By Edgar Johnson

Novels

UNWEAVE A RAINBOW: A SENTIMENTAL FANTASY

THE PRAYING MANTIS

Criticism

ONE MIGHTY TORRENT: THE DRAMA OF BIOGRAPHY

Biography

CHARLES DICKENS: HIS TRAGEDY AND TRIUMPH

THE HEART OF CHARLES DICKENS: HIS LETTERS TO
ANGELA BURDETT-COUTTS

Anthologies

A TREASURY OF BIOGRAPHY

A TREASURY OF SATIRE

THE
DICKENS
THEATRICAL
READER

Edgar Johnson is Chairman of the Department of English and has been professor of English for some time at City College of New York. He is the editor and author of CHARLES DICKENS: HIS TRAGEDY AND TRIUMPH, THE HEART OF CHARLES DICKENS: HIS LETTERS TO ANGELA BURDETT-COUTTS, and other books.

THE
DICKENS
THEATRICAL
READER

Edited with a Prologue and Notes

by EDGAR and ELEANOR JOHNSON

With Illustrations

LITTLE, BROWN AND COMPANY · BOSTON · TORONTO

The editors' and publisher's profound thanks are due to the Houghton
Library of Harvard University and to Mr. William H. Bond thereof in
particular for their courteous help with the illustrations between pages
178-179. The Cruikshank and Phiz engravings from *Sketches by Boz*
and *Nicholas Nickleby*, respectively, were photographed in the library
from marvelously clean copies of the first editions.

For Miranda and Mark Steven
who arrived just in time
to be greeted with love
from the "Aged Grand-P's"

Prefatory Note

DICKENS'S WRITINGS on the theater are far too entertaining to be presented only to scholars (although even they are entitled to have fun). This volume is therefore addressed to the general reader. It is selective, not exhaustive; but it ranges the gamut of Dickens's enthusiastic interest in plays, in actors, and in acting, and it includes all his more important comments, and some which may not even be widely familiar among scholars.

It does *not* include the eight or nine plays he wrote, collaborated on, or gave some help in writing. Whatever vitality these may have had in the nineteenth century has trickled out of them, leaving them flabby and lifeless dummies. Anyone desiring through either skepticism or a gloomy sense of duty to read them may locate them in various other printed sources; he will not find them here. We wish rather that we had some of the imaginary plays Dickens only joked about writing, like his supposititious comedy called *The One Thing Needed, or a Part is Better than the Whole*, or "that soul-stirring drama" entitled *The Larboard Fin*, "which looks to me," Dickens said, "like an undiscovered play by Shakespeare surreptitiously modernized."

We have included all the *Sketches by Boz* that are devoted to the entertainment world and to actors and acting, both amateur and professional. We have included most of the scenes from Dickens's novels in which mummers of all kinds appear — from clowns, giants, dwarfs, jugglers, and acrobats to performers in the comic and tragic drama. And from his periodical writings we have dramatic criticism, articles on the popular theater, comments on cabarets and minstrel shows, ballet dancers, pantomimes, and marionettes, even on ventriloquists, magicians, and "grimaciers."

From Dickens's letters we have extracted a generous selection of passages dealing with plays and acting performances that amused or excited him, and several sequences that convey the enormous energy and enthusiasm — and the brilliant skill — that he flung into producing, directing, and acting in the plays he himself staged for amusement, charity, or profit. A number of the quoted texts are taken from previously unpublished autograph letters, and others are corrected from the original manuscripts. Finally, there is one of his half dozen or so speeches at the dinners of the General Theatrical Fund, and "Mr. Bob Sawyer's Party," one of the readings into which he threw so much of his genius as an actor.

EDGAR JOHNSON
ELEANOR JOHNSON

Contents

THE
DICKENS
THEATRICAL
READER

Prologue

I

In a way, the complete works of Dickens, with the entire story of his life thrown in as well, might constitute one extended and monumental Theatrical Reader. His imagination and personality were steeped in the stage; the world in which his spirit dwelt was a world brilliant in theatrical hue and violent in theatrical movement, crammed with a huge cast of fantastic actors. Not only strangers in the street and mere acquaintances, but his dearest friends were to him always characters in a series of wild farces and roaring melodramas. Life itself glared in a circle of stage fire.

His own father discoursed with the improbable and ludicrous grandiloquence of Micawber. His mother gabbled with the scatter-brained volubility of Mrs. Nickleby. The most outrageous characteristics of Sairey Gamp, the oleaginous Pecksniff, and the airy Skimpole were literal renditions of living originals, and the thunderous Boythorn was, Dickens confided, "a most exact portrait of Walter Savage Landor." Pompous London merchants, stuffing themselves at public banquets while opposing the most necessary social reforms, swell in his letters into "sleek, slobbering, bow-paunched, over-fed, apoplectic, snorting cattle," voicing sentiments at which "any moderately intelligent dustman would have blushed through his cindery bloom." An ill-considered parsimony could overnight transform his publishers from his "trusty friends" and "the best of booksellers, past, present, and to come," into scaly-headed vultures rubbing "the tenderest parts" of his "eyelids with bay-salt." Everyone recognized his close friend John Forster in the mannerisms of Podsnap — the indignant reddening of the face, the sweeping gesture of dismissal, the pomposity carried to such towering heights that often Dickens rolled on a sofa in agonies of enjoyment at some grotesque revelation of Forster "impregnably mailed in self-complacency." There was no need of greasepaint and footlights to make all the world a stage, and all its men and women players in thronging scenes of tears and laughter.

Dickens's own personality, indeed, was theatrical. In youth he looked the hero of a romantic comedy, with long, flowing brown hair waving about his brow, flashing eyes, an actor's mobile mouth, and vivacious movements. That sapient theatrical manager, Mr. Vincent Crummles, might well have said to Dickens, as he did to Nicholas Nickleby, "There's genteel comedy in your walk and manner, juvenile tragedy in your eye, and touch-and-go farce in your laugh." Although he did not, of course, employ the jerky jargon of Mr. Jingle, numerous observers, even in the years of his fame, felt that he displayed more than a trace of that strolling actor's boundless exuberance and superb assurance. Into assemblies of dimmer personalities he blazed like a star making an entrance.

He dressed with dashing dandyism; at the age of twenty-one he could be seen striding along the Adelphi in a "handsome blue cloak with velvet facings, the corner of which he threw over his shoulder à l'Espagnol." No sooner had he attained literary success than he burst out in a glitter of gold rings, jeweled tiepins, watch chains, and fobs. His blue dress-coat was gorgeous with brass buttons and his embroidered shirt-bosoms as gay as a butterfly. Gleaming patent leather encased his feet, primrose-yellow gloves his hands. His waistcoats were sensational — green and crimson velvet, black satin embroidered with flowers, broad stripes of blue and purple. At a soirée where he wore a "black-and-white or magpie waistcoat" he was gratified to hear guests exclaiming, "What is it? Is it a waistcoat? No, it's a shirt." In middle age he still garbed himself like a juvenile lead, billowing in the richest of cravats and touching up his grizzling side-locks with brilliantine.

But in more than manner, and in more than thus displaying the innocent sartorial vanity of the actor, Dickens was theatrical. His very way of feeling and rendering experience was drenched in the drama. The characters in his novels often behave stagily and speak the rhetoric of the theater. The frustrated Carker foams at the mouth while Edith Dombey confronts him with the proud scorn of a tragedy queen. Ralph Nickleby grinds his teeth as he sees his designs crashing into ruin; to the nephew who has defeated him he rasps, "My curse, my bitter, deadly, curse, upon you, boy!" The novels are filled to overflowing with the well-worn devices of melodrama — cruel fathers and stepfathers, scheming misers, heartless skinflints, generous benefactors, smooth and artful villains, stolen children, lost wills, missing heirs, masquerades and disguises, men returning from the dead, horrendous secrets starting up out of the buried past, midnight assignations, plots overheard and betrayed.

All these artificialities are ample proof — if there be any reader who feels he needs it — of the degree to which Dickens's work is permeated by the conventions of the stage. This is not the place in which to analyze how his art not merely triumphs over these conventions but even molds them into instruments of a profound and serious vision of life. Such a demonstration belongs rather in a discussion of his achievement as a novelist than in an anthology of his writings about the theater and actors. It may be noted, however, that from the beginning he was keenly aware of the dangers he was skirting, and well knew how easily pathos collapses into bathos and melodrama fizzles into absurdity. Even in the youthful *Sketches by Boz* he observes the tendency of stage fathers "to discover, all of a sudden, that somebody whom they have been in constant communication with, during three long acts, without the slightest suspicion, is their own child: in which case they exclaim, 'Ah! what do I see? This bracelet! That smile! These documents! Those eyes! Can I believe my senses? — It must be! — Yes — it is, it is my child!' — 'My father!' exclaims the child; and they fall into each other's arms, and look over each other's shoulders, and the audience give three rounds of applause."

Over and over again, throughout his later work, he has hilarious fun with the imbecilities of hack drama, the ludicrous posturings of ham actors, and the ridiculous world of stage illusion their imaginations come to mistake for reality. In *Nicholas Nickleby* he brilliantly distinguishes between the theatricality of his serious characters and that of the actors and actresses in Vincent Crummles's company. Though Kate and Nicholas and Ralph Nickleby often talk an inflated stage diction, the springs of their behavior are not false to human nature. Mr. Folair's and Miss Snevellicci's very emotions, however, are blown up into theatricality; their life *is* stylized melodrama.

Mr. Lenville really *believes* it psychologically convincing to work a lively jig into a tearful melodrama by having a distressed mother say, "Do you remember that dance, my honest friend, which in happier days you practised with this sweet angel?" (Her little daughter.) "Oh, let me see it once again before I die!" "There it is —" Lenville concludes triumphantly, "— cue for the band, *before I die* — and off they go."

II

It is no surprise to learn that Dickens made an early acquaintance with the stage. As a child of seven he was taken up to London to behold the splendors of the Christmas pantomimes, and clapped his small hands at the comic feats of Joe Grimaldi, greatest of buffoons. He delighted in the beautiful white-and-red complexions of the clowns and gloried in their greed for sausages, reveled in the antics of Harlequin and Pantaloon, and fell in love with the wispy-skirted loveliness of Columbine. To marry her, he thought deliriously, "would be to attain the highest pitch of all human felicity!" In Chatham at fair time a pantomime came lumbering into town in Richardson's wagons, and he sat in a row of white-frilled little boys, sniffing up the smell of sawdust and orangepeel, and exulting in the defeat of the crafty wizard who had been holding the delicious heroine in bondage.

Long before being "forced by a relentless parent into" his "first pair of boots," the youngster had seen Edmund Kean and Charles Mathews, and was familiar with the little Theatre Royal in Rochester. What intoxication to pass through its two-columned portico lit by a wrought-iron lantern and wait for the magic moment when the curtain rose! What bouts of glorious laughter, what peaks of excitement, at its bills of farce, melodrama, comedy, and tragedy! Dickens himself distils for us the essence of that enchantment:

Richard the Third, in a very uncomfortable cloak, had first appeared to me there, and had made my heart leap with terror by backing up against the stage-box in which I was posted, while struggling for life against the virtuous Richmond. It was within those walls that I had learnt as from a page of English history, how that wicked King slept in war-time on a sofa much too short for him, and how fearfully his conscience troubled his boots.

There, too, had I first seen the funny countryman, but countryman of noble principles, in a flowered waistcoat, crunch up his little hat and throw it on the ground, and pull off his coat, saying, "Dom thee, squire, coom on with thy fistes then!" At which the lovely young woman who kept company with him (and who went out gleaning, in a narrow white muslin apron with five beautiful bars of five different coloured ribbons across it) was so frightened for his sake, that she fainted away. Many wondrous secrets of Nature had I come to the knowledge of in that sanctuary: of which not the least terrific were, that the witches in Macbeth bore an awful resemblance to the Thanes and other proper inhabitants of Scotland; and that the good King Duncan couldn't rest in his grave, but was constantly coming out of it and calling himself somebody else.

As soon as his mother had taught him to read and he was able to distinguish "the easy good nature of O and Q and S" from each other, he plunged into the thrilling adventures of Jack and the Bean Stalk, Red Riding Hood, Valentine and Orson, Robin Hood, the Yellow Dwarf, Mother Bunch. But it was not long before his imagination was responding to a summons still more dramatic and masterful — as imperious as those hammer blows of Fate that sound their commanding notes in the *Eroica*. Stowed away forgotten in an attic next to his bedroom he found a cheap reprint series of novels, and radiance burst around him. "From that blessed little room, *Roderick Random, Peregrine Pickle, Humphrey Clinker, Tom Jones, The Vicar of Wakefield, Don Quixote, Gil Blas*, and *Robinson Crusoe* came out, a glorious host, to keep me company . . . they and the *Arabian Nights*, and the *Tales of the Genii*," as well as the *Tatler* and *Spectator* papers, Goldsmith's *Citizen of the World*, and Mrs. Inchbald's *Collection of Farces*.

When I think of it, the picture always rises in my mind, of a summer evening, the boys at play in the churchyard, and I sitting on my bed, reading as if for life. Every barn in the neighbourhood, every stone in the church, and every foot of the churchyard, had some association of its own, in my mind, connected with these books, and stood for some locality made famous in them. I have seen Tom Pipes go climbing up the church-steeple; I have watched Strap, with the knapsack on his back, stopping to rest himself upon the wicket-gate; and I *know* that Commodore Trunnion held that club with Mr. Pickle, in the parlour of our little village alehouse.

Carried away, he began — before he was nine years old — scribbling stories and plays himself, "and became famous in his childish circle for having written a tragedy called *Misnar, the Sultan of India,* founded (and very literally founded, no doubt) on one of the *Tales of the Genii.*" More exciting still, in invented solitary games he acted out in long extemporaneous dramas his favorite characters from these enthralling stories.

I have been Tom Jones (a child's Tom Jones, a harmless creature) for a week together. I have sustained my own idea of Roderick Random for a month at a stretch, I verily believe. I had a greedy relish for a few volumes of Voyages and Travels — I forget what, now — that were on those shelves; and for days and days I can remember to have gone about my region of our house, armed with the centre-piece out of an old set of boot-trees — the perfect realisation of Captain Somebody, of the Royal British Navy, in danger of being beset by savages, and resolved to sell his life at a great price.

These dramatic impersonations came to an end with those dark days of family misfortune that incarcerated his father as a debtor in the Marshalsea Prison and subjected the youngster to tearful enslavement in the blacking warehouse. As a toiling factory child, washing and tying up bottles, he had no room in his overburdened young heart for anything but the dreadful weight of his unhappiness. Creeping every hopeless day from Camden Town to the tumbledown old warehouse in Hungerford Stairs, trying to apportion his few half-pence for the saveloy or slice of pudding that constituted his solitary lunch, wandering through the back streets of the Adelphi or staring dismally at the pineapples in Covent Garden Market, he felt utterly abandoned to despair.

Only after long months was his father discharged from prison and only after what seemed an eternity of darkness he himself released from his painful drudgery. But then, at last, he was sent to school in London, the sun shone again, and he could gradually blot from his mind the shadow of the blacking warehouse. In their free time he and his fellow-pupils at Wellington House Academy amused themselves by staging plays in a toy theater, with brightly colored scenery created by a boy named Beverley (who later became a well-known scene painter), and with trained mice as actors.

The boys trained the mice, much better than the masters trained the boys. We recall one white mouse, who lived in the cover of a Latin dictionary, who ran up ladders, drew Roman chariots, shouldered muskets, turned wheels, and even made a very creditable appearance on the stage as the Dog of Montargis. He might have achieved greater things, but for having the misfortune to mistake his way in a triumphal procession to the Capitol, when he fell into a deep inkstand, and was dyed black and drowned.

The Dog of Montargis, a melodrama by W. H. Arnold, was one of these plays; another was *Cherry and Fair Star*, a dramatic version of Mme. d'Aulnoy's fairy tale, *La Princesse Belle-Étoile et le Prince Chéri*. One of their great successes was Pocock's exciting *The Miller and His Men*, a lurid play about robbers innocently disguised as millers by day. Young Beverley ingeniously constructed the mill so that at the climax it could be made to tumble to pieces by means of exploding firecrackers, which it did with such noisy realism that the police came pounding on the schoolhouse door.

Soon after his fifteenth birthday Charles dropped out of school and became an office boy for a firm of attorneys. With pocket money of his own, he began splurging on the theater. Admission to the galleries at Covent Garden, Drury Lane, and the Haymarket was only a shilling, and after nine o'clock prices were reduced to half. Since, in addition to the main attraction, an evening's bill usually included a farce and an interlude, a wealth of entertainment could be had at small expense. Besides these so-called "major" theaters, there were a good many even less expensive "minor" theaters, which pretended that they were not competing with the serious drama of the licensed theaters by inserting a few songs in their performances and calling them "burlettas."

Across Westminster Bridge, in the East End, and to the north and west, there were still other theaters which presented everything from farce to melodrama. Astley's, in Westminster Bridge Road, was a circus that also put on plays about wild Indians and despotic Oriental monarchs. The Surrey, in Blackfriars Road, did nautical melodramas with pirates and gallant sailors. The Pavilion, in Whitechapel Road, dealt in murderous criminals. Greenwich Fair, besides its public houses and gingerbread booths, had wild-beast shows, giants and dwarfs, pantomimes, dramas about Mexican chiefs and ancient Romans, and melodramas involving rightful and wrongful heirs, ghosts, and assassins. The Grecian Saloon, in Britannia Field, Hoxton, was a cabaret with a Moorish band and drinks served at its garden tables.

Nor was this all. In Wilson Street, Gray's Inn Lane, and Catharine Street there were "private" theaters where aspirants to the boards paid the owners a fee to be allowed to play Captain Absolute, Shylock, Charles Surface, and Macbeth. Behind these footlights stagestruck copying clerks and youths from countinghouses ranted and postured under such impressive professional names as Belville, Berkeley, Treville, Byron, and St. Clair; for two pounds anybody could be the villainous Richard III, make love to the Lady Ann, shout "Orf with his 'ed!" and clash swords in the frenzy of the finale. Dickens was rapidly caught up in the glamor of this mimic world of greasepaint, stage business, and bright costumes, and the knowing greenroom description of his sketch "Private Theatres" shows clearly that his experience was not limited to the spectators' side of the proscenium.

For a time, indeed — before he obtained the newspaper engagement that led to his rapid success as a reporter, then to his first efforts in fiction and the glorious popularity of *Pickwick Papers* — Dickens even thought seriously of going on the stage. He had fallen deliriously in love with a bewitching and flirtatious little beauty named Maria Beadnell; he must with all speed, he decided impetuously, achieve a position in the world. Seemingly it did not occur to him to question whether Maria's banker father would be much impressed by even the most glittering theatrical laurels. Untroubled by any such doubts, he set to work with characteristic energy.

This was at the time [he wrote years later] when I was at Doctors' Commons as a shorthand writer for the proctors. It wasn't a very good living (though not a *very* bad one), and was wearily uncertain; which made me think of the Theatre in quite a business-like way. I went to some theatre every night, with a very few exceptions, for at least three years; really studying the bills first, and going to where there was the best acting: and always to see Mathews whenever he played. I practised immensely (even such things as walking in and out, and sitting down in a chair): often four, five, six hours a day: shut up in my own room, or walking about in the fields. I prescribed to myself, too, a sort of Hamiltonian system for learning parts; and learnt a great number.

When I was about twenty, and knew three or four successive years of Mathews's At Homes from sitting in the pit to hear them, I wrote to Bartley, who was stage-manager, and told him how young I was, and exactly what I thought I could do; and that I believed I had a strong perception of character and oddity, and a natural power of reproducing in my own person what I observed in others. . . . There must have been something in my letter that struck the authorities, for Bartley wrote to me almost immediately to say . . . that they would communicate with me again in a fortnight. Punctual to the time another letter came, with an appointment to do anything of Mathews's I pleased, before him and Charles Kemble, on a certain day at the theatre. My sister Fanny was in the secret, and was to go with me to play the songs. I was laid up when the day came, with a terrible bad cold and an inflammation of the face; the beginning, by the bye, of that annoyance in one ear to which I am subject to this day. I wrote to say so, and added that I would resume my application next season.

But the application was never renewed. Only a few weeks later Dickens obtained a post as a Parliamentary reporter. "See how near I may have been," he exclaimed, "to another way of life." In the Reporters' Gallery, as he himself said, he "made a great splash." Among the eighty or ninety reporters there, many of them veterans in the occupation, this youth of twenty rapidly strode to the highest rank, "not merely for accuracy in reporting, but for marvellous quickness in transcript." Said one of his colleagues, "There never *was* such a shorthand writer!" Within little more than a year his outstanding pre-eminence brought him a position on the *Morning Chronicle,* the only important rival to the *Times.* Soon he was the *Chronicle's* star reporter, dashing from the reception for Lord Grey at Edinburgh to the Stroud by-election at which Lord John Russell was defeated, covering the scandalous Melbourne-Norton trial and the spectacular fire at Hatfield House in which the Marchioness of Salisbury was burned to death. He began writing fictional sketches which were eagerly snapped up by magazines and newspapers, and his plan of becoming a professional actor was laid aside.

But not his enthusiasm for footlights and greasepaint. During the debates over the Irish Coercion Bill in 1833, Dickens and his family were putting on amateur theatricals in his father's house in Bentinck Street. The play was *Clari, the Maid of Milan,* now remembered mainly for the song "Home, Sweet Home," but the bill also included "the favourite Interlude of *The Married Bachelor*," and the farce of *Amateurs and Actors*. Dickens dominated the production, made himself director and stage manager, designed scenery, worried with the stage carpenter about simulating moonlight, played an accordion in the band, tyrannously rehearsed the entire cast, and assumed not only the role of Rolamo but three other parts as well. Later that year there were more theatricals in the Dickens home, for which Dickens himself wrote a burlesque extravaganza entitled *O'Thello*, with his father swelling his way through a role teasingly named "The Great Unpaid."

Even in the midst of his rising popularity as the author of *Sketches by Boz*, Dickens still hankered after acclaim as a writer for the stage. He readily agreed to do the book and lyrics of an operetta for the music of a young composer, John Hullah, although he transformed the musician's idea of a play with a Venetian background, to be called *The Gondoliers*, into a bucolic drama of rural maidens, would-be seducers, and virtuous farmers, entitled *The Village Coquettes*. At almost the same time, on the invitation of the comic actor John Pritt Harley, he began writing a one-act farce which he remolded from his story "The Great Winglebury Duel" and called *The Strange Gentleman*. Meanwhile he had also started *Pickwick Papers*; all three progressed simultaneously during the slow discouraging months in 1836 when the opening numbers of that serial novel lingered unsold on booksellers' shelves and seemed a complete failure.

Suddenly, however, during the summer, *Pickwick* caught fire; it skyrocketed to spectacular and hilarious fame; and his two stage pieces reached the boards amid a blaze of popularity. *The Strange Gentleman* is a mechanical imbroglio of cross-purposes and mistaken identities, but in performance its rapid-fire action was made wildly comical, and Harley was a riot as the "strange gentleman" fleeing a duel and appalled at believing himself to have landed in an innful of maniacs. It ran for sixty nights — no small success — and was revived the following year. *The Village Coquettes* did not do so well; reviewers derided the book, but praised Hullah's music. Audiences, however, enjoyed the pretty tunes and the eighteenth-century costumes, and the operetta had a fair run. A "comic burletta" called *Is She His Wife?* which Dickens turned out in the following year met with only a lukewarm reception. But the wild furore over *Pickwick* followed the hardly less fantastic triumph of *Oliver Twist;* if Dickens's talents as a playwright seemed doubtful he was now assured of supremacy as a novelist.

In later years he made no independent endeavors at original composition for the stage, but he often lent a hand on the work of others. He added so many contributions to his friend Mark Lemon's ludicrous farce *Mr. Nightingale's Diary* that the piece turned into a virtual collaboration. Throughout a series of benefit amateur theatricals in 1851 the two men were a screaming success in acting it — Dickens himself, with rapid changes of costume and make-up, assuming no fewer than six parts, ranging from a Sam Wellerish waiter to a gabbling Sairey Gamplike old woman. During the 1860's Dickens aided the Anglo-French actor Charles Fechter as a "play doctor," adapting Bellew's *The King's Butterfly* to more effective stage production, and giving much assistance in putting on *The Master of Ravenswood,* a dramatization of Scott's *The Bride of Lammermoor.*

In a number of plays written by his friend Wilkie Collins, Dickens's share was even greater. He made fruitful suggestions about Collins's melodrama *The Lighthouse* and enthusiastically acted its principal role in amateur performances. The manuscript of *The Frozen Deep* is so criss-crossed with emendations, additions, and alterations in Dickens's hand that he might almost have claimed co-authorship. And although Collins did most of the writing of *No Thoroughfare,* it was dramatized with Dickens's aid from a Christmas story they had done together in 1867 and was shaped in hundreds of ways by Dickens's criticism. Even after the play had been running for five roaring months at the Adelphi, on his return from his second American trip Dickens tightened its structure and suggested poetic sound-effects, then dashed over to Paris, where it was opening under the title of *L'Abîme,* to show the French actors how it should be done.

In addition to these theatrical activities, Dickens had what amounted to a brilliant second career as an amateur actor and producer. Whenever he felt in need of distraction, whenever he was restless, bored, or unhappy, he broke out in a violent bout of theatricals. Playing at the drama as hard as if it were work, he drained off some of his feverish disquiet. During his first visit to America in 1842, he put on at Montreal a benefit performance of Morton's A

Roland for an Oliver, Mathews's *Past Two O'Clock in the Morning*,
and Poole's *Deaf as a Post*, blazing away as manager and universal
director, and taking parts in all three. His Snobbington, in the
second of them, clad in an absurd yellow wig surmounted by two
nightcaps, had the whole audience laughing uncontrollably. "Everybody was told they would have to submit to the most iron despotism," he wrote; "and didn't I come Macready over them? Oh no. By
no means. Certainly not."

Three years later, even in the midst of all the turmoil of founding
the *Daily News*, of which he became the first editor, Dickens got up
a production of Jonson's *Every Man in His Humour*, with a distinguished cast of writers and artists. Scenery was new-painted, bright
seventeenth-century costumes designed. Dickens gloriously ran everything. "I am half dead with Managerial work," he lamented happily,
"— and with actual work in shirt-sleeves; with a dirty face, a hammer, and a bag of nails." He himself, said one of his fellow-actors,
was "glorious in Bobadil," assuming an "air of supreme conceit
and frothy pomp." "He literally floated in braggadocio." Public
excitement about the play became so extravagant that the amateurs
put on a benefit performance for Dr. Southwood Smith's Sanatorium,
which was attended by a distinguished audience including the Duke of
Wellington, the Duke of Devonshire, Lord Melbourne, and Prince
Albert. On January 3, 1846, the same company of amateurs acted
Massinger and Fletcher's *The Elder Brother* for the benefit of the
retired actress Frances Kelly.

In the summer of 1847 and again in 1848 Dickens had still another theatrical outburst, this time for the benefit of Leigh Hunt and
the desperately impoverished dramatists John Poole and Sheridan
Knowles. Grandiosely he decided to do not only *Every Man in His
Humour* but *The Merry Wives of Windsor*. Again he coaxed,
bullied, drilled; taught everybody natural gesture, clear articulation,
graceful movement; wore his fellow-workers out and kept them in
good humor. The two performances, in Manchester and Liverpool
respectively, fired such enthusiasm that the following year Dickens
had to schedule an entire series of repetitions, at the Theatre Royal,
Haymarket, and in Liverpool, Birmingham, Manchester, Edinburgh,
and Glasgow. The sensation created by Dickens's Bobadil was even

surpassed by the stormy applause that engulfed his Shallow, a wonderful mingling of shaky decrepitude and pretended vigor.

For three nights in the winter of 1850 he revived *Every Man in His Humour* before an audience of Sir Edward Bulwer Lytton's invited guests at Knebworth. "Ah, sir," said the master carpenter of Miss Kelly's theater, where the last rehearsal took place, "it's a universal observation in the profession, sir, that it was a great loss to the public when you took to writing books!" Hard upon these festivities Dickens had the fun of doing *A Day After the Wedding, Used Up,* and *Animal Magnetism* at Rockingham Castle in Northamptonshire, the home of his friends the Honorable Mr. and Mrs. Richard Watson.

The Knebworth theatricals inspired Dickens and Lytton to the idea of the Guild of Literature and Art, a foundation to promote the welfare of artists and writers. Lytton wrote a comedy, *Not So Bad as We Seem,* all the earnings of which he dedicated to the endowment; Dickens once more assembled his company of literary men and artists to act the play. On May 16, 1851, Queen Victoria and Prince Albert attended the first night at Devonshire House, the palatial residence of the Duke of Devonshire in Piccadilly. Then came performances in the Hanover Square Rooms, and for all the next year the company gloriously barnstormed all over England. With the thirty or so actors, the orchestra and its conductor, the carpenters, gasmen, tailors, barbers, property men, dressers, and servants, they sometimes took up all the rooms of the smaller provincial hotels. Everywhere the performances were a triumph; they earned the Guild around £5,000.

These repeated and almost professional engagements were far from exhausting Dickens's theatrical enthusiasm. In earlier years at his home in Devonshire Terrace he had given children's Christmas parties at which he surprised everyone with expert feats of conjuring and magic; after his move to Tavistock House, in 1852, on each Twelfth Night he transformed the schoolroom into a miniature theater and staged gorgeous pantomimes — first Albert Smith's *Guy Fawkes,* and then in successive years Brough's *William Tell,* Fielding's *Tom Thumb,* and Planché's *Fortunio and His Seven Gifted Servants.*

In June 1855 the same little theater saw Collins's *The Lighthouse.* Dickens played the part of Aaron Gurnock, the old lighthouse-

keeper, with such pathos that the well-known actress Mrs. Frederick
Yates wept large red circles around her eyes and exclaimed, "O Mr.
Dickens what a pity it is you can do anything else!" Within less than
a year Dickens was urging Collins to write the arctic melodrama that
became *The Frozen Deep*; by autumn it was in rehearsal; its first
night was January 6, 1857. Dickens's performance as Richard Wardour, its hero, Wilkie Collins regarded as the very peak of his achievement as an actor. "The trite phrase is the true phrase," said Collins,
"to describe that magnificent piece of acting. He literally electri-
fied the audience."

Dickens's own emotions speedily exploded him into a series of
benefits. A friend and fellow-writer, Douglas Jerrold, had just died,
leaving his family in narrow circumstances. Eagerly, Dickens seized
the opportunity. Though sympathy was, of course, a motive, it was
not the only one. His galvanic restlessness had been increasing; his
indignation at the evils of society, against which he had directed the
gigantic cannonadings of *Bleak House, Hard Times*, and *Little Dorrit*, had mounted to an almost intolerable fiery incandescence; and
his married life had slowly through the years been growing more and
more unhappy and was now heading inexorably toward crisis. "Why
is it," he lamented, "that . . . a sense comes always crushing on me
now, when I fall into low spirits, as of one happiness I have missed
in life, and one friend and companion I have never made?"

Some anodyne had become a desperate need to drug a misery that
now gave him no peace. Not until later that summer, to be sure, was
he brought into close association with the fair-haired young actress
Ellen Ternan who was to sweep him away on a compelling tide of
longing. But he was tinder for such a passion. The central theme of
The Frozen Deep — Richard Wardour dying in the dreadful frustration of an unhappy love — filled him with intense emotion. When
during the last act he rushed from the stage in anguish, he tossed the
other men aside like a charging bull, often leaving them black and
blue. His death scene was so heartrending that his fellow-actors were
in tears and the audience sobbed.

The Frozen Deep was the last play in which Dickens acted, but it
was not his farewell to the stage. Within another year he had opened
up a new dramatic career for himself. For some years past — and always with enormous success — he had been giving occasional benefit

readings from A *Christmas Carol*, *The Chimes*, and *The Cricket on the Hearth*. Now he decided on a series of public readings for his own profit. Into the amazing entertainment he devised he poured all his years of acquired skill as an actor and all his instinct and talent for the dramatic. In simple evening dress, standing in the center of the platform, only by gesture, changes of voice, and facial expression, he peopled his stage with a throng of characters.

His face could flash from the miserly harshness of Scrooge to the timidity of Bob Cratchit, his voice from Scrooge's grating snarl to Bob's meek gasp or the cry of the plump sister at the Christmas party: "It's your uncle Scroo-o-o-ooge!" Merely by drumming on his desk with his fingers he suggested the dash and gaiety of the dance at old Fezziwig's ball, by licking his lips Trotty Veck's relish of tripe. His features swelled out with the bullying pomposity of Alderman Cute or sharpened themselves to a sly London street arab. As he added other readings to his repertory — from *Pickwick*, from *Nicholas Nickleby*, little Dombey, Mrs. Gamp — he assumed countless other voices, innumerable faces. He did Justice Stareleigh in convulsive snorts and starts, Paul Dombey in the alto of a weary child, Mrs. Gamp with a snuffy and oozing unctuousness. He could be a schoolboy, a country yokel, a cockney medical student, a stout old gentleman with a yawn in his very tones.

Even as his marriage was breaking up, in the final arrangements for a separation, Dickens added new triumphs to his career as a public entertainer. Unknown to the mass of his readers and listeners, Ellen Ternan took her place in his life, but she did not assuage his restlessness. As if driven by some demon of unease he kept on — hurtling through long railway journeys in England, Ireland and Scotland, dashing across the channel to Paris, ploughing the Atlantic to the United States, broiling himself beneath the glare of gas-lamps, exulting in the applause and adulation of his audiences, and slowly killing himself with the impossible exertion.

Everywhere he went, for these last dozen suicidal years, the readings were a sensation. In New York people stood in line in front of the box office throughout all of a cold winter's night to be able to buy tickets in the morning. In Washington the President, the Cabinet, the Supreme Court, ambassadors, congressmen and brilliantly uniformed officers came almost in a body, and roared in a chorus of laughter. In

Paris "gorgeous beauties all radiant with diamonds, clasped their fans between their two hands, and rolled about in ecstasy." Said Thomas Carlyle, "Charley, you carry a whole company under your own hat"; and to his sister, "Dickens . . . acts better than any Macready in the world; a whole tragic comic heroic *theatre* visible." In the last two years of Dickens's life, when he added the "Murder" reading from *Oliver Twist*, he threw all his genius as an actor into bringing to horrible life the oily and crafty Fagin, the ferocious Sikes, and Nancy's terrifying shrieks. At almost every performance there was a contagion of fainting. Dickens's old friend the actor William Charles Macready voiced his own judgment upon the success of the rendering: "TWO MACBETHS!"

Throughout all these histrionic activities, behind the footlights and beneath the blazing gas of his reading platform, carried on while he unceasingly performed his editorial duties as the conductor of a highly successful weekly magazine and as he pursued his major career as a novelist, Dickens never lost his delight in being part of an audience as well. During the last month of his life he attended the theater with Lady Molesworth and Lord Redesdale in such high spirits that he and his companions never stopped "laughing at the majesty of his own absurdities." Just one week before he died he took charge of some private theatricals at the home of his London neighbors, Mr. and Mrs. Freake.

Walking with a friend only a few days earlier, he had paused in the shadow of Westminster Abbey — where his body now rests — and summarized his lifelong love affair with the theater: "What do you think," he demanded, "would be the realization of one of my most cherished day-dreams?" It would be, he said eagerly, to "hold supreme authority" in the direction of a great theater, with "a skilled and noble company." "The pieces should be dealt with according to my pleasure, and touched up here and there in obedience to my own judgment; the players as well as the plays being absolutely under my command. That," he concluded, laughing and glowing, *"that's* my day-dream!"

III

Throughout Dickens's entire literary career, from his youthful days as a reporter to the very end of his life, his enthusiasm for the theater overflowed in a rich outpouring through all his work. His very last known letter quotes Friar Laurence in *Romeo and Juliet:* "These violent delights have violent ends." No fewer than five of the early *Sketches by Boz* range over the entertainment world, from the cheerful clamor of Greenwich Fair to the equestrian melodrama of Astley's Circus, and from the gleaming lanterns and fireworks of Vauxhall Gardens to the mishaps of stagestruck amateurs both in middle-class homes and in the greenrooms of the private theaters. Among his periodical contributions to dramatic criticism are articles on Macready's revival of *King Lear* and his performance as Benedick in *Much Ado About Nothing.* Later we find brilliant accounts of Italian marionette theaters, pieces on ballet dancers, on sailors' cabarets, on traveling Flemish acting companies, and a whole series of articles on the popular theater.

Actors and acting and theatrical doings are constantly popping up in Dickens's novels. Out of the entire fourteen, no fewer than seven either introduce stage performers or give some of their major characters the festive excitement of going to a play. David Copperfield rises into a fever of romantic admiration at Covent Garden over the Roman heroism of *Julius Caesar* and falls into a less noble species of intoxication during a later night at the theater. In *The Old Curiosity Shop* Kit Nubbles and his family, together with Barbara, are enchanted by the gilding and mirrors at Astley's Circus and by the delightful smell of horses and sawdust and the excitement of its equine drama; and in the same novel there are Little Nell's experiences with Codlin and Short's Punch-and-Judy Show, the giants and dwarfs and performing dogs, and Mrs. Jarley's Wax-work. In *Hard Times* there is Sleary's Circus, with its acrobats, jugglers, bareback riders, and tightrope walkers; in *Little Dorrit* we see a ballet rehearsal at the theater where Fanny Dorrit is one of the dancers. *Great Expectations* has Mr. Wopsle's hilariously lugubrious performance as Hamlet, with the church in the graveyard scene resembling a "small ecclesiastical washhouse" and the Danish nobility represented by "a noble boy in the wash-leather boots of a gigantic ancestor" and "a venerable Peer with a dirty face, who seemed to have arisen from the people late in life."

Perhaps most superb of all, *Nicholas Nickleby* rejoices in the wonderful constellation of the Vincent Crummles troupe, ranging from Mr. Crummles himself and the Infant Phenomenon to the impudent Mr. Folair, the jealous Mr. Lenville, and Miss Snevellicci with her delightful skipping gait. Even *Bleak House* has "Little Swills" and his popular comic songs at the local pub; and I am not certain that if one searched carefully in *Barnaby Rudge* and *Dombey and Son* one could not find Sir John Chester getting some new idea for villainy by listening to Joseph Surface in *The School for Scandal* or come upon Florence Dombey timorously looking down from a box at the opera.

Dickens's letters, finally, abound in vignettes of real actors and theatrical performances, vivid appreciations, penetrating comments. Even his slightest observations are often amusing, as when he describes a wild-beast show at Broadstairs, where a dirty young woman in shining scaly armor pretended to fall asleep reclining on a lion, while an adenoidal keeper exclaimed "Be'old the abazick power of woobbud!" Repeatedly Dickens gleams a rich response or a sharp twist of analysis, an amused insight, a glimpse of histrionic absurdity, or a deeply moved awareness of some revelation of truth and beauty. In many ways his letters are a lightning-flash chronicle of the nineteenth-century stage. And how vibrant with the very life and essence of the theater are his letters dealing with the plays he himself acted and directed, from *Clari* to *The Frozen Deep*, and from the moment of their first conception to the last curtain call. No letters ever written convey more glowingly all the turmoil, labor, excitement, tension, and emotional rewards filling the world of the drama.

But this prologue should be drawing to a close. The young manager of *Clari*, all grimy, is waiting in the wings, and, nudging him impatiently, Mrs. Joseph Porter and Mr. Sempronius Gattleton, at Rose Villa, are eager for the amateur performance of *Othello* to begin. In the parlor the lamps are dimmed; before the proscenium the footlights are blazing. Let us ring up the curtain.

The Young Impresario: A Brief Glimpse

[*The performance of* Clari *in Bentinck Street took place on the evening of Saturday, April 27, 1833, grandly introduced by a printed playbill headed "Private Theatricals. Stage Manager, Mr. Charles Dickens." In addition to his principal role as Rolamo, Dickens spoke in the prologue and played the parts of Sir Charles Courtall in* The Married Bachelor *and* Wing, *"a poor Country Actor," in* Amateurs and Actors.]

To Henry Kolle

Bentinck Street, Tuesday Morning [*April 1833*]
. . . As Saturday is fast approaching, I should really be much obliged to you if you will (if you can find the time) write me a word in answer to these two questions. In the first place, do you play the Nobleman? I have the dress and if you are disinclined to play the character I must intrust it to other hands. In the second place, when may I send for your scene, as it requires fitting up, lighting, & c.?

[*April 1833*]
. . . I expect an excellent rehearsal, and "Look to yourself." The scenery is progressing at a very rapid rate, the machinery is excellent, the decorations are very good and ditto expensive; and in short the whole affair is in excellent train.

Bentinck Street, Monday morning [*April 15? 1833*]
I received your note the other day and of course much regretted the absence of any member of my company on the occasion of a

grand rehearsal. . . . May I ask you to spare one evening this week for the purpose of doing your two pair of side scenes. I would not ask you, but I really have no other resource. The time is fast approaching and I am rather nervous. Will you write and tell me when you will come and when I may send for your scene. Thursday is a rehearsal of Clari with the band and Friday week a dress rehearsal.

You shall have your bills when I see you. An immense audience are invited, including many judges. Write me an answer to these queries as soon as possible pray.

The family are busy. The corps dramatic are all anxiety. The scenery is all completing rapidly; the machinery is finished, the curtain hemmed, the orchestra complete, and the manager grimy.

Five Sketches

[*Of the sketches that follow, four* ("Mrs. Joseph Porter," "Astley's," "Greenwich Fair," and "Private Theatres") are from Sketches by Boz, and one ("The Theatrical Young Gentleman") is from Sketches of Young Gentlemen.]

MRS. JOSEPH PORTER

Most extensive were the preparations at Rose Villa, Clapham Rise, in the occupation of Mr. Gattleton (a stock-broker in especially comfortable circumstances), and great was the anxiety of Mr. Gattleton's interesting family, as the day fixed for the representation of the Private Play which had been "many months in preparation," approached. The whole family was infected with the mania for Private Theatricals; the house, usually so clean and tidy, was, to use Mr. Gattleton's expressive description, "regularly turned out o' windows"; the large dining-room, dismantled of its furniture and ornaments, presented a strange jumble of flats, flies, wings, lamps, bridges, clouds, thunder and lightning, festoons and flowers, daggers and foil, and various other messes in theatrical slang included under the comprehensive name of "properties." The bedrooms were crowded with scenery, the kitchen was occupied by carpenters. Rehearsals took place every other night in the drawing-room, and every sofa in the house was more or less damaged by the perseverance and spirit with which Mr. Sempronius Gattleton, and Miss Lucina, rehearsed the smothering scene in "Othello"— it having been determined that that tragedy should form the first portion of the evening's entertainments.

"When we're a *leetle* more perfect, I think it will go admirably," said Mr. Sempronius, addressing his *corps dramatique*, at the conclusion of the hundred and fiftieth rehearsal. In consideration of his sustaining the trifling inconvenience of bearing all the expenses of the play, Mr. Sempronius had been, in the most handsome manner, unanimously elected stage-manager. "Evans," continued Mr. Gattleton, the younger, addressing a tall, thin, pale young gentleman, with extensive whiskers, "Evans, you play *Roderigo* beautifully."

"Beautifully," echoed the three Miss Gattletons; for Mr. Evans was pronounced by all his lady friends to be "quite a dear." He looked so interesting, and had such lovely whiskers: to say nothing of his talent for writing verses in albums and playing the flute! *Roderigo* simpered and bowed.

"But I think," added the manager, "you are hardly perfect in the — fall — in the fencing-scene, where you are — you understand?"

"It's very difficult," said Mr. Evans, thoughtfully; "I've fallen about, a good deal, in our counting-house lately, for practice, only I find it hurts one so. Being obliged to fall backward, you see, it bruises one's head a good deal."

"But you must take care you don't knock a wing down," said Mr. Gattleton, the elder, who had been appointed prompter, and who took as much interest in the play as the youngest of the company. "The stage is very narrow, you know."

"Oh! don't be afraid," said Mr. Evans, with a very self-satisfied air: "I shall fall with my head 'off,' and then I can't do any harm."

"But, egad," said the manager, rubbing his hands, "we shall make a decided hit in 'Masaniello.' Harleigh sings that music admirably."

Everybody echoed the sentiment. Mr. Harleigh smiled, and looked foolish — not an unusual thing with him — hummed "Behold how brightly breaks the morning," and blushed as red as the fisherman's night-cap he was trying on.

"Let's see," resumed the manager, telling the number on his fingers, "we shall have three dancing female peasants, besides *Fenella*, and four fishermen. Then, there's our man Tom; he can have a pair of ducks of mine, and a check shirt of Bob's, and a red night-cap, and he'll do for another — that's five. In the choruses, of course, we can sing at the sides; and in the market-scene we can walk about in cloaks and things. When the revolt takes place, Tom must keep rushing in on one side and out on the other, with a pickaxe, as fast as he can.

The effect will be electrical; it will look exactly as if there were an immense number of 'em. And in the eruption scene we must burn the red fire, and upset the tea-trays, and make all sorts of noises—and it's sure to do."

"Sure! sure!" cried all the performers *unâ voce* — and away hurried Mr. Sempronius Gattleton to wash the burnt cork off his face, and superintend the "setting up" of some of the amateur-painted, but never-sufficiently-to-be-admired, scenery.

Mrs. Gattleton was a kind, good-tempered, vulgar soul, exceedingly fond of her husband and children, and entertaining only three dislikes. In the first place, she had a natural antipathy to anybody else's unmarried daughters; in the second, she was in bodily fear of anything in the shape of ridicule; lastly — almost a necessary consequence of this feeling — she regarded, with feelings of the utmost horror, one Mrs. Joseph Porter over the way. However, the good folks of Clapham and its vicinity stood very much in awe of scandal and sarcasm; and thus Mrs. Joseph Porter was courted, and flattered, and caressed, and invited, for much the same reason that induces a poor author, without a farthing in his pocket, to behave with extraordinary civility to a twopenny postman.

"Never mind, ma," said Miss Emma Porter, in colloquy with her respected relative, and trying to look unconcerned; "if they had invited me, you know that neither you nor pa would have allowed me to take part in such an exhibition."

"Just what I should have thought from your high sense of propriety," returned the mother. "I am glad to see, Emma, you know how to designate the proceeding." Miss P., by the bye, had only the week before made "an exhibition" of herself for four days, behind a counter at a fancy fair, to all and every of her Majesty's liege subjects who were disposed to pay a shilling each for the privilege of seeing some four dozen girls flirting with strangers, and playing at shop.

"There!" said Mrs. Porter, looking out of window; "there are two rounds of beef and a ham going in — clearly for sandwiches; and Thomas, the pastrycook, says, there have been twelve dozen tarts ordered, besides blanc-mange and jellies. Upon my word! think of the Miss Gattletons in fancy dresses, too!"

"Oh, it's too ridiculous!" said Miss Porter, hysterically.

"I'll manage to put them a little out of conceit with the business, however," said Mrs. Porter; and out she went on her charitable errand.

"Well, my dear Mrs. Gattleton," said Mrs. Joseph Porter, after they had been closeted for some time, and when, by dint of indefatigable pumping, she had managed to extract all the news about the play, "well, my dear, people may say what they please; indeed we know they will, for some folks are *so* ill-natured. Ah, my dear Miss Lucina, how d' ye do? I was just telling your mamma that I have heard it said, that —"

"What?"

"Mrs. Porter is alluding to the play, my dear," said Mrs. Gattleton; "she was, I am sorry to say, just informing me that —"

"Oh, now pray don't mention it," interrupted Mrs. Porter; "it's most absurd — quite as absurd as young What's-his-name saying he wondered how Miss Caroline, with such a foot and ankle, could have the vanity to play *Fenella*."

"Highly impertinent, whoever said it," said Mrs. Gattleton, bridling up.

"Certainly, my dear," chimed in the delighted Mrs. Porter; "most undoubtedly! Because, as I said, if Miss Caroline *does* play *Fenella*, it doesn't follow, as a matter of course, that she should think she has a pretty foot; — and then — such puppies as these young men are — he had the impudence to say, that —"

How far the amiable Mrs. Porter might have succeeded in her pleasant purpose, it is impossible to say, had not the entrance of Mr. Thomas Balderstone, Mrs. Gattleton's brother, familiarly called in the family, "Uncle Tom," changed the course of conversation, and suggested to her mind an excellent plan of operation on the evening of the play.

Uncle Tom was very rich, and exceedingly fond of his nephews and nieces: as a matter of course, therefore, he was an object of great importance in his own family. He was one of the best-hearted men in existence: always in a good temper, and always talking. It was his boast that he wore top-boots on all occasions, and had never worn a black silk neckerchief; and it was his pride that he remembered all the principal plays of Shakespeare from beginning to end — and so he did. The result of this parrot-like accomplishment was, that he was not only perpetually quoting himself, but that he could never sit by, and hear a misquotation from the "Swan of Avon" without setting the unfortunate delinquent right. He was also something of a wag; never missed an opportunity of saying what he considered a good thing, and invariably laughed until he cried at anything that appeared to him mirth-moving or ridiculous.

"Well, girls!" said Uncle Tom, after the preparatory ceremony of kissing and how-d' ye-do-ing had been gone through — "how d' ye get on? Know your parts, eh? — Lucina, my dear, act ii., scene 1 — place, left — cue — 'Unknown fate,' — What's next, eh? — Go on — 'The heavens — '"

"Oh, yes," said Miss Lucina, "I recollect —

'The heavens forbid
But that our loves and comforts should increase
Even as our days do grow!'"

"Make a pause here and there," said the old gentleman, who was a great critic. "'But that our loves and comforts should increase' — emphasis on the last syllable, 'crease,' — loud 'even,' — one, two, three, four; then loud again, 'as our days do grow'; emphasis on *days*. That's the way, my dear; trust to your uncle for emphasis. Ah! Sem, my boy, how are you?"

"Very well, thank'ee, uncle," returned Mr. Sempronius, who had just appeared, looking something like a ringdove, with a small circle round each eye: the result of his constant corking. "Of course we see you on Thursday."

"Of course, of course, my dear boy."

"What a pity it is your nephew didn't think of making you prompter, Mr. Balderstone!" whispered Mrs. Joseph Porter; "you would have been invaluable."

"Well, I flatter myself, I *should* have been tolerably up to the thing," responded Uncle Tom.

"I must bespeak sitting next you on the night," resumed Mrs. Porter; "and then, if our dear young friends here, should be at all wrong, you will be able to enlighten me. I shall be so interested."

"I am sure I shall be most happy to give you any assistance in my power."

"Mind, it's a bargain."

"Certainly."

"I don't know how it is," said Mrs. Gattleton to her daughters, as they were sitting round the fire in the evening, looking over their parts, "but I really very much wish Mrs. Joseph Porter wasn't coming on Thursday. I am sure she's scheming something."

"She can't make *us* ridiculous, however," observed Mr. Sempronius Gattleton, haughtily.

The long-looked-for Thursday arrived in due course, and brought with it, as Mr. Gattleton, senior, philosophically observed, "no disappointments, to speak of." True, it was yet a matter of doubt whether *Cassio* would be enabled to get into the dress which had been sent for him from the masquerade warehouse. It was equally uncertain whether the principal female singer would be sufficiently recovered from the influenza to make her appearance; Mr. Harleigh, the *Masaniello* of the night, was hoarse, and rather unwell, in consequence of the great quantity of lemon and sugar-candy he had eaten to improve his voice; and two flutes and a violoncello had pleaded severe colds. What of that? the audience were all coming. Everybody knew his part: the dresses were covered with tinsel and spangles; the white plumes looked beautiful; Mr. Evans had practised falling until he was bruised from head to foot and quite perfect; *Iago* was sure that, in the stabbing-scene, he should make "a decided hit." A self-taught deaf gentleman, who had kindly offered to bring his flute, would be a most valuable addition to the orchestra; Miss Jenkins's talent for the piano was too well known to be doubted for an instant; Mr. Cape had practised the violin accompaniment with her frequently; and Mr. Brown, who had kindly undertaken, at a few hours' notice, to bring his violoncello, would, no doubt, manage extremely well.

Seven o'clock came, and so did the audience; all the rank and fashion of Clapham and its vicinity was fast filling the theatre. There were the Smiths, the Gubbinses, the Nixons, the Dixons, the Hicksons, people with all sorts of names, two aldermen, a sheriff in perspective, Sir Thomas Glumper (who had been knighted in the last reign for carrying up an address on somebody's escaping from nothing); and last, not least, there were Mrs. Joseph Porter and Uncle Tom, seated in the centre of the third row from the stage; Mrs. P. amusing

Uncle Tom with all sorts of stories, and Uncle Tom amusing everyone else by laughing most immoderately.

Ting, ting, ting! went the prompter's bell at eight o'clock precisely, and dash went the orchestra into the overture to "The Men of Prometheus." The pianoforte player hammered away with laudable perseverance; and the violoncello, which struck in at intervals, "sounded very well, considering." The unfortunate individual, however, who had undertaken to play the flute accompaniment "at sight," found, from fatal experience, the perfect truth of the old adage, "out of sight, out of mind"; for being very near-sighted, and being placed at a considerable distance from his music-book, all he had an opportunity of doing was to play a bar now and then in the wrong place, and put the other performers out. It is, however, but justice to Mr. Brown to say that he did this to admiration. The overture, in fact, was not unlike a race between the different instruments; the piano came in first by several bars, and the violoncello next, quite distancing the poor flute; for the deaf gentleman *too-too'd* away, quite unconscious that he was at all wrong, until apprised, by the applause of the audience, that the overture was concluded. A considerable bustle and shuffling of feet was then heard upon the stage, accompanied by whispers of "Here's a pretty go! — what's to be done?" etc. The audience applauded again, by way of raising the spirits of the performers; and then Mr. Sempronius desired the prompter, in a very audible voice, to "clear the stage, and ring up."

Ting, ting, ting! went the bell again. Everybody sat down; the curtain shook; rose sufficiently high to display several pair of yellow boots paddling about; and there remained.

Ting, ting, ting! went the bell again. The curtain was violently convulsed, but rose no higher; the audience tittered; Mrs. Porter looked at Uncle Tom; Uncle Tom looked at everybody, rubbing his hands, and laughing with perfect rapture. After as much ringing with the little bell as a muffin-boy would make in going down a tolerably long street, and a vast deal of whispering, hammering, and calling for nails and cord, the curtain at length rose, and discovered Mr. Sempronius Gattleton *solus*, and decked for *Othello*. After three distinct rounds of applause, during which Mr. Sempronius applied his right hand to his left breast, and bowed in the most approved manner, the manager advanced and said —

"Ladies and Gentlemen — I assure you it is with sincere regret, that I regret to be compelled to inform you, that *Iago* who was to have played Mr. Wilson — I beg your pardon, Ladies and Gentlemen, but I am naturally somewhat agitated (applause) — I mean, Mr. Wilson, who was to have played *Iago*, is — that is, has been — or, in other words, Ladies and Gentlemen, the fact is, that I have just received a note, in which I am informed that *Iago* is unavoidably detained at the Post-office this evening. Under these circumstances, I trust — a — a — amateur performance — a — another gentleman undertaken to read the part — request indulgence for a short time — courtesy and kindness of a British audience." Overwhelming applause. Exit Mr. Sempronius Gattleton, and curtain falls.

The audience were, of course, exceedingly good-humoured; the whole business was a joke; and accordingly they waited for an hour with the utmost patience, being enlivened by an interlude of rout-cakes and lemonade. It appeared by Mr. Sempronius's subsequent explanation, that the delay would not have been so great, had it not so happened that when the substitute *Iago* had finished dressing, and just as the play was on the point of commencing, the original *Iago* unexpectedly arrived. The former was therefore compelled to undress, and the latter to dress for his part; which, as he found some difficulty in getting into his clothes, occupied no inconsiderable time. At last, the tragedy began in real earnest. It went off well enough, until the third scene of the first act, in which *Othello* addresses the Senate: the only remarkable circumstance being, that as *Iago* could not get on any of the stage boots, in consequence of his feet being violently swelled with the heat and excitement, he was under the necessity of playing the part in a pair of Wellingtons, which contrasted rather oddly with his richly embroidered pantaloons. When *Othello* started with his address to the Senate (whose dignity was represented by, the *Duke,* a carpenter, two men engaged on the recommendation of the gardener, and a boy), Mrs. Porter found the opportunity she so anxiously sought.

Mr. Sempronius proceeded —

> " 'Most potent, grave, and reverend signiors,
> My very noble and approv'd good masters,
> That I have ta'en away this old man's daughter,
> It is most true; — rude am I in my speech — ' "

"Is that right?" whispered Mrs. Porter to Uncle Tom.

"No."

"Tell him so, then."

"I will. Sem!" called out Uncle Tom, "that's wrong, my boy."

"What's wrong, Uncle?" demanded *Othello,* quite forgetting the dignity of his situation.

"You've left out something. 'True I have married —' "

"Oh, ah!" said Mr. Sempronius, endeavouring to hide his confusion as much and as ineffectually as the audience attempted to conceal their half-suppressed tittering, by coughing with extraordinary violence —

—— " 'true I have married her; —
The very head and front of my offending
Hath this extent; no more.'

(*Aside*) Why don't you prompt, father?"

"Because I've mislaid my spectacles," said poor Mr. Gattleton, almost dead with the heat and bustle.

"There, now it's 'rude am I,' " said Uncle Tom.

"Yes, I know it is," returned the unfortunate manager, proceeding with his part.

It would be useless and tiresome to quote the number of instances in which Uncle Tom, now completely in his element, and instigated by the mischievous Mrs. Porter, corrected the mistakes of the performers; suffice it to say, that having mounted his hobby, nothing could induce him to dismount; so, during the whole remainder of the play, he performed a kind of running accompaniment, by muttering everybody's part as it was being delivered, in an undertone. The audience were highly amused, Mrs. Porter delighted, the performers embarrassed; Uncle Tom never was better pleased in all his life; and Uncle Tom's nephews and nieces had never, although the declared heirs to his large property, so heartily wished him gathered to his fathers as on that memorable occasion.

Several other minor causes, too, united to damp the ardour of the *dramatis personae.* None of the performers could walk in their tights, or move their arms in their jackets; the pantaloons were too small, the boots too large, and the swords of all shapes and sizes. Mr. Evans, naturally too tall for the scenery, wore a black velvet hat with immense white plumes, the glory of which was lost in "the flies"; and the only other inconvenience of which was, that when it was off his head he could not put it on, and when it was on he could not take it off. Notwithstanding all his practice, too, he fell with his head and shoulders as neatly through one of the side-scenes, as a harlequin would jump through a panel in a Christmas pantomime. The piano-forte player, overpowered by the extreme heat of the room, fainted away at the commencement of the entertainments, leaving the music of "Masaniello" to the flute and violoncello. The orchestra com-plained that Mr. Harleigh put them out, and Mr. Harleigh declared that the orchestra prevented his singing a note. The fishermen, who were hired for the occasion, revolted to the very life, positively refus-ing to play without an increased allowance of spirits; and, their de-mand being complied with, getting drunk in the eruption scene as naturally as possible. The red fire, which was burnt at the conclusion of the second act, not only nearly suffocated the audience, but nearly set the house on fire into the bargain; and, as it was, the remainder of the piece was acted in a thick fog.

In short, the whole affair was, as Mrs. Joseph Porter triumphantly told everybody, "a complete failure." The audience went home at four o'clock in the morning, exhausted with laughter, suffering from severe headaches, and smelling terribly of brimstone and gunpowder. The Messrs. Gattleton, senior and junior, retired to rest, with the vague idea of emigrating to Swan River early in the ensuing week.

Rose Villa has once again resumed its wonted appearance; the dining-room furniture has been replaced; the tables are as nicely polished as formerly; the horsehair chairs are ranged against the wall, as regularly as ever; Venetian blinds have been fitted to every window in the house to intercept the prying gaze of Mrs. Joseph Porter. The subject of theatricals is never mentioned in the Gattleton family, un-less, indeed, by Uncle Tom, who cannot refrain from sometimes ex-pressing his surprise and regret at finding that his nephews and nieces appear to have lost the relish they once possessed for the beauties of Shakespeare, and quotations from the works of that immortal bard.

ASTLEY'S

We never see any very large, staring, black Roman capitals, in a book,
or shop-window, or placarded on a wall, without their immediately
recalling to our mind an indistinct and confused recollection of the
time when we were first initiated in the mysteries of the alphabet. We
almost fancy we see the pin's point following the letter, to impress its
form more strongly on our bewildered imagination; and wince involuntarily, as we remember the hard knuckles with which the reverend
old lady who instilled into our mind the first principles of education
for ninepence per week, or ten and sixpence per quarter, was wont
to poke our juvenile head occasionally, by way of adjusting the confusion of ideas in which we were generally involved. The same kind
of feeling pursues us in many other instances, but there is no place
which recalls so strongly our recollections of childhood as Astley's.
It was not a "Royal Amphitheatre" in those days, nor had Ducrow
arisen to shed the light of classic taste and portable gas over the sawdust of the circus; but the whole character of the place was the same,
the pieces were the same, the clown's jokes were the same, the riding-
masters were equally grand, the comic performers equally witty, the
tragedians equally hoarse, and the "highly-trained chargers" equally
spirited. Astley's has altered for the better — we have changed for
the worse. Our histrionic taste is gone, and with shame we confess,.
that we are far more delighted and amused with the audience, than
with the pageantry we once so highly appreciated.

We like to watch a regular Astley's party in the Easter or Midsummer holidays — pa and ma, and nine or ten children, varying
from five foot six to two foot eleven: from fourteen years of age to
four. We had just taken our seat in one of the boxes, in the centre of
the house, the other night, when the next was occupied by just such
a party as we should have attempted to describe, had we depicted our
beau ideal of a group of Astley's visitors.

First of all, there came three little boys and a little girl, who, in
pursuance of pa's directions, issued in a very audible voice from the
box-door, occupied the front row; then two more little girls were
ushered in by a young lady, evidently the governess. Then came three
more little boys, dressed like the first, in blue jackets and trousers,

with lay-down shirtcollars: then a child in a braided frock and high state of astonishment, with very large round eyes, opened to their utmost width, was lifted over the seats — a process which occasioned a considerable display of little pink legs — then came ma and pa, and then the eldest son, a boy of fourteen years old, who was evidently trying to look as if he did not belong to the family.

The first five minutes were occupied in taking the shawls off the little girls, and adjusting the bows which ornamented their hair; then it was providentially discovered that one of the little boys was seated behind a pillar and could not see, so the governess was stuck behind the pillar, and the boy lifted into her place. Then pa drilled the boys, and directed the stowing away of their pocket-handkerchiefs, and ma having first nodded and winked to the governess to pull the girls' frocks a little more off their shoulders, stood up to review the little troop — an inspection which appeared to terminate much to her own satisfaction, for she looked with a complacent air at pa, who was standing up at the further end of the seat. Pa returned the glance, and blew his nose very emphatically; and the poor governess peeped out from behind the pillar, and timidly tried to catch ma's eye, with a look expressive of her high admiration of the whole family. Then two of the little boys who had been discussing the point whether Astley's was more than twice as large as Drury Lane, agreed to refer it to "George" for his decision; at which "George," who was no other than the young gentleman before noticed, waxed indignant, and remonstrated in no very gentle terms on the gross impropriety of having his name repeated in so loud a voice at a public place, on which all the children laughed very heartily, and one of the little boys wound up by expressing his opinion, that "George began to think himself quite a man now," whereupon both pa and ma laughed too; and George (who carried a dress cane and was cultivating whiskers) muttered that "William always was encouraged in his impertinence"; and assumed a look of profound contempt, which lasted the whole evening.

The play began, and the interest of the little boys knew no bounds. Pa was clearly interested too, although he very unsuccessfully endeavoured to look as if he wasn't. As for ma, she was perfectly overcome by the drollery of the principal comedian, and laughed till every one of the immense bows on her ample cap trembled, at which the governess peeped out from behind the pillar again, and whenever she could catch ma's eye, put her handkerchief to her mouth, and appeared, as in duty bound, to be in convulsions of laughter also. Then when the man in the splendid armour vowed to rescue the lady or perish in the attempt, the little boys applauded vehemently, especially one little fellow who was apparently on a visit to the family, and had been carrying on a child's flirtation, the whole evening, with a small coquette of twelve years old, who looked like a model of her mamma on a reduced scale; and who, in common with the other little girls (who generally speaking have even more coquettishness about them than much older ones), looked very properly shocked, when the knight's squire kissed the princess's confidential chambermaid.

When the scenes in the circle commenced, the children were more delighted than ever; and the wish to see what was going forward, completely conquering pa's dignity, he stood up in the box, and applauded as loudly as any of them. Between each feat of horsemanship, the governess leant across to ma, and retailed the clever remarks of the children on that which had preceded: and ma, in the openness of her heart, offered the governess an acidulated drop, and the governess, gratified to be taken notice of, retired behind her pillar again with a brighter countenance: and the whole party seemed quite happy, except the exquisite in the back of the box, who, being too grand to take any interest in the children, and too insignificant to be taken notice of by anybody else, occupied himself, from time to time, in rubbing the place where the whiskers ought to be, and was completely alone in his glory.

We defy any one who has been to Astley's two or three times, and is consequently capable of appreciating the perseverance with which precisely the same jokes are repeated night after night, and season after season, not to be amused with one part of the performances at least — we mean the scenes in the circle. For ourself, we know that when the hoop, composed of jets of gas, is let down, the curtain drawn up for the convenience of the half-price on their ejectment from the ring, the orange-peel cleared away, and the sawdust shaken, with mathematical precision, into a complete circle, we feel as much enlivened as the youngest child present; and actually join in the laugh which follows the clown's shrill shout of "Here we are!" just for old acquaintance' sake. Nor can we quite divest ourself of our old feeling of reverence for the riding-master, who follows the clown with a long whip in his hand, and bows to the audience with graceful dignity. He is none of your second-rate riding-masters in nankeen dressing-gowns, with brown frogs, but the regular gentleman-attendant on the principal riders, who always wears a military uniform with a tablecloth inside the breast of the coat, in which costume he forcibly reminds one of a fowl trussed for roasting. He is — but why should we attempt to describe that of which no description can convey an adequate idea? Everybody knows the man, and everybody remembers his polished boots, his graceful demeanour, stiff, as some misjudging persons have in their jealousy considered it, and the splendid head of black hair, parted high on the forehead, to impart to the countenance an appearance of deep thought and poetic melancholy. His soft and pleasing voice, too, is in perfect unison with his noble bearing, as he humours the clown by indulging in a little badinage; and the striking recollection of his own dignity, with which he exclaims, "Now, sir, if you please, inquire for Miss Woolford, sir," can never be forgotten. The graceful air, too, with which he introduces Miss Woolford into the arena, and, after assisting her to the saddle, follows her fairy courser round the circle, can never fail to create a deep impression in the bosom of every female servant present.

When Miss Woolford, and the horse, and the orchestra, all stop together to take breath, he urbanely takes part in some such dialogue as the following (commenced by the clown): "I say, sir!" — "Well, sir?" (it's always conducted in the politest manner). — "Did you ever happen to hear I was in the army, sir?" — "No, sir." — "Oh, yes, sir — I can go through my exercise, sir." — "Indeed, sir!" — "Shall I do it now, sir?" — "If you please, sir; come, sir — make haste" (a cut with the long whip, and "Ha' done now — I don't like it," from the clown). Here the clown throws himself on the ground, and goes through a variety of gymnastic convulsions, doubling himself up, and untying himself again, and making himself look very like a man in the most hopeless extreme of human agony, to the vociferous delight of the gallery, until he is interrupted by a second cut from the long whip, and a request to see "what Miss Woolford's stopping for?" On which, to the inexpressible mirth of the gallery, he exclaims, "Now, Miss Woolford, what can I come for to go, for to fetch, for to bring, for to carry, for to do, for you, ma'am?" On the lady's announcing

with a sweet smile that she wants the two flags, they are, with sun-
dry grimaces, procured and handed up; the clown facetiously observing after the performance of the latter ceremony — "He, he, oh! I
say, sir, Miss Woolford knows me; she smiled at me." Another cut
from the whip, a burst from the orchestra, a start from the horse, and
round goes Miss Woolford again on her graceful performance, to the
delight of every member of the audience, young or old. The next
pause affords an opportunity for similar witticisms, the only additional fun being that of the clown making ludicrous grimaces at the
riding-master every time his back is turned; and finally quitting the
circle by jumping over his head, having previously directed his attention another way.

Did any of our readers ever notice the class of people, who hang
about the stage-doors of our minor theatres in the daytime. You will
rarely pass one of these entrances without seeing a group of three or
four men conversing on the pavement, with an indescribable public-
house-parlour swagger, and a kind of conscious air, peculiar to people
of this description. They always seem to think they are exhibiting;
the lamps are ever before them. That young fellow in the faded
brown coat, and very full light green trousers, pulls down the wristbands of his check shirt, as ostentatiously as if it were of the finest
linen, and cocks the white hat of the summer-before-last as know-
ingly over his right eye, as if it were a purchase of yesterday. Look at
the dirty white Berlin gloves, and the cheap silk-handkerchief stuck
in the bosom of his threadbare coat. Is it possible to see him for an
instant, and not come to the conclusion that he is the walking gentleman who wears a blue surtout, clean collar, and white trousers, for
half an hour, and then shrinks into his worn-out scanty clothes: who
has to boast night after night of his splendid fortune, with the painful consciousness of a pound a week and his boots to find: to talk of
his father's mansion in the country, with a dreary recollection of his
own two-pair back, in the New Cut; and to be envied and flattered
as the favoured lover of a rich heiress, remembering all the while that
the ex-dancer at home is in the family way, and out of an engagement?

Next to him, perhaps, you will see a thin pale man, with a very
long face, in a suit of shining black, thoughtfully knocking that part
of his boot which once had a heel, with an ash stick. He is the man

who does the heavy business, such as prosy fathers, virtuous servants, curates, landlords, and so fourth.

By the way, talking of fathers, we should very much like to see some piece in which all the dramatis personae were orphans. Fathers are invariably great nuisances on the stage, and always have to give the hero or heroine a long explanation of what was done before the curtain rose, usually commencing with "It is now nineteen years, my dear child, since your blessed mother (here the old villain's voice falters) confided you to my charge. You were then an infant," etc., etc. Or else they have to discover, all of a sudden, that somebody whom they have been in constant communication with, during three long acts, without the slightest suspicion, is their own child: in which case they exclaim, "Ah! what do I see? This bracelet! That smile! These documents! Those eyes! Can I believe my senses? — It must be! — Yes — it is, it is my child!" — "My father!" exclaims the child; and they fall into each other's arms, and look over each other's shoulders, and the audience give three rounds of applause.

To return from this digression, we were about to say, that these are the sort of people whom you see talking, and attitudinising, outside the stage-doors of our minor theatres. At Astley's they are always more numerous than at any other place. There is generally a groom or two, sitting on the window-sill, and two or three dirty shabby-genteel men in checked neckerchiefs, and sallow linen, lounging about, and carrying, perhaps, under one arm, a pair of stage shoes badly wrapped up in a piece of old newspaper. Some years ago we used to stand looking, open-mouthed, at these men, with a feeling of mysterious curiosity, the very recollection of which provokes a smile at the moment we are writing. We could not believe that the beings of light and elegance, in milk-white tunics, salmon-coloured legs, and blue scarfs, who flitted on sleek cream-coloured horses before our eyes at night, with all the aid of lights, music, and artificial flowers, could be the pale, dissipated-looking creatures we beheld by day.

We can hardly believe it now. Of the lower class of actors we have seen something, and it requires no great exercise of imagination to identify the walking gentleman with the "dirty swell," the comic singer with the public-house chairman, or the leading tragedian with drunkenness and distress; but these other men are mysterious beings, never seen out of the ring, never beheld but in the costume of gods and sylphs. With the exception of Ducrow, who can scarcely be classed among them, who ever knew a rider at Astley's, or saw him but on horseback? Can our friend in the military uniform, ever appear in threadbare attire, or descend to the comparatively unwadded costume of everyday life? Impossible! We cannot — we will not — believe it.

GREENWICH FAIR

If the Parks be "the lungs of London," we wonder what Greenwich Fair is — a periodical breaking out, we suppose, a sort of spring-rash: a three days' fever, which cools the blood for six months afterwards, and at the expiration of which London is restored to its old habits of plodding industry, as suddenly and completely as if nothing had ever happened to disturb them.

In our earlier days, we were a constant frequenter of Greenwich Fair, for years. We have proceeded to, and returned from it, in almost every description of vehicle. We cannot conscientiously deny the charge of having once made the passage in a spring-van, accompanied by thirteen gentlemen, fourteen ladies, an unlimited number of children, and a barrel of beer; and we have a vague recollection of having, in later days, found ourself the eighth outside, on the top of a hackney-coach, at something past four o'clock in the morning, with a rather confused idea of our own name, or place of residence. We have grown older since then, and quiet, and steady: liking nothing better than to spend our Easter, and all our other holidays, in some quiet nook, with people of whom we shall never tire; but we think we still remember something of Greenwich Fair, and of those who resort to it. At all events we will try.

The road to Greenwich during the whole of Easter Monday, is in a state of perpetual bustle and noise. Cabs, hackney-coaches, "shay" carts, coal-waggons, stages, omnibuses, sociables, gigs, donkey-chaises — all crammed with people (for the question never is, what the horse can draw, but what the vehicle will hold), roll along at their utmost speed; the dust flies in clouds, ginger-beer corks go off in volleys, the balcony of every public-house is crowded with people, smoking and drinking, half the private houses are turned into tea-shops, fiddles are in great request, every little fruit-shop displays its stall of gilt ginger-bread and penny toys; turnpike men are in despair; horses won't go on, and wheels will come off; ladies in "carawans" scream with fright at every fresh concussion, and their admirers find it necessary to sit remarkably close to them, by way of encouragement; servants of all work, who are not allowed to have followers, and have got a holiday for the day, make the most of their time with the faithful admirer who waits for a stolen interview at the corner of the street every night, when they go to fetch the beer — apprentices grow senti-mental, and straw-bonnet makers kind. Everybody is anxious to get on, and actuated by the common wish to be at the fair, or in the park, as soon as possible.

Pedestrians linger in groups at the roadside, unable to resist the allurements of the stout proprietress of the "Jack-in-the-box, three shies a penny," or the more splendid offers of the man with three thimbles and a pea on a little round board, who astonishes the be-wildered crowd with some such address as, "Here's the sort o' game to make you laugh seven years arter you're dead, and turn ev'ry air on your ed gray vith delight! Three thimbles and vun little pea — with a vun, two, three, and a two, three, vun: catch him who can, look on, keep your eyes open, and niver say die! niver mind the charge, and the expense: all fair and above board: them as don't play can't vin, and luck attend the ryal sportsman! Bet any gen'l'm'n any sum of money, from harf-a-crown up to a suverin, as he doesn't name the thimble as kivers the pea!" Here some greenhorn whispers his friend that he distinctly saw the pea roll under the middle thimble — an impression which is immediately confirmed by a gentleman in top-boots, who is standing by, and who, in a low tone, regrets his own inability to bet, in consequence of having unfortunately left his purse at home, but strongly urges the stranger not to neglect such a golden opportunity. The "plant" is successful, the bet is made, the stranger of course loses: and the gentleman with the thimbles consoles him, as he pockets the money, with an assurance that it's 'all the fortin of war! this time I vin, next time you vin: niver mind the loss of two bob and a bender! Do it up in a small parcel, and break out in a fresh place. Here's the sort o' game,' etc. — and the eloquent ha-rangue, with such variations as the speaker's exuberant fancy suggests, is again repeated to the gaping crowd, reinforced by the accession of several new comers.

The chief place of resort in the daytime, after the public-houses, is the park, in which the principal amusement is to drag young ladies up the steep hill which leads to the Observatory, and then drag them down again, at the very top of their speed, greatly to the derangement of their curls and bonnet-caps, and much to the edification of lookers-on from below. "Kiss in the Ring," and "Threading my Grandmother's Needle," too, are sports which receive their full share of patronage. Love-sick swains, under the influence of gin-and-water, and the tender passion, become violently affectionate: and the fair objects of their regard enhance the value of stolen kisses, by a vast deal of struggling, and holding down of heads, and cries of "Oh! Ha' done, then, George — Oh, do tickle him for me, Mary — Well, I never!" and similar Lucretian ejaculations. Little old men and women, with a small basket under one arm, and a wine-glass, without a foot, in the other hand, tender "a drop o' the right sort" to the different groups; and young ladies, who are persuaded to indulge in a drop of the aforesaid right sort, display a pleasing degree of reluctance to taste it, and cough afterwards with great propriety.

The old pensioners, who, for the moderate charge of a penny, exhibit the mast-house, the Thames and shipping, the place where the men used to hang in chains, and other interesting sights, through a telescope, are asked questions about objects within the range of the glass, which it would puzzle a Solomon to answer; and requested to find out particular houses in particular streets, which it would have been a task of some difficulty for Mr. Horner (not the young gentleman who ate mince-pies with his thumb, but the man of Colosseum notoriety) to discover. Here and there, where some three or four couples are sitting on the grass together, you will see a sunburnt woman in a red cloak "telling fortunes" and prophesying husbands, which it requires no extraordinary observation to describe, for the originals are before her. Thereupon, the lady concerned laughs and blushes, and ultimately buries her face in an imitation cambric handkerchief, and the gentleman described looks extremely foolish, and squeezes her hand, and fees the gipsy liberally; and the gipsy goes away, perfectly satisfied with herself, and leaving those behind her perfectly satisfied also: and the prophecy, like many other prophecies of greater importance, fulfils itself in time.

But it grows dark: the crowd has gradually dispersed, and only a few stragglers are left behind. The light in the direction of the church shows that the fair is illuminated; and the distant noise proves it to be filling fast. The spot, which half an hour ago was ringing with the shouts of boisterous mirth, is as calm and quiet as if nothing could ever disturb its serenity; the fine old trees, the majestic building at their feet, with the noble river beyond, glistening in the moonlight, appear in all their beauty, and under their most favourable aspect; the voices of the boys, singing their evening hymn, are borne gently on the air; and the humblest mechanic who has been lingering on the grass so pleasant to the feet that beat the same dull round from week to week in the paved streets of London, feels proud to think, as he surveys the scene before him, that he belongs to the country which has selected such a spot as a retreat for its oldest and best defenders in the decline of their lives.

Five minutes' walking brings you to the fair; a scene calculated to awaken very different feelings. The entrance is occupied on either side by the vendors of gingerbread and toys: the stalls are gaily lighted up, the most attractive goods profusely disposed, and unbonneted young ladies, in their zeal for the interest of their employers, seize you by the coat, and use all the blandishments of "Do, dear" — "There's a love" — "Don't be cross, now," etc., to induce you to purchase half a pound of the real spice nuts, of which the majority of the regular fair-goers carry a pound or two as a present supply, tied up in a cotton pocket-handkerchief. Occasionally you pass a deal table, on which are exposed pen'orths of pickled salmon (fennel included), in little white saucers: oysters, with shells as large as cheese-plates, and divers specimens of a species of snail (*wilks*, we think they are called), floating in a somewhat bilious-looking green liquid. Cigars, too, are in great demand; gentlemen must smoke, of course, and here they are, two a penny, in a regular authentic cigar-box, with a lighted tallow candle in the centre.

Imagine yourself in an extremely dense crowd, which swings you to and fro, and in and out, and every way but the right one; add to this the screams of women, the shouts of boys, the clanging of gongs, the firing of pistols, the ringing of bells, the bellowings of speaking-trumpets, the squeaking of penny dittoes, the noise of a dozen bands, with three drums in each, all playing different tunes at the same time, the hallooing of showmen, and an occasional roar from the wild-beast shows; and you are in the very centre and heart of the fair.

This immense booth, with the large stage in front, so brightly illuminated with variegated lamps, and pots of burning fat, is "Richardson's," where you have a melodrama (with three murders and a ghost), a pantomime, a comic song, an overture, and some incidental music, all done in five-and-twenty minutes.

The company are now promenading outside in all the dignity of wigs, spangles, red-ochre, and whitening. See with what a ferocious air the gentleman who personates the Mexican chief, paces up and down, and with what an eye of calm dignity the principal tragedian gazes on the crowd below, or converses confidentially with the harlequin! The four clowns, who are engaged in a mock broadsword combat, may be all very well for the low-minded holiday-makers; but these are the people for the reflective portion of the community. They look so noble in those Roman dresses, with their yellow legs and arms, long black curly heads, bushy eyebrows, and scowl expressive of assassination, and vengeance, and everything else that is grand and solemn. Then, the ladies — were there ever such innocent and awful-looking beings; as they walk up and down the platform in twos and threes, with their arms round each other's waists, or leaning for support on one of those majestic men? Their spangled muslin dresses and blue satin shoes and sandals (a *leetle* the worse for wear) are the admiration of all beholders; and the playful manner in which they check the advances of the clown, is perfectly enchanting.

"Just a going to begin! Pray come for'erd, come for'erd," exclaims the man in the countryman's dress, for the seventieth time: and people force their way up the steps in crowds. The band suddenly strikes up, the harlequin and columbine set the example, reels are formed in less than no time, the Roman heroes place their arms akimbo, and dance with considerable agility; and the leading tragic actress, and the gentleman who enacts the "swell" in the pantomime, foot it to perfection. "All in to begin," shouts the manager, when no more people can be induced to "come for'erd," and away rush the leading members of the company to do the dreadful in the first piece.

A change of performance takes place every day during the fair, but the story of the tragedy is always pretty much the same. There is a rightful heir, who loves a young lady, and is beloved by her; and a wrongful heir, who loves her too, and isn't beloved by her; and the wrongful heir gets hold of the rightful heir, and throws him into a dungeon, just to kill him off when convenient, for which purpose he hires a couple of assassins — a good one and a bad one — who, the moment they are left alone, get up a little murder on their own account, the good one killing the bad one, and the bad one wounding the good one. Then the rightful heir is discovered in prison, carefully holding a long chain in his hands, and seated despondingly in a large arm-chair; and the young lady comes in to two bars of soft music, and embraces the rightful heir; and then the wrongful heir comes in to two bars of quick music (technically called "a hurry"), and goes on in the most shocking manner, throwing the young lady about as if she was nobody, and calling the rightful heir "Ar-recreant — ar-wretch!" in a very loud voice, which answers the double purpose of displaying his passion, and preventing the sound being deadened by the sawdust. The interest becomes intense; the wrongful heir draws his sword, and rushes on the rightful heir; a blue smoke is seen, a gong is heard, and a tall white figure (who has been all this time, behind the arm-chair, covered over with a table-cloth), slowly rises to the tune of "Oft in the stilly night." This is no other than the ghost of the rightful heir's father, who was killed by the wrongful heir's father, at sight of which the wrongful heir becomes apoplectic, and is literally "struck all of a heap," the stage not being large enough to admit of his falling down at full length. Then the good assassin staggers in, and says he was hired in conjunction with the bad assassin, by the wrongful heir, to kill the rightful heir; and he's killed a good many people in his time, but he's very sorry for it, and won't do so any more — a promise which he immediately redeems, by dying off-hand without any nonsense about it. Then the rightful heir throws down his chain; and then two men, a sailor, and a young woman (the tenentry of the rightful heir) come in, and the ghost makes dumb motions to them, which they, by supernatural interference understand — for no one else can; and the ghost (who can't do anything without blue fire) blesses the rightful heir and the young lady, by half suffocating them with smoke: and then a muffin-bell rings, and the curtain drops.

The exhibitions next in popularity to these itinerant theatres are the travelling menageries, or, to speak more intelligibly, the "Wild-beast shows," where a military band in beefeaters' costume, with leopard-skin caps, play incessantly; and where large highly-coloured representations of tigers tearing men's heads open, and a lion being burnt with red-hot irons to induce him to drop his victim, are hung up outside, by way of attracting visitors.

The principal officer at these places is generally a very tall, hoarse man, in a scarlet coat, with a cane in his hand, with which he occasionally raps the pictures we have just noticed, by way of illustrating his description — something in this way. "Here, here, here; the lion, the lion (tap), exactly as he is represented on the canvas outside (three taps) : no waiting, remember; no deception. The fe-rocious lion (tap, tap) who bit off the gentleman's head last Cambervel vos a twelvemonth, and has killed on the awerage three keepers a year ever since he arrived at matoority. No extra charge on this account recollect; the price of admission is only sixpence." This address never fails to produce a considerable sensation, and sixpences flow into the treasury with wonderful rapidity.

The dwarfs are also objects of great curiosity, and as a dwarf, a giantess, a living skeleton, a wild Indian, "a young lady of singular beauty, with perfectly white hair and pink eyes," and two or three other natural curiosities, are usually exhibited together for the small charge of a penny, they attract very numerous audiences. The best thing about a dwarf is, that he has always a little box, about two feet six inches high, into which, by long practice, he can just manage to get, by doubling himself up like a boot-jack; this box is painted outside like a six-roomed house, and as the crowd see him ring a bell, or fire a pistol out of the first-floor window, they verily believe that it is his ordinary town residence, divided like other mansions into drawing-rooms, dining-parlour, and bed-chambers. Shut up in this case, the unfortunate little object is brought out to delight the throng by holding a facetious dialogue with the proprietor: in the course of which, the dwarf (who is always particularly drunk) pledges himself to sing a comic song inside, and pays various compliments to the ladies, which induce them to "come for'erd" with great alacrity. As a giant is not so easily moved, a pair of indescribables of most capacious dimensions, and a huge shoe, are usually brought out, into which two or three stout men get all at once, to the enthusiastic delight of the crowd, who are quite satisfied with the solemn assurance that these habiliments form part of the giant's everyday costume.

The grandest and most numerously-frequented booth in the whole fair, however, is "the Crown and Anchor" — a temporary ballroom — we forget how many hundred feet long, the price of admission to which is one shilling. Immediately on your right hand as you enter, after paying your money, is a refreshment place, at which cold beef, roast and boiled, French rolls, stout, wine, tongue, ham, even fowls, if we recollect right, are displayed in tempting array. There is a raised orchestra, and the place is boarded all the way down, in patches, just wide enough for a country dance.

There is no master of the ceremonies in this artificial Eden — all is primitive, unreserved, and unstudied. The dust is blinding, the heat insupportable, the company somewhat noisy, and in the highest spirits possible: the ladies, in the height of their innocent animation, dancing in the gentlemen's hats, and the gentlemen promenading the "gay and festive scene" in the ladies' bonnets, or with the more expensive ornaments of false noses, and low-crowned, tinder-box-looking hats: playing children's drums, and accompanied by ladies on the penny trumpet.

The noise of these various instruments, the orchestra, the shouting, the "scratchers," and the dancing, is perfectly bewildering. The dancing, itself beggars description — every figure lasts about an hour, and the ladies bounce up and down the middle, with a degree of spirit which is quite indescribable. As to the gentlemen, they stamp their feet against the ground, every time "hands four round" begins, go down the middle and up again, with cigars in their mouths, and silk handkerchiefs in their hands, and whirl their partners round, nothing loth, scrambling and falling, and embracing, and knocking up against the other couples, until they are fairly tired out, and can move no longer. The same scene is repeated again and again (slightly varied by an occasional "row") until a late hour at night: and a great many clerks and 'prentices find themselves next morning with aching heads, empty pockets, damaged hats, and a very imperfect recollection of how it was they did *not* get home.

THE THEATRICAL YOUNG GENTLEMAN

All gentlemen who love the drama — and there are few gentlemen who are not attached to the most intellectual and rational of all our amusements — do not come within this definition. As we have no mean relish for theatrical entertainments ourself, we are disinterestedly anxious that this should be perfectly understood.

The theatrical young gentleman has early and important information on all theatrical topics. "Well," says he, abruptly, when you meet him in the street, "here's a pretty to-do. Flimkins has thrown up his part in the melodrama at the Surrey." — "And what's to be done?" you inquire with as much gravity as you can counterfeit. "Ah, that's the point," replies the theatrical young gentleman, looking very serious; "Boozle declines it; positively declines it. From all I am told, I should say it was decidedly in Boozle's line, and that he would be very likely to make a great hit in it; but he objects on the ground of Flimkins having been put up in the part first, and says no earthly power shall induce him to take the character. It's a fine part, too — excellent business, I'm told. He has to kill six people in the course of the piece, and to fight over a bridge in red fire, which is as safe a card, you know, as can be. Don't mention it; but I hear that the last scene, when he is first poisoned, and then stabbed, by Mrs. Flimkins as Vengedora, will be the greatest thing that has been done these many years." With this piece of news, and laying his finger on his lips as a caution for you not to excite the town with it, the theatrical young gentleman hurries away.

The theatrical young gentleman, from often frequenting the different theatrical establishments, has pet and familiar names for them all. Thus Covent-Garden is the garden, Drury-Lane the lane, the Victoria the vic, and the Olympic the pic. Actresses, too, are always designated by their surnames only, as Taylor, Nisbett, Faucit, Honey; that talented and lady-like girl Sheriff, that clever little creature Horton, and so on. In the same manner he prefixes Christian names when he mentions the actors, as Charley Young, Jemmy Buckstone, Fred Yates, Paul Bedford. When he is at a loss for a Christian name, the word "old" applied indiscriminately answers quite as well: as old Charley Matthews at Vestris's, old Harley, and old Braham. He has a great knowledge of the private proceedings of actresses, especially of their getting married, and can tell you in a breath half a dozen who have changed their names without avowing it. Whenever an alteration of this kind is made in the playbills, he will remind you that he let you into the secret six months ago.

The theatrical young gentleman has a great reverence for all that is connected with the stage department of the different theatres. He would, at any time, prefer going a street or two out of his way, to omitting to pass a stage-entrance, into which he always looks with a curious and searching eye. If he can only identify a popular actor in the street, he is in a perfect transport of delight; and no sooner meets him, then he hurries back, and walks a few paces in front of him, so that he can turn round from time to time, and have a good stare at his features. He looks upon a theatrical-fund dinner as one of the most enchanting festivities ever known; and thinks that to be a member of the Garrick Club, and see so many actors in their plain clothes, must be one of the highest gratifications the world can bestow.

The theatrical young gentleman is a constant half-price visitor at one or other of the theatres, and has an infinite relish for all pieces which display the fullest resources of the establishment. He likes to place implicit reliance upon the play-bills when he goes to see a show-piece, and works himself up to such a pitch of enthusiasm, as not only to believe (if the bills say so) that there are three hundred and seventy-five people on the stage at one time in the last scene, but is highly indignant with you, unless you believe it also. He considers that if the stage be opened from the foot-lights to the back wall, in any new play, the piece is a triumph of dramatic writing, and applauds accordingly. He has a great notion of trap-doors too; and thinks any character going down or coming up a trap (no matter whether he be an angel or a demon — they both do it occasionally) one of the most interesting feats in the whole range of scenic illusion.

Besides these acquirements, he has several veracious accounts to communicate of the private manners and customs of different actors, which, during the pauses of a quadrille, he usually communicates to his partner, or imparts to his neighbour at a supper table. Thus he is advised, that Mr. Liston always had a footman in gorgeous livery waiting at the side-scene with a brandy bottle and tumbler, to administer half a pint or so of spirit to him every time he came off, without which assistance he must infallibly have fainted. He knows for a fact, that, after an arduous part, Mr. George Bennett is put between two feather beds, to absorb the perspiration; and is credibly informed, that Mr. Baker has, for many years, submitted to a course of lukewarm toast-and-water, to qualify him to sustain his favourite characters. He looks upon Mr. Fitz-Ball as the principal dramatic genius and poet of the day; but holds that there are great writers extant besides him, — in proof whereof he refers you to various dramas and melodramas recently produced, of which he takes in all the sixpenny and threepenny editions as fast as they appear.

The theatrical young gentleman is a great advocate for violence of emotion and redundancy of action. If a father has to curse a child upon the stage, he likes to see it done in the thorough-going style, with no mistake about it: to which end it is essential that the child should follow the father on her knees, and be knocked violently over on her face by the old gentleman as he goes into a small cottage, and shuts the door behind him. He likes to see a blessing invoked upon the young lady, when the old gentleman repents, with equal earnestness, and accompanied by the usual conventional forms, which consist of the old gentleman looking anxiously up into the clouds, as if to see whether it rains, and then spreading an imaginary tablecloth in the air over the young lady's head — soft music playing all the while. Upon these, and other points of a similar kind, the theatrical young gentleman is a great critic indeed. He is likewise very acute in judging of natural expressions of the passions, and knows precisely the frown, wink, nod, or leer, which stands for any of them, or the means by which it may be converted into any other; as jealousy, with a good stamp of the right foot, becomes anger; or wildness, with the hands clasped before the throat, instead of tearing the wig, is passionate love. If you venture to express a doubt of the accuracy of any of these portraitures, the theatrical young gentleman assures you, with a haughty smile, that it always has been done in that way, and he supposes they are not going to change it at this time of day to please you; to which, of course, you meekly reply that you suppose not.

There are innumerable disquisitions of this nature, in which the theatrical young gentleman is very profound, especially to ladies whom he is most in the habit of entertaining with them; but as we have no space to recapitulate them at greater length, we must rest content with calling the attention of the young ladies in general to the theatrical young gentlemen of their own acquaintance.

PRIVATE THEATRES

"RICHARD THE THIRD. — DUKE OF GLOUCESTER, 2 £.; EARL OF RICHMOND, 1 £.; DUKE OF BUCKINGHAM, 15s.; CATESBY, 12s.; TRESSEL, 10s. 6d.; LORD STANLEY, 5s.; LORD MAYOR OF LONDON, 2s. 6d."

Such are the written placards wafered up in the gentlemen's dressing-room, in the green-room (where there is any), at a private theatre; and such are the sums extracted from the shop-till, or overcharged in the office expenditure, by the donkeys who are prevailed upon to pay for permission to exhibit their lamentable ignorance and boobyism on the stage of a private theatre. This they do, in proportion to the scope afforded by the character for the display of their imbecility. For instance, the Duke of Glo'ster is well worth two pounds, because he has it all to himself; he must wear a real sword, and what is better still, he must draw it, several times in the course of the piece. The soliloquies alone are well worth fifteen shillings; then there is the stabbing of King Henry — decidedly cheap at three-and-sixpence, that's eighteen-and-sixpence; bullying the coffin-bearers — say eighteen-pence, though it's worth much more — that's a pound. Then the love scene with Lady Anne, and the bustle of the fourth act can't be dear at ten shillings more — that's only one pound ten, including the "off with his head!" — which is sure to bring down the applause, and it is very easy to do — "Orf with his ed" (very quick and loud; — then slow and sneeringly) — "So much for Bu-u-u-uckingham!" Lay the emphasis on the "uck"; get yourself gradually into a corner, and work with your right hand, while you're saying it, as if you were feeling your way, and it's sure to do. The tent scene is confessedly worth half-a-sovereign, and so you have the fight in, gratis, and everybody knows what an effect may be produced by a good combat. One — two — three — four — over; then, one — two — three — four — under; then thrust; then dodge and slide about; then fall down on one knee; then fight upon it, and then get up again and stagger. You may keep on doing this, as long as it seems to take — say ten minutes — and then fall down (backwards, if you can manage it without hurting yourself), and die game: nothing like it for producing an effect. They always do it at Astley's and Sadler's Wells, and if they don't know how to do this sort of thing, who in the world does? A small child, or a female in white, increases the interest of a combat materially — indeed, we are not aware that a regular legitimate terrific broadsword combat could be done without; but it would be rather difficult, and somewhat unusual, to introduce this effect in the last scene of Richard the Third, so the only thing to be done, is, just to make the best of a bad bargain, and be as long as possible fighting it out.

The principal patrons of private theatres are dirty boys, low copying-clerks in attorneys' offices, capacious-headed youths from City counting-houses, Jews whose business, as lenders of fancy dresses, is a sure passport to the amateur stage, shop-boys who now and then mistake their masters' money for their own; and a choice miscellany of idle vagabonds. The proprietor of a private theatre may be an ex-scene-painter, a low coffee-house-keeper, a disappointed eighth-rate actor, a retired smuggler, or uncertificated bankrupt. The theatre itself may be in Catherine Street, Strand, the purlieus of the city, the neighbourhood of Gray's Inn Lane, or the vicinity of Sadler's Wells; or it may, perhaps, form the chief nuisance of some shabby street, on the Surrey side of Waterloo Bridge.

The lady performers pay nothing for their characters, and, it is needless to add, are usually selected from one class of society; the audiences are necessarily of much the same character as the performers, who receive, in return for their contributions to the management, tickets to the amount of the money they pay.

All the minor theatres in London, especially the lowest, constitute the centre of a little stage-struck neighbourhood. Each of them has an audience exclusively its own; and at any you will see dropping into the pit at half-price, or swaggering into the back of a box, if the price of admission be a reduced one, divers boys of from fifteen to twenty-one years of age, who throw back their coat and turn up their wristbands, after the portraits of Count D'Orsay, hum tunes and whistle when the curtain is down, by way of persuading the people near them, that they are not at all anxious to have it up again, and speak familiarly of the inferior performers as Bill Such-a-one, and

Ned So-and-so, or tell each other how a new piece called *The Unknown Bandit of the Invisible Cavern,* is in rehearsal; how Mister
Palmer is to play *The Unknown Bandit;* how Charley Scarton is to
take the part of an English sailor, and fight a broadsword combat
with six unknown bandits, at one and the same time (one theatrical
sailor is always equal to half a dozen men at least); how Mister
Palmer and Charley Scarton are to go through a double hornpipe in
fetters in the second act; how the interior of the invisible cavern is to
occupy the whole extent of the stage; and other town-surprising theatrical announcements. These gentlemen are the amateurs — the
Richards, Shylocks, Beverleys, and *Othellos* — the *Young Dorn-
tons, Rovers, Captain Absolutes,* and *Charles Surfaces* — of a private
theatre.

See them at the neighbouring public-house or the theatrical coffee-
shop! They are the kings of the place, supposing no real performers to
be present; and roll about, hats on one side, and arms akimbo, as if
they had actually come into possession of eighteen shillings a week,
and a share of a ticket night. If one of them does but know an Astley's supernumerary he is a happy fellow. The mingled air of envy and
admiration with which his companions will regard him, as he converses familiarly with some mouldy-looking man in a fancy neckerchief, whose partially corked eyebrows, and half-rouged face, testify
to the fact of his having just left the stage or the circle, sufficiently
shows in what high admiration these public characters are held.

With the double view of guarding against the discovery of friends
or employers, and enhancing the interest of an assumed character,
by attaching a high-sounding name to its representative, these gen-
iuses assume fictitious names, which are not the least amusing part
of the play-bill of a private theatre. Belville, Melville, Treville, Berkeley, Randolph, Byron, St. Clair, and so forth, are among the humblest; and the less imposing titles of Jenkins, Walker, Thomson,
Barker, Solomons, etc., are completely laid aside. There is something
imposing in this, and it is an excellent apology for shabbiness into
the bargain. A shrunken, faded coat, a decayed hat, a patched and
soiled pair of trousers — nay, even a very dirty shirt (and none of
these appearances are very uncommon among the members of the
corps dramatique), may be worn for the purpose of disguise, and to
prevent the remotest chance of recognition. Then it prevents any
troublesome inquiries or explanations about employments and pur-

suits; everybody is a gentleman at large, for the occasion, and there are none of those unpleasant and unnecessary distinctions to which even genius must occasionally succumb elsewhere. As to the ladies (God bless them), they are quite above any formal absurdities; the mere circumstance of your being behind the scenes is a sufficient introduction to their society — for of course they know that none but strictly respectable persons would be admitted into that close fellowship with them, which acting engenders. They place implicit reliance on the manager, no doubt; and as to the manager, he is all affability when he knows you well — or, in other words, when he has pocketed your money once, and entertains confident hopes of doing so again.

A quarter before eight — there will be a full house to-night — six parties in the boxes, already; four little boys and a woman in the pit; and two fiddles and a flute in the orchestra, who have got through five overtures since seven o'clock (the hour fixed for the commencement of the performances), and have just begun the sixth. There will be plenty of it, though, when it does begin, for there is enough in the bill to last six hours at least.

That gentleman in the white hat and checked shirt, brown coat and brass buttons, lounging behind the stage-box on the O. P. side, is Mr. Horatio St. Julien, alias Jem Larkins. His line is genteel comedy — his father's coal and potato. He *does* Alfred Highflier in the last piece, and very well he'll do it — at the price. The party of gentlemen in the opposite box, to whom he has just nodded, are friends and supporters of Mr. Beverley (otherwise Loggins), the *Macbeth* of the night. You observe their attempts to appear easy and gentlemanly, each member of the party, with his feet cocked upon the cushion in front of the box! They let them do these things here, upon the same humane principle which permits poor people's children to knock double-knocks at the door of an empty house — because they can't do it anywhere else. The two stout men in the centre box, with an opera-glass ostentatiously placed before them, are friends of the proprietor — opulent country managers, as he confidentially informs every individual among the crew behind the curtain — opulent country managers looking out for recruits; a representation which Mr. Nathan, the dresser, who is in the manager's interest, and has just arrived with the costumes, offers to confirm upon oath if required — corroborative evidence, however, is quite unnecessary, for the gulls believe it at once.

The stout Jewess who has just entered, is the mother of the pale
bony little girl, with the necklace of blue glass beads, sitting by her;
she is being brought up to "the profession." Pantomime is to be her
line, and she is coming out to-night, in a hornpipe after the tragedy.
The short thin man beside Mr. St. Julien, whose white face is so
deeply seared with the small-pox, and whose dirty shirt-front is inlaid
with open-work, and embossed with coral studs like ladybirds, is the
low comedian and comic singer of the establishment. The remainder of the audience — a tolerably numerous one by this time — are a
motley group of dupes and blackguards.

The foot-lights have just made their appearance: the wicks of the
six little oil lamps round the only tier of boxes, are being turned up,
and the additional light thus afforded serves to show the presence of
dirt, and absence of paint, which form a prominent feature in the
audience part of the house. As these preparations, however, announce
the speedy commencement of the play, let us take a peep "behind,"
previous to the ringing-up.

The little narrow passages beneath the stage are neither especially
clean nor too brilliantly lighted; and the absence of any flooring, together with the damp mildewy smell which pervades the place, does
not conduce in any great degree to their comfortable appearance.
Don't fall over this plate-basket — it's one of the "properties" — the
cauldron for the witches' cave; and the three uncouth-looking figures,
with broken clothes-props in their hands, who are drinking gin-and-
water out of a pint pot, are the weird sisters. This miserable room,
lighted by candles in sconces placed at lengthened intervals round
the wall, is the dressing-room, common to the gentlemen performers,
and the square hole in the ceiling is *the* trap-door of the stage above.
You will observe that the ceiling is ornamented with the beams that
support the boards, and tastefully hung with cobwebs.

The characters in the tragedy are all dressed, and their own clothes
are scattered in hurried confusion over the wooden dresser which
surrounds the room. That snuff-shop-looking figure, in front of the
glass, is *Banquo:* and the young lady with the liberal display of legs,
who is kindly painting his face with a hare's foot, is dressed for
Fleance. The large woman, who is consulting the stage directions in
Cumberland's edition of *Macbeth,* is the *Lady Macbeth* of the night;
she is always selected to play the part, because she is tall and stout,
and *looks* a little like Mrs. Siddons — at a considerable distance.

That stupid-looking milksop, with light hair and bow legs — a kind of man whom you can warrant town-made — is fresh caught; he plays *Malcolm* to-night, just to accustom himself to an audience. He will get on better by degrees; he will play *Othello* in a month, and in a month more, will very probably be apprehended on a charge of embezzlement. The black-eyed female with whom he is talking so earnestly, is dressed for the "gentlewoman." It is *her* first appearance, too — in that character. The boy of fourteen who is having his eyebrows smeared with soap and whitening, is *Duncan*, King of Scotland; and the two dirty men with the corked countenances, in very old green tunics, and dirty drab boots, are the "army."

"Look sharp below there, gents," exclaims the dresser, a red-headed and red-whiskered Jew, calling through the trap, "they're a going to ring up. The flute says he'll be blowed if he plays any more, and they're getting precious noisy in front." A general rush immediately takes place to the half-dozen little steep steps leading to the stage, and the heterogeneous group are soon assembled at the side scenes, in breathless anxiety and motley confusion.

"Now," cries the manager, consulting the written list which hangs behind the first P. S. wing, "Scene 1, open country — lamps down — thunder and lightning — all ready, White?" [This is addressed to one of the army.] "All ready." — "Very well. Scene 2, front chamber. Is the front chamber down?" — "Yes." — "Very well." — "Jones" [to the other army who is up in the flies.] "Hallo!" — "Wind up the open country when we ring up." — "I'll take care." — "Scene 3, back perspective with practical bridge. Bridge ready, White? Got the tressels there?" — "All right."

"Very well. Clear the stage," cries the manager, hastily packing every member of the company into the little space there is between the wings and the wall, and one wing and another. "Places, places. Now then, Witches — Duncan — Malcolm — bleeding officer — where's the bleeding officer?" — "Here!" replies the officer, who has been rose-pinking for the character. "Get ready, then; now, White, ring the second music-bell." The actors who are to be discovered, are hastily arranged, and the actors who are not to be discovered place themselves, in their anxiety to peep at the house, just where the audience can see them. The bell rings, and the orchestra, in acknowledgment of the call, play three distinct chords. The bell rings — the tragedy(!) opens — and our description closes.

First Flight as a Dramatist

[The young composer John Hullah's proposal of an operetta with its scenes laid among the canals and piazzas of Venice (which Dickens so characteristically and coolly seized upon and transported to the lanes of rural England) was made in November 1835. Eight months later he had completed the libretto. Meanwhile Dickens's father-in-law George Hogarth, who was music critic of the Morning Chronicle, *had introduced him to the famous tenor John Braham, then just about to open the new St. James's Theatre, magnificent with its red-and-gold decor. Braham expressed interest in producing the operetta, and his leading comedian, John Pritt Harley, asked Dickens to write a farce for the same theater.* The Strange Gentleman *was finished first, and opened on September 29, 1836;* The Village Coquettes *followed on December 6, with the farce repeated on the same bill. "Cramer's" were the music publishers who brought out the score.]*

To J. P. HULLAH

13 Furnivals Inn, [*6th November 1835*]

What I am anxious to suggest to you is, the expediency of dropping the Venetian idea altogether, and making the drama an English one. I really cannot please myself with any of the sketches I have made for an opera to which the title of The Gondolier would be applicable; and remembering the popularity and beauty of many of the old English operas, I am strongly prejudiced in favor of a simple rural story. I am the more induced to favor this notion when I consider with how little expence such a piece might be produced, and how very effective its situations might be made; while the Gondolier on the other hand would require a great many supernumeraries, and some rather costly scenery. Add to these considerations, the increased ease and effect with which we could both work on an English drama where the characters would act and talk like people we see and hear every day, and I think you will be of my opinion.

I have a little story by me which I have not yet published, which I think would dramatize well. If you approve of my idea, it is done in a twinkling; if not I will work out your original notion, but I will frankly confess that while I am at home in England, I am in Venice abroad indeed.

Furnivals Inn, [1836]

I enclose both the Duett and song. For the latter, I have found a very dramatic situation, and I think you will find the words sufficiently passionate for display. The duett carries on the plot, and I have therefore been able to dispense with a page of dialogue. Bring either the inclosed, or legible copies, with you to the Theatre tomorrow.

When, oh *when,* will this music be ready. I really begin to grow alarmed lest Braham think we are playing him some nonsense; and there is every reason to fear that he will have left town, *long* before it reaches his hands. A day's loss now, may be a month's after the season has commenced. It is very disheartening.

I want to see you about Cramer's & Co. to relate what passed between them and Hogarth, who has acted godfather for us, and promised and vowed in our names, that no one else shall have the opera without their being first communicated with. They say they should be *very sorry to let it slip through their hands.*

Mr. Hogarth has just been here, with news which I think you will be glad to hear. He was with Braham yesterday, who was *far more full* of the opera, than he ever was; speaking highly of my works and "fame" (!) and expressing an earnest desire to be the first to introduce me to the Public, as a dramatic Writer. He said that he intended opening at Michaelmas; and added (unasked) that it was his intention to produce the opera, within *one month* of his first night. He wants a low comedy part introduced, without singing: thinking it will take with the audience. As he is desirous of explaining to me, what he means, and who he intends to play it, I am to see him on Sunday morning. Full particulars of the Interview shall be duly announced.

Petersham, [29th August 1836]

Since I called on you this morning, I have not had time to look over the words of "the child and the old man." It occurs to me, as I shall see you on Wednesday *Morning,* that the best plan will be for you to bring the music (if you possibly can) without the words, and we can put them in then. Of course this observation applies only to that particular song.

Braham having sent to me, about the farce, I called on him this morning. Harley wrote, when he had read the whole of the opera, saying "It's a sure card — nothing wrong *there.* Bet you ten pounds it runs fifty nights. Come, don't be afraid. I will be the gainer by it, and you needn't mind betting; it's a capital custom." They tell the story with infinite relish. I saw the fair manageress, who is fully of Harley's opinion, so is Braham. The only difference is, that they are far more enthusiastic than ourselves, even. That's a bold word, isn't it? It is a true one, nevertheless.

"Depend upon it, Sir," said Braham to Hogarth yesterday, when he went there to say I should be in town to-day, "Depend upon it, Sir, that there has been no such music since the days of Sheil, and no such piece since the Duenna." — "Everybody is delighted with it," he added to me to-day. "I played it to Stansbury, who is by no means an excitable person, and he was *charmed.*" This was said with great emphasis, but I have forgotten the grand point. It was not "I played it to Stansbury," but "I sang it — all through"! ! !

[11th September 1836]

Harley . . . dragged me home with him, and forced me into town, again to-day. He is delighted with the farce, and it will certainly be got up well. He has copied out his part in The Village Coquettes, himself, for the convenience of learning, and looks over it daily. They want to open, if they possibly can, *tomorrow fortnight.*

[17th September 1836]

I am most happy to report that the Miss Smiths are very nice-looking, well-dressed, agreeable-mannered, lady-like girls. I should say that Rose especially, is a very knowing little person, *rather* fat, but not a bit too much so, with a very nice smiling pretty face. The father is all bows and politeness; and they all readiness and satisfaction. I don't think you could have picked out a nicer looking girl for the part, if you had picked all London through.

The farce is in active rehearsal, and the company have begun *business*. I would rather you didn't see it, till they drop the written parts (about the end of the week) but you will find me at the Theatre every day at half past 12 o'clock.

[*11th December 1836*]

Have you seen the Examiner? It is *rather* depreciatory of the opera, but like all their inveterate critiques against Braham, so well done that I cannot help laughing at it, for the life and soul of me.

I have seen the Sunday Times, the Dispatch, and the Satirist, all of which blow their little trumpets against unhappy me, most lustily. Either I must have grievously awakened the ire of all the "adapters" and their friends, or the drama must be decidedly bad. I haven't made up my mind yet, which of the two is the fact.

I have not seen the John Bull or any other of the Sunday papers except the Spectator. If you have any of them, bring 'em with you on Tuesday. I am afraid that for "dirty Cummins's" allusion to Hogarth, I shall be reduced to the necessity of being valorous the next time I meet him.

Memoirs of Joseph Grimaldi

(Edited by "Boz")

[*Dickens's editorial work on these memoirs consisted mainly of drastic abridgment, except for an introductory and possibly a concluding chapter. The volume was published early in 1838. The following paragraphs are from the introductory chapter.*]

It is some years now since we first conceived a strong veneration for Clowns, and an intense anxiety to know what they did with themselves out of pantomime time, and off the stage. As a child, we were accustomed to pester our relations and friends with questions out of number concerning these gentry; — whether their appetite for sausages and suchlike wares was always the same, and if so, at whose expense they were maintained; whether they were ever taken up for pilfering other people's goods, or were forgiven by everybody because it was only done in fun; how it was they got such beautiful complexions, and where they lived; and whether they were born Clowns, or gradually turned into Clowns as they grew up. On these and a thousand other points our curiosity was insatiable. Nor were our speculations confined to Clowns alone; they extended to Harlequins, Pantaloons, and Columbines, all of whom we believed to be real and veritable personages, existing in the same forms and characters all the year round. How often have we wished that the Pantaloon were our godfather! and how often thought that to marry a Columbine would be to attain the highest pitch of all human felicity!

The delights — the ten thousand million delights of a pantomime — come streaming upon us now, — even of the pantomime which came lumbering down in Richardson's waggons at fair time to the dull little town in which we had the honour to be brought up, and which a long row of small boys, with frills as white as they could be washed, and hands as clean as they would come, were taken to behold the glories of, in fair daylight.

We feel again all the pride of standing in a body on the platform, the observed of all observers in the crowd below, while the junior usher pays away twenty-four ninepences to a stout gentleman under a Gothic arch, with a hoop of variegated lamps swinging over his head. Again we catch a glimpse (too brief, alas!) of the lady with a green parasol in her hand, on the outside stage of the next show but one, who supports herself on one foot, on the back of a majestic horse, blotting-paper coloured and white; and once again our eyes open wide with wonder, and our hearts throb with emotion, as we deliver our card-board check into the very hands of the Harlequin himself, who, all glittering with spangles, and dazzling with many colours, deigns to give us a word of encouragement and commendation as we pass into the booth!

But what was this — even this — to the glories of the inside, where, amid the smell of sawdust, and orange-peel, sweeter far than violets to youthful noses, the first play being over, the lovers united, the Ghost appeased, the Baron killed, and everything made comfortable and pleasant, — the pantomime itself began! What words can describe the deep gloom of the opening scene, where a crafty Magician holding a young lady in bondage was discovered, studying an enchanted book to the soft music of a gong! — or in what terms can we express the thrill of ecstasy with which, his magic power opposed by superior art, we beheld the monster himself converted into Clown! What mattered it that the stage was three yards wide, and four deep? We never saw it. We had no eyes, ears, or corporeal senses but for the pantomime. And when its short career was run, and the Baron previously slaughtered, coming forward with his hand upon his heart, announced that for that favour Mr. Richardson returned his most sincere thanks, and the performances would commence again in a quarter of an hour, what jest could equal the effects of the Baron's indignation and surprise, when the Clown, unexpectedly peeping from behind the curtain, requested the audience "not to believe it, for it was all gammon!" Who but a Clown could have called forth the roar of laughter that succeeded; and what witchery but a Clown's could have caused the junior usher himself to declare aloud, as he shook his sides and smote his knee in a moment of irrepressible joy, that that was the very best thing he had ever heard said!

The Great Vincent Crummles and His Thespian Galaxy

[Nicholas Nickleby *appeared in monthly installments between April 1838 and October 1839. The Crummles episodes, streaming from Dickens's pen with hilarious bravura and irresistible pace, are a triumph of frolicsome invention. The parts given here represent almost all of Chapters 22-25, 29-30, and 49.*]

NICHOLAS ENCOUNTERS MR. VINCENT CRUMMLES

[*Nicholas and his protégé Smike, after having left Squeers's school, Dotheboys Hall, have been journeying on foot to Portsmouth. At an inn twelve miles from town, the landlord introduces them to Crummles, the actor-manager of a traveling theatrical troupe.*]

Nicholas was prepared for something odd, but not for something quite so odd as the sight he encountered. At the upper end of the room were a couple of boys, one of them very tall and the other very short, both dressed as sailors — or at least as theatrical sailors, with belts, buckles, pigtails, and pistols complete—fighting what is called in playbills, a terrific combat, with two of those short broadswords with basket hilts which are commonly used at our minor theatres. The short boy had gained a great advantage over the tall boy, who was reduced to mortal strait, and both were overlooked by a large, heavy man, perched against the corner of a table, who emphatically adjured them to strike a little more fire out of the swords, and they couldn't fail to bring the house down on the very first night.

"Mr. Vincent Crummles," said the landlord, with an air of great deference, "this is the young gentleman."

Mr. Vincent Crummles received Nicholas with an inclination of the head, something between the courtesy of a Roman emperor and the nod of a pot-companion; and bade the landlord shut the door and begone.

"There's a picture," said Mr. Crummles, motioning Nicholas not to advance and spoil it. "There the little 'un has him; if the big 'un doesn't knock under in three seconds, he's a dead man. Do that again, boys."

The two combatants went to work afresh, and chopped away until the swords emitted a shower of sparks; to the great satisfaction of Mr. Crummles, who appeared to consider this a very great point indeed. The engagement commenced with about two hundred chops administered by the short sailor and the tall sailor alternately, without producing any particular result, until the short sailor was chopped down on one knee; but this was nothing to him, for he worked himself about on the one knee with the assistance of his left hand, and fought most desperately until the tall sailor chopped his sword out of his grasp. Now, the inference was, that the short sailor, reduced to this extremity, would give in at once and cry quarter, but instead of that, he all of a sudden drew a large pistol from his belt and presented it at the face of the tall sailor, who was so overcome at this (not expecting it) that he let the short sailor pick up his sword and begin again. Then the chopping recommenced, and a variety of fancy chops were administered on both sides; such as chops dealt with the left hand, and under the leg, and over the right shoulder, and over the left; and when the short sailor made a vigorous cut at the tall sailor's legs, which would have shaved them clean off if it had taken effect, the tall sailor jumped over the short sailor's sword, wherefore to balance the matter, and make it all fair, the tall sailor administered the same cut, and the short sailor jumped over *his* sword. After this, there was a good deal of dodging about, and hitching up of the inexpressibles in the absence of braces, and then the short sailor (who was the moral character evidently, for he always had the best of it) made a violent demonstration and closed with the tall sailor, who, after a few unavailing struggles, went down, and expired in great torture as the short sailor put his foot upon his breast, and bored a hole in him through and through.

"That'll be a double *encore* if you take care, boys," said Mr. Crummles. "You had better get your wind now, and change your clothes."

Having addressed these words to the combatants, he saluted Nicholas, who then observed that the face of Mr. Crummles was quite proportionate in size to his body; that he had a very full under-lip, a hoarse voice, as though he were in the habit of shouting very much, and very short, black hair, shaved off nearly to the crown of his head — to admit (as he afterwards learned) of his more easily wearing character wigs of any shape or pattern.

"What did you think of that, sir?" inquired Mr. Crummles.

"Very good, indeed — capital," answered Nicholas.

"You won't see such boys as those very often, I think," said Mr. Crummles.

Nicholas assented — observing that if they were a little better match —

"Match!" cried Mr. Crummles.

"I mean if they were a little more of a size," said Nicholas, explaining himself.

"Size!" repeated Mr. Crummles; "why, it's the essence of the combat that there should be a foot or two between them. How are you to get up the sympathies of the audience in a legitimate manner, if there isn't a little man contending against a big one — unless there's at least five to one, and we haven't hands enough for that business in our company."

"I see," replied Nicholas. "I beg your pardon. That didn't occur to me, I confess."

"It's the main point," said Mr. Crummles. "I open at Portsmouth the day after to-morrow. If you're going there, look into the theatre, and see how that'll tell."

Nicholas promised to do so if he could, and drawing a chair near the fire, fell into conversation with the manager at once. He was very talkative and communicative, stimulated, perhaps, not only by his natural disposition, but by the spirits and water he sipped very plentifully, or the snuff he took in large quantities from a piece of whity-brown paper in his waistcoat pocket. He laid open his affairs without the smallest reserve, and descanted at some length upon the merits of his company, and the acquirements of his family; of both of which the two broadsword boys formed an honourable portion. There was to be a gathering, it seemed, of the different ladies and gentlemen of Portsmouth on the morrow, whither the father and sons were proceeding (not for the regular season, but in the course of a wandering speculation), after fulfilling an engagement at Guildford with the greatest applause.

"You are going that way?" asked the manager.

"Ye-yes," said Nicholas. "Yes, I am."

"Do you know the town at all?" inquired the manager, who seemed to consider himself entitled to the same degree of confidence as he had himself exhibited.

"No," replied Nicholas.

"Never there?"

"Never."

Mr. Vincent Crummles gave a short, dry cough, as much as to say, "If you won't be communicative, you won't"; and took so many pinches of snuff from the piece of paper, one after another, that Nicholas quite wondered where it all went to.

While he was thus engaged, Mr. Crummles looked, from time to time, with great interest at Smike, with whom he had appeared considerably struck from the first. He had now fallen asleep, and was nodding in his chair.

"Excuse my saying so," said the manager, leaning over to Nicholas, and sinking his voice, "but what a capital countenance your friend has got!"

"Poor fellow!" said Nicholas, with a half smile, "I wish it were a little more plump and less haggard."

"Plump!" exclaimed the manager, quite horrified, "you'd spoil it for ever."

"Do you think so?"

"Think so, sir! Why, as he is now," said the manager, striking his knee emphatically, "without a pad upon his body, and hardly a touch of paint upon his face, he'd make such an actor for the starved business as was never seen in this country. Only let him be tolerably well up in the Apothecary in 'Romeo and Juliet,' with the slightest possible dab of red on the tip of his nose, and he'd be certain of three rounds the moment he put his head out of the practicable door in the front grooves O.P."

"You view him with a professional eye," said Nicholas, laughing.

"And well I may," rejoined the manager. "I never saw a young fellow so regularly cut out for that line since I've been in the profession, and I played the heavy children when I was eighteen months old."

The appearance of the beefsteak pudding, which came in simultaneously with the junior Vincent Crummleses, turned the conversation to other matters, and, indeed, for a time stopped it altogether. These two young gentlemen wielded their knives and forks with scarcely less address than their broadswords, and as the whole party were quite as sharp set as either class of weapons, there was no time for talking until the supper had been disposed of.

The Masters Crummles had no sooner swallowed the last procurable morsel of food than they evinced, by various half-suppressed yawns and stretchings of their limbs, an obvious inclination to retire for the night, which Smike had betrayed still more strongly; he having, in the course of the meal, fallen asleep several times while in the very act of eating. Nicholas therefore proposed that they should break up at once, but the manager would by no means hear of it, vowing that he had promised himself the pleasure of inviting his new acquaintance to share a bowl of punch, and that if he declined he should deem it very unhandsome behaviour.

"Let them go," said Mr. Vincent Crummles, "and we'll have it snugly and cosily together by the fire."

Nicholas was not much disposed to sleep, being, in truth, too anxious; so, after a little demur, he accepted the offer, and having exchanged a shake of the hand with the young Crummleses, and the manager having on his part bestowed a most affectionate benediction on Smike, he sat himself down opposite to that gentleman by the fireside, to assist in emptying the bowl, which soon afterwards appeared, steaming in a manner which was quite exhilarating to behold, and sending forth a most grateful and inviting fragrance.

But despite the punch and the manager, who told a variety of stories, and smoked tobacco from a pipe, and inhaled it in the shape of snuff, with a most astonishing power, Nicholas was absent and dispirited. His thoughts were in his old home, and when they reverted to his present condition, the uncertainty of the morrow cast a gloom upon him, which his utmost efforts were unable to dispel. His attention wandered; although he heard the manager's voice, he was deaf to what he said; and when Mr. Vincent Crummles concluded the history of the adventure with a loud laugh, and an inquiry what Nicholas would have done under the same circumstances, he was obliged to make the best apology in his power, and to confess his entire ignorance of all he had been talking about.

"Why, so I saw," observed Mr. Crummles. "You're uneasy in your mind. What's the matter?"

Nicholas could not refrain from smiling at the abruptness of the question; but, thinking it scarcely worth while to parry it, owned that he was under some apprehensions lest he might not succeed in the object which had brought him to that part of the country.

"And what's that?" asked the manager.

"Getting something to do which will keep me and my poor fellow-traveller in the common necessaries of life," said Nicholas. "That's the truth. You guessed it long ago, I dare say, so I may as well have the credit of telling it you with a good grace."

"What's to be got to do at Portsmouth more than anywhere else?" asked Mr. Vincent Crummles, melting the sealing-wax on the stem of his pipe in the candle, and rolling it out afresh with his little finger.

"There are many vessels leaving the port, I suppose," replied Nicholas. "I shall try for a berth in some ship or other. There is meat and drink there, at all events."

"Salt meat and new rum; pease pudding and chaff biscuits," said the manager, taking a whiff at his pipe to keep it alight, and returning to his work of embellishment.

"One may do worse than that," said Nicholas. "I can rough it, I believe, as well as most men of my age and previous habits."

"You need be able to," said the manager, "if you go on board ship; but you won't."

"Why not?"

"Because there's not a skipper or mate that would think you worth your salt, when he could get a practised hand," replied the manager; "and they as plentiful there as the oysters in the streets."

"What do you mean?" asked Nicholas, alarmed by this prediction, and the confident tone in which it had been uttered. "Men are not born able seamen. They must be reared, I suppose?"

Mr. Vincent Crummles nodded his head. "They must; but not at your age, or from young gentlemen like you."

There was a pause. The countenance of Nicholas fell, and he gazed ruefully at the fire.

"Does no other profession occur to you, which a young man of your figure and address could take up easily, and see the world to advantage in?" asked the manager.

"No," said Nicholas, shaking his head.

"Why, then, I'll tell you one," said Mr. Crummles, throwing his pipe into the fire, and raising his voice. "The stage."

"The stage!" cried Nicholas, in a voice almost as loud.

"The theatrical profession," said Mr. Vincent Crummles. "I am in the theatrical profession myself, my wife is in the theatrical profession, my children are in the theatrical profession. I had a dog that lived and died in it from a puppy; and my chaise-pony goes on in 'Timour the Tartar.' I'll bring you out, and your friend, too. Say the word. I want a novelty."

"I don't know anything about it," rejoined Nicholas, whose breath had been almost taken away by this sudden proposal. "I never acted a part in my life, except at school."

"There's genteel comedy in your walk and manner, juvenile tragedy in your eye, and touch-and-go farce in your laugh," said Mr. Vincent Crummles. "You'll do as well as if you had thought of nothing else but the lamps from your birth downwards."

Nicholas thought of the small amount of small change that would remain in his pocket after paying the tavern bill, and he hesitated.

"You can be useful to us in a hundred ways," said Crummles. "Think what capital bills a man of your education could write for the shop windows."

"Well, I think I could manage that department," said Nicholas.

"To be sure you could," replied Mr. Crummles. " 'For further particulars see small hand-bills'— we might have half a volume in every one of 'em. Pieces, too; why, you could write us a piece to bring out the whole strength of the company, whenever we wanted one."

"I am not quite so confident about that," replied Nicholas. "But I dare say I could scribble something now and then that would suit you."

"We'll have a new show-piece out directly," said the manager. "Let me see — peculiar resources of this establishment — new and splendid scenery — you must manage to introduce a real pump and two washing-tubs."

"Into the piece?" said Nicholas.

"Yes," replied the manager. "I bought 'em cheap, at a sale the other day, and they'll come in admirably. That's the London plan. They look up some dresses and properties, and have a piece written to fit them. Most of the theatres keep an author on purpose."

"Indeed!" cried Nicholas.

"Oh, yes," said the manager; "a common thing. It'll look very well in the bills in separate lines — Real pump! — Splendid tubs! — Great attraction! You don't happen to be anything of an artist, do you?"

"That is not one of my accomplishments," rejoined Nicholas.

"Ah! Then it can't be helped," said the manager. "If you had been, we might have had a large woodcut of the last scene for the posters, showing the whole depth of the stage, with the pump and tubs in the middle; but, however, if you're not, it can't be helped."

"What should I get for all this?" inquired Nicholas, after a few moments' reflection. "Could I live by it?"

"Live by it!" said the manager. "Like a prince! With your own salary, and your friend's, and your writings, you'd make a pound a week!"

"You don't say so!"

"I do, indeed; and, if we had a run of good houses, nearly double the money."

Nicholas shrugged his shoulders; but sheer destitution was before him; and if he could summon fortitude to undergo the extremes of want and hardship, for what had he rescued his helpless charge if it were only to bear as hard a fate as that from which he had wrested him? It was easy to think of seventy miles as nothing, when he was in the same town with the man who had treated him so ill and roused his bitterest thoughts; but now it seemed far enough. What if he went abroad, and his mother or Kate were to die the while?

Without more deliberation he hastily declared that it was a bargain, and gave Mr. Vincent Crummles his hand upon it.

TREATS OF THE COMPANY OF MR. VINCENT CRUMMLES, AND
OF HIS AFFAIRS, DOMESTIC AND THEATRICAL

As Mr. Crummles had a strange four-legged animal in the inn stables
which he called a pony, and a vehicle of unknown design on which
he bestowed the appellation of a four-wheeled phaeton, Nicholas proceeded on his journey next morning with greater ease than he had expected: the manager and himself occupying the front seat; and the
Masters Crummles and Smike being packed together behind, in company with a wicker basket defended from wet by a stout oilskin, in
which were the broadswords, pistols, pigtails, nautical costumes, and
other professional necessaries of the aforesaid young gentlemen.

The pony took his time upon the road, and — possibly in consequence of his theatrical education — evinced, every now and then, a
strong inclination to lie down. However, Mr. Vincent Crummles kept
him up pretty well by jerking the rein and plying the whip; and when
these means failed, and the animal came to a stand, the elder Master
Crummles got out and kicked him. By dint of these encouragements,
he was persuaded to move from time to time, and they jogged on
(as Mr. Crummles truly observed) very comfortably for all parties.

"He's a good pony at bottom," said Mr. Crummles, turning to
Nicholas.

He might have been at bottom, but he certainly was not at top,
seeing that his coat was of the roughest and most ill-favoured kind.
So Nicholas merely observed that he shouldn't wonder if he was.

"Many and many is the circuit this pony has gone," said Mr.
Crummles, flicking him skilfully on the eyelid for old acquaintance'
sake. "He is quite one of us. His mother was on the stage."

"Was she?" rejoined Nicholas.

"She ate apple-pie at a circus for upwards of fourteen years," said
the manager; "fired pistols, and went to bed in a nightcap; and, in
short, took the low comedy entirely. His father was a dancer."

"Was he at all distinguished?"

"Not very," said the manager. "He was rather a low sort of pony.
The fact is, he had been originally jobbed out by the day, and he
never quite got over his old habits. He was clever in melodrama, too,

but too broad — too broad. When the mother died, he took the port wine business."

"The port wine business!" cried Nicholas.

"Drinking port wine with the clown," said the manager; "but he was greedy, and one night bit off the bowl of the glass, and choked himself, so his vulgarity was the death of him at last."

The descendant of this ill-starred animal requiring increased attention from Mr. Crummles as he progressed in his day's work, that gentleman had very little time for conversation. Nicholas was thus left at leisure to entertain himself with his own thoughts, until they arrived at the drawbridge at Portsmouth, when Mr. Crummles pulled up.

"We'll get down here," said the manager, "and the boys will take him round to the stable, and call at my lodgings with the luggage. You had better let yours be taken there for the present."

Thanking Mr. Vincent Crummles for his obliging offer, Nicholas jumped out, and, giving Smike his arm, accompanied the manager up High Street on their way to the theatre, feeling nervous and uncomfortable enough at the prospect of an immediate introduction to a scene so new to him.

They passed a great many bills, pasted against the walls and displayed in windows, wherein the names of Mr. Vincent Crummles, Mrs. Vincent Crummles, Master Crummles, Master P. Crummles, and Miss Crummles, were printed in very large letters, and everything else in very small ones; and turning at length into an entry, in which was a strong smell of orange-peel and lamp-oil, with an under-current of sawdust, groped their way through a dark passage, and, descending a step or two, threaded a little maze of canvas screens and paint-pots, and emerged upon the stage of the Portsmouth Theatre.

"Here we are," said Mr. Crummles.

It was not very light, but Nicholas found himself close to the first entrance on the prompter's side, among bare walls, dusty scenes, mildewed clouds, heavily daubed draperies, and dirty floors. He looked about him; ceiling, pit, boxes, gallery, orchestra, fittings and decorations of every kind — all looked coarse, cold, gloomy, and wretched.

"Is this a theatre?" whispered Smike, in amazement; "I thought it was a blaze of light and finery."

"Why, so it is," replied Nicholas, hardly less surprised; "but not by day, Smike — not by day."

The manager's voice recalled him from a more careful inspection of the building, to the opposite side of the proscenium, where, at a small mahogany table with rickety legs and of an oblong shape, sat a stout, portly female, apparently between forty and fifty, in a tarnished silk cloak, with her bonnet dangling by the strings in her hand, and her hair (of which she had a great quantity) braided in a large festoon over each temple.

"Mr. Johnson," said the manager (for Nicholas had given the name which Newman Noggs had bestowed upon him in his conversation with Mrs. Kenwigs), "let me introduce Mrs. Vincent Crummles."

"I am glad to see you, sir," said Mrs. Vincent Crummles, in a sepulchral voice. "I am very glad to see you, and still more happy to hail you as a promising member of our corps."

The lady shook Nicholas by the hand as she addressed him in these terms; he saw it was a large one, but had not expected quite such an iron grip as that with which she honoured him.

"And this," said the lady, crossing to Smike, as tragic actresses cross when they obey a stage direction, "and this is the other. You, too, are welcome, sir."

"He'll do, I think, my dear?" said the manager, taking a pinch of snuff.

"He is admirable," replied the lady. "An acquisition, indeed."

As Mrs. Vincent Crummles recrossed back to the table, there bounded on to the stage, from some mysterious inlet, a little girl in a dirty white frock with tucks up to the knees, short trousers, sandalled shoes, white spencer, pink gauze bonnet, green veil, and curl-papers; who turned a pirouette, cut twice in the air, turned another pirouette, then, looking off at the opposite wing, shrieked, bounded forward to within six inches of the footlights, and fell into a beautiful attitude of terror, as a shabby gentleman in an old pair of buff slippers came in at one powerful slide, and, chattering his teeth, fiercely brandished a walking-stick.

"They are going through the 'Indian Savage and the Maiden,' " said Mrs. Crummles.

"Oh," said the manager, "the little ballet interlude. Very good, go on. A little this way, if you please, Mr. Johnson. That'll do. Now!"

The manager clapped his hands as a signal to proceed, and the savage, becoming ferocious, made a slide towards the maiden; but the maiden avoided him in six twirls, and came down, at the end of the last one, upon the very points of her toes. This seemed to make some impression upon the savage; for, after a little more ferocity and chasing of the maiden into corners, he began to relent, and stroked his face several times with his right thumb and four fingers, thereby intimating that he was struck with admiration of the maiden's beauty. Acting upon the impulse of this passion, he (the savage) began to hit himself severe thumps in the chest, and to exhibit other indications of being desperately in love, which being rather a prosy proceeding, was very likely the cause of the maiden's falling asleep; whether it was or no, asleep she did fall, sound as a church, on a sloping bank, and the savage perceiving it, leaned his left ear on his left hand, and nodded sideways, to intimate to all whom it might concern that she *was* asleep, and no shamming. Being left to himself, the savage had a dance all alone. Just as he left off the maiden woke up, rubbed her eyes, got off the bank, and had a dance all alone too — such a dance that the savage looked on in ecstasy all the while, and when it was done plucked from a neighbouring tree some botanical curiosity, resembling a small pickled cabbage, and offered it to the maiden, who at first wouldn't have it; but, on the savage shedding tears, relented. Then the savage jumped for joy; then the maiden jumped for rapture at the sweet smell of the pickled cabbage. Then the savage and the maiden danced violently together; and finally the savage dropped down on one knee, and the maiden stood on one leg upon his other knee; thus concluding the ballet, and leaving the spectators in a state of pleasing uncertainty whether she would ultimately marry the savage or return to her friends.

"Very well indeed," said Mr. Crummles; "bravo!"

"Bravo!" cried Nicholas, resolved to make the best of everything. "Beautiful!"

"This, sir," said Mr. Vincent Crummles, bringing the maiden forward, "this is the infant phenomenon — Miss Ninetta Crummles."

"Your daughter?" inquired Nicholas.

"My daughter — my daughter," replied Mr. Vincent Crummles;

"the idol of every place we go into, sir. We have had complimentary letters about this girl, sir, from the nobility and gentry of almost every town in England."

"I am not surprised at that," said Nicholas; "she must be quite a natural genius."

"Quite a —!" Mr. Crummles stopped; language was not powerful enough to describe the infant phenomenon. "I'll tell you what, sir," he said, "the talent of this child is not to be imagined. She must be seen, sir — seen — to be ever so faintly appreciated. There; go to your mother, my dear."

"May I ask how old she is?" inquired Nicholas.

"You may, sir," replied Mr. Crummles, looking steadily in his questioner's face, as some men do when they have doubts about being implicitly believed in what they are going to say. "She is ten years of age, sir."

"Not more!"

"Not a day."

"Dear me!" said Nicholas, "it's extraordinary."

It was; for the infant phenomenon, though of short stature, had a comparatively aged countenance; and had, moreover, been precisely the same age — not, perhaps, to the full extent of the memory of the oldest inhabitant, but certainly for five good years. But she had been kept up late every night, and put upon an unlimited allowance of gin-and-water from infancy, to prevent her growing tall; and perhaps this system of training had produced in the infant phenomenon these additional phenomena.

While this short dialogue was going on, the gentleman who had enacted the savage came up, with his walking shoes on his feet, and his slippers in his hand, to within a few paces, as if desirous of joining in the conversation. Deeming this a good opportunity, he put in his word.

"Talent there, sir," said the savage, nodding towards Miss Crummles.

Nicholas assented.

"Ah!" said the actor, setting his teeth together, and drawing in his breath with a hissing sound, "she oughtn't to be in the provinces, she oughtn't."

"What do you mean?" asked the manager.

"I mean to say," replied the other warmly, "that she is too good for country boards, and that she ought to be in one of the large houses in London, or nowhere; and I tell you more, without mincing the matter, that if it wasn't for envy and jealousy in some quarter that you know of, she would be. Perhaps you'll introduce me here, Mr. Crummles."

"Mr. Folair," said the manager, presenting him to Nicholas.

"Happy to know you, sir." Mr. Folair touched the brim of his hat with his forefinger, and then shook hands. "A recruit, sir, I understand?"

"An unworthy one," replied Nicholas.

"Did you ever see such a set-out as that?" whispered the actor, drawing him away, as Crummles left them to speak to his wife.

"As what?"

Mr. Folair made a funny face from his pantomime collection, and pointed over his shoulder.

"You don't mean the infant phenomenon?"

"Infant humbug, sir," replied Mr. Folair. There isn't a female child of common sharpness in a charity school that couldn't do better than that. She may thank her stars she was born a manager's daughter."

"You seem to take it to heart," said Nicholas, with a smile.

"Yes, by Jove, and well I may," said Mr. Folair, drawing his arm through his, and walking him up and down the stage. Isn't it enough to make a man crusty to see that little sprawler put up in the best business every night, and actually keeping money out of the house by being forced down people's throats, whilst other people are passed over? Isn't it extraordinary to see a man's confounded family conceit blinding him even to his own interest? Why, I *know* of fifteen-and-sixpence that came to Southampton one night last month to see me dance the Highland Fling; and what's the consequence? I've never been put up in it since — never once — while the 'infant phenomenon' has been grinning through artificial flowers at five people and a baby in the pit, and two boys in the gallery, every night."

"If I may judge of what I have seen of you," said Nicholas, "you must be a valuable member of the company."

"Oh!" replied Mr. Folair, beating his slippers together to knock the dust out; "I *can* come it pretty well — nobody better, perhaps, in my own line — but having such business as one gets here is like putting lead on one's feet instead of chalk, and dancing in fetters without the credit of it. Hollo! old fellow, how are you?"

The gentleman addressed in these latter words was a dark-complexioned man, inclining, indeed, to sallow, with long, thick, black hair, and very evident indications (although he was close shaved) of a stiff beard, and whiskers of the same deep shade. His age did not appear to exceed thirty, though many at first sight would have considered him much older, as his face was long and very pale, from the constant application of stage paint. He wore a checked shirt, an old green coat, with new gilt buttons, a neckerchief of broad red and green stripes, and full blue trousers; he carried, too, a common ash walking-stick, apparently more for show than use, as he flourished it about, with the hooked end downwards, except when he raised it, for a few seconds, and throwing himself into a fencing attitude, made a pass or two at the side-scenes, or at any other object, animate or inanimate, that chanced to afford him a pretty good mark at the moment.

"Well, Tommy," said this gentleman, making a thrust at his friend, who parried it dexterously with his slipper, "what's the news?"

"A new appearance, that's all," replied Mr. Folair, looking at Nicholas.

"Do the honours, Tommy, do the honours," said the other gentleman, tapping him reproachfully on the crown of the hat with his stick.

"This is Mr. Lenville, who does our first tragedy, Mr. Johnson," said the pantomimist.

"Except when old bricks and mortar takes it into his head to do it himself, you should add, Tommy," remarked Mr. Lenville. "You know who bricks and mortar is, I suppose, sir?"

"I do not, indeed," replied Nicholas.

"We call Crummles that, because his style of acting is rather in the heavy and ponderous way," said Mr. Lenville. "I mustn't be cracking jokes, though, for I've got a part of twelve lengths here, which I must be up in to-morrow night, and I haven't had time to look at it yet; I'm a confounded quick study, that's one comfort."

Consoling himself with this reflection, Mr. Lenville drew from his coat pocket a greasy and crumpled manuscript, and having made another pass at his friend, proceeded to walk to and fro, conning it to himself, and indulging occasionally in such appropriate action as his imagination and the text suggested.

A pretty general muster of the company had by this time taken place; for besides Mr. Lenville and his friend Tommy, there were present a slim young gentleman with weak eyes, who played the low-spirited lovers and sang tenor songs, and who had come arm-in-arm with the comic countryman — a man with a turned-up nose, large mouth, broad face, and staring eyes. Making himself very amiable to the infant phenomenon, was an inebriated elderly gentleman, in the last depths of shabbiness, who played the calm and virtuous old men; and paying especial court to Mrs. Crummles was another elderly gentleman, a shade more respectable, who played the irascible old men — those funny fellows who have nephews in the army, and perpetually run about with thick sticks to compel them to marry heiresses. Besides these, there was a roving-looking person in a rough greatcoat, who strode up and down in front of the lamps, flourishing a dress cane, and rattling away, in an undertone, with great vivacity, for the amusement of an ideal audience. He was not quite so young as he had been, and his figure was rather running to seed; but there was an air of exaggerated gentility about him, which bespoke the hero of swaggering comedy. There was, also, a little group of three or four young men, with lantern jaws and thick eyebrows, who were conversing in one corner; but they seemed to be of secondary importance, and laughed and talked together without attracting any attention.

The ladies were gathered in a little knot by themselves round the rickety table before mentioned. There was Miss Snevellicci — who could do anything, from a medley dance to Lady Macbeth, and always played some part in blue silk knee-smalls at her benefit — glancing, from the depths of her coal-scuttle straw bonnet, at Nicholas, and affecting to be absorbed in the recital of a diverting story to her friend Miss Ledrook, who had brought her work, and was making up a ruff in the most natural manner possible. There was Miss Belvawney — who seldom aspired to speaking parts, and usually went on as a page in white silk hose, to stand with one leg bent, and contemplate the audience, or to go in and out after Mr. Crummles in stately tragedy — twisting up the ringlets of the beautiful Miss Bravassa, who had once had her likeness taken "in character" by an engraver's apprentice, whereof impressions were hung up for sale in the pastry-cook's window, and the greengrocer's, and at the circulating library, and the box-office, whenever the announce bills came out for her annual night. There was Mrs. Lenville, in a very limp bonnet and veil, decidedly in that way in which she would wish to be if she truly loved Mr. Lenville; there was Miss Gazingi, with an imitation ermine boa tied on a loose knot round her neck, flogging Mr. Crummles, junior, with both ends, in fun. Lastly, there was Mrs. Grudden, in a brown cloth pelisse and a beaver bonnet, who assisted Mrs. Crummles in her domestic affairs, and took money at the doors, and dressed the ladies, and swept the house, and held the prompt-book when everybody else was on for the last scene, and acted any kind of part on any emergency without ever learning it, and was put down in the bills under any name or names whatever that occurred to Mr. Crummles as looking well in print.

Mr. Folair, having obligingly confided these particulars to Nicholas, left him to mingle with his fellows; the work of personal introduction was completed by Mr. Vincent Crummles, who publicly heralded the new actor as a prodigy of genius and learning.

"I beg your pardon," said Miss Snevellicci, sidling towards Nicholas, "but did you ever play at Canterbury?"

"I never did," replied Nicholas.

"I recollect meeting a gentleman at Canterbury," said Miss Snevellicci, "only for a few moments, for I was leaving the company as he joined it, so like you that I felt almost certain it was the same."

"I see you now for the first time," rejoined Nicholas, with all due gallantry. "I am sure I never saw you before; I couldn't have forgotten it."

"Oh, I'm sure — it's very flattering of you to say so," retorted Miss Snevellicci, with a graceful bend. "Now I look at you again, I see that the gentleman at Canterbury hadn't the same eyes as you; you'll think me very foolish for taking notice of such things, won't you?"

"Not at all," said Nicholas. "How can I feel otherwise than flattered by your notice in any way?"

"Oh! you men are such vain creatures!" cried Miss Snevellicci.

Whereupon she became charmingly confused, and, pulling out her pocket-handkerchief from a faded pink silk reticule with a gilt clasp, called to Miss Ledrook —

"Led, my dear," said Miss Snevellicci.

"Well, what is the matter?" said Miss Ledrock.

"It's not the same."

"Not the same what?"

"Canterbury — you know what I mean. Come here! I want to speak to you."

But Miss Ledrook wouldn't come to Miss Snevellicci, so Miss Snevellicci was obliged to go to Miss Ledrook, which she did in a skipping manner that was quite fascinating; and Miss Ledrook evidently joked Miss Snevellicci about being struck with Nicholas; for, after some playful whispering, Miss Snevellicci hit Miss Ledrook very hard on the backs of her hands, and retired up, in a state of pleasing confusion.

"Ladies and gentlemen," said Mr. Vincent Crummles, who had been writing on a piece of paper, "we'll call the 'Mortal Struggle' to-morrow at ten; everybody for the procession. 'Intrigue,' and 'Ways and Means,' you're all up in; so we shall only want one rehearsal. Everybody at ten, if you please."

"Everybody at ten," repeated Mrs. Grudden, looking about her.

"On Monday morning we shall read a new piece," said Mr. Crummles; "the name's not known yet, but everybody will have a good part. Mr. Johnson will take care of that."

"Hollo!" said Nicholas, starting, "I —"

"On Monday morning," repeated Mr. Crummles, raising his voice, to drown the unfortunate Mr. Johnson's remonstrance; "that'll do, ladies and gentlemen."

The ladies and gentlemen required no second notice to quit, and in a few minutes the theatre was deserted, save by the Crummles family, Nicholas, and Smike.

"Upon my word," said Nicholas, taking the manager aside, "I don't think I can be ready by Monday."

"Pooh, pooh," replied Mr. Crummles.

"But really I can't," returned Nicholas; "my invention is not accustomed to these demands, or possibly I might produce —"

"Invention! what the devil's that got to do with it?" cried the manager hastily.

"Everything, my dear sir."

"Nothing, my dear sir," retorted the manager, with evident impatience. "Do you understand French?"

"Perfectly well."

"Very good," said the manager, opening the table-drawer, and giving a roll of paper from it to Nicholas. "There! Just turn that into English, and put your name on the tilt-page. Damn me," said Mr. Crummles angrily, "if I haven't often said that I wouldn't have a man or woman in my company that wasn't master of the language, so that they might learn it from the original, and play it in English, and by that means save all this trouble and expense."

Nicholas smiled, and pocketed the play.

"What are you going to do about your lodgings?" said Mr. Crummles.

Nicholas could not help thinking that, for the first week, it would be an uncommon convenience to have a turn-up bedstead in the pit; but he merely remarked that he had not turned his thoughts that way.

"Come home with me, then," said Mr. Crummles, "and my boys shall go with you after dinner, and show you the most likely place."

The offer was not to be refused; Nicholas and Mr. Crummles gave Mrs. Crummles an arm each, and walked up the street in stately array. Smike, the boys, and the phenomenon, went home by a shorter cut, and Mrs. Grudden remained behind to take some cold Irish stew and a pint of porter in the box-office.

Mrs. Crummles trod the pavement as if she were going to immediate execution with an animating consciousness of innocence, and that heroic fortitude which virtue alone inspires. Mr. Crummles, on the other hand, assumed the look and gait of a hardened despot; but they both attracted some notice from many of the passers-by, and when they heard whisper of "Mr. and Mrs. Crummles!" or saw a little boy run back to stare them in the face, the severe expression of their countenances relaxed, for they felt it was popularity.

Mr. Crummles lived in St. Thomas's Street, at the house of one Bulph, a pilot, who sported a boat-green door, with window frames of the same colour, and had the little figure of a drowned man on his parlour mantel-shelf with other maritime and natural curiosities. He displayed also a brass knocker, a brass plate, and a brass bell-handle, all very bright and shining; and had a mast, with a vane on the top of it, in his back yard.

"You are welcome," said Mrs. Crummles, turning round to Nicholas when they reached the bow-windowed front room on the first floor.

Nicholas bowed his acknowledgments, and was unfeignedly glad to see the cloth laid.

"We have but a shoulder of mutton with onion sauce," said Mrs. Crummles, in the same charnel-house voice; "but such as our dinner is, we beg you to partake of it."

"You are very good," replied Nicholas; "I shall do it ample justice."

"Vincent," said Mrs. Crummles, "what is the hour?"

"Five minutes past dinner-time," said Mr. Crummles.

Mrs. Crummles rang the bell. "Let the mutton and onion sauce appear."

The slave who attended upon Mr. Bulph's lodgers disappeared, and after a short interval reappeared with the festive banquet. Nicholas and the infant phenomenon opposed each other at the Pembroke table, and Smike and the Masters Crummles dined on the sofa-bedstead.

"Are they very theatrical people here?" asked Nicholas.

"No," replied Mr. Crummles, shaking his head, "far from it."

"I pity them," observed Mrs. Crummles.

"So do I," said Nicholas; "if they have no relish for theatrical entertainments, properly conducted."

"Then they have none, sir," rejoined Mr. Crummles. "To the infant's benefit, last year, on which occasion she repeated three of her most popular characters, and also appeared in the 'Fairy Porcupine,' as originally performed by her, there was a house of no more than four pound twelve."

"Is it possible?" cried Nicholas.

"And two pound of that was trust, pa," said the phenomenon.

"And two pound of that was trust," repeated Mr. Crummles. "Mrs. Crummles herself has played to mere handfuls."

"But they are always a taking audience, Vincent," said the manager's wife.

"Most audiences are, when they have good acting — real good acting — the real thing," replied Mr. Crummles forcibly.

"Do you give lessons, ma'am?" inquired Nicholas.

"I do," said Mrs. Crummles.

"There is no teaching here, I suppose?"

"There has been," said Mrs. Crumlmes. "I have received pupils here. I imparted tuition to the daughter of a dealer in ships' provision; but it afterwards appeared that she was insane when she first came to me. It was very extraordinary that she should come, under such circumstances."

Not feeling quite so sure of that, Nicholas thought it best to hold his peace.

"Let me see," said the manager, cogitating after dinner. "Would you like some nice little part with the infant?"

"You are very good," replied Nicholas hastily; "but I think perhaps it would be better if I had somebody of my own size at first, in case I should turn out awkward. I should feel more at home, perhaps."

"True," said the manager. "Perhaps you would. And you could play up to the infant in time, you know."

"Certainly," replied Nicholas, devoutly hoping that it would be a very long time before he was honoured with this distinction.

"Then I'll tell you what we'll do," said Mr. Crummles. "You shall study Romeo when you've done that piece — don't forget to throw the pump and tubs in, by the bye — Juliet, Miss Snevellicci, old Grudden, the nurse — Yes, that'll do very well. Rover, too — you might get up Rover while you were about it, and Cassio, and Jeremy Diddler. You can easily knock them off: one part helps the other so much. Here they are, cues and all."

With these hasty general directions, Mr. Crummles thrust a number of little books into the faltering hands of Nicholas, and bidding his eldest son go with him and show where lodgings were to be had, shook him by the hand, and wished him good-night.

There is no lack of comfortable furnished apartments in Portsmouth, and no difficulty in finding some that are proportionate to very slender finances; but the former were too good, and the latter too bad, and they went into so many houses, and came out unsuited, that Nicholas seriously began to think he should be obliged to ask permission to spend the night in the theatre after all.

Eventually, however, they stumbled upon two small rooms up three pair of stairs, or rather two pair and a ladder, at a tobacconist's shop, on the Common Hard, a dirty street leading to the dockyard. These Nicholas engaged, only too happy to have escaped any request for payment of a week's rent beforehand.

"There! Lay down our personal property, Smike," he said, after showing young Crummles downstairs. "We have fallen upon strange times, and God only knows the end of them; but I am tired with the events of these three days, and will postpone reflection till to-morrow — if I can."

OF THE GREAT BESPEAK FOR MISS SNEVELLICCI, AND THE FIRST APPEARANCE OF NICHOLAS UPON ANY STAGE

Nicholas was up betimes in the morning; but he had scarcely begun to dress, notwithstanding, when he heard footsteps ascending the stairs, and was presently saluted by the voices of Mr. Folair, the pantomimist, and Mr. Lenville, the tragedian.

"House, house, house!" cried Mr. Folair.

"What, ho! within there!" said Mr. Lenville, in a deep voice.

"Confound these fellows!" thought Nicholas; "they have come to breakfast, I suppose. I'll open the door directly, if you'll wait an instant."

The gentlemen entreated him not to hurry himself; and, to beguile the interval, had a fencing bout with their walking-sticks on the very small landing-place, to the unspeakable discomposure of all the other lodgers downstairs.

"Here, come in," said Nicholas, when he had completed his toilet. "In the name of all that's horrible, don't make that noise outside."

"An uncommon snug little box this," said Mr. Lenville, stepping into the front room, and taking his hat off before he could get in at all. "Pernicious snug."

"For a man at all particular in such matters it might be a trifle too snug," said Nicholas; "for although it is, undoubtedly, a great convenience to be able to reach anything you want from the ceiling or the floor, or either side of the room, without having to move from your chair, still these advantages can only be had in an apartment of the most limited size."

"It isn't a bit too confined for a single man," returned Mr. Lenville. "That reminds me — my wife, Mr. Johnson — I hope she'll have some good part in this piece of yours?"

"I glanced at the French copy last night," said Nicholas. "It looks very good, I think."

"What do you mean to do for me, old fellow?" asked Mr. Lenville, poking the struggling fire with his walking-stick, and afterwards wiping it on the skirt of his coat. "Anything in the gruff and grumble way?"

"You turn your wife and child out of doors," said Nicholas; "and, in a fit of rage and jealousy, stab your eldest son in the library."

"Do I though!" exclaimed Mr. Lenville. "That's very good business."

"After which," said Nicholas, "you are troubled with remorse till the last act, and then you make up your mind to destroy yourself. But just as you are raising the pistol to your head, a clock strikes — ten."

"I see," cried Mr. Lenville. "Very good."

"You pause," said Nicholas; "you recollect to have heard a clock strike ten in your infancy. The pistol falls from your hand — you are overcome — you burst into tears, and become a virtuous and exemplary character for ever afterwards."

"Capital!" said Mr. Lenville; "that's a sure card, a sure card. Get the curtain down with a touch of nature like that, and it'll be a triumphant success."

"Is there anything good for me?" inquired Mr. Folair anxiously.

"Let me see," said Nicholas. "You play the faithful and attached servant; you are turned out of doors with the wife and child."

"Always coupled with that infernal phenomenon," sighed Mr. Folair; "and we go into poor lodgings, where I won't take any wages, and talk sentiment, I suppose?"

"Why — yes," replied Nicholas; "that is the course of the piece."

"I must have a dance of some kind, you know," said Mr. Folair. "You'll have to introduce one for the phenomenon, so you'd better make it a *pas de deux*, and save time."

"There's nothing easier than that," said Mr. Lenville, observing the disturbed looks of the young dramatist.

"Upon my word I don't see how it's to be done," rejoined Nicholas.

"Why, isn't it obvious?" reasoned Mr. Lenville. "Gadzooks! who can help seeing the way to do it? — you astonish me! You get the distressed lady, and the little child, and the attached servant, into the poor lodgings, don't you? Well, look here. The distressed lady sinks into a chair, and buries her face in her pocket-handkerchief. 'What makes you weep, mamma?' says the child. 'Don't weep, mamma, or you'll make me weep too!' 'And me!' says the faithful servant, rubbing his eyes with his arm. 'What can we do to raise your spirits, dear mamma?' says the little child. 'Aye, what *can* we do?' says the faithful servant. 'Oh, Pierre!' says the distressed lady; 'would that I could shake off these painful thoughts.' 'Try ma'am, try,' says the faithful servant; 'rouse yourself, ma'am; be amused.' 'I will,' says the lady — 'I will learn to suffer with fortitude. Do you remember that dance, my honest friend, which in happier days you practised with this sweet angel? It never failed to calm my spirits then. Oh, let me see it once again before I die!' There it is — cue for the band, *before I die* — and off they go. That's the regular thing; isn't it, Tommy?"

"That's it," replied Mr. Folair. "The distressed lady, overpowered by old recollections, faints at the end of the dance, and you close in with a picture."

Profiting by these and other lessons, which were the result of the personal experience of the two actors, Nicholas willingly gave them the best breakfast he could, and, when he at length got rid of them, applied himself to his task, by no means displeased to find that it was so much easier than he had at first supposed. He worked very hard all day, and did not leave his room until the evening, when he went down to the theatre, whither Smike had repaired before him to go on with another gentleman as a general rebellion.

Here all the people were so much changed that he scarcely knew them. False hair, false colour, false calves, false muscles — they had become different beings. Mr. Lenville was a blooming warrior of most exquisite proportions; Mr. Crummles, his large face shaded by a profusion of black hair, a Highland outlaw of most majestic bearing; one of the old gentlemen a jailer, and the other a venerable patriarch; the comic countryman, a fighting-man of great valour, relieved by a touch of humour; each of the Masters Crummles, a prince in his own right; and the low-spirited lover, a desponding captive. There was a gorgeous banquet ready spread for the third act, consisting of two pasteboard vases, one plate of biscuits, a black bottle, and a vinegar-cruet; and, in short, everything was on a scale of the utmost splendour and preparation.

Nicholas was standing with his back to the curtain, now contemplating the first scene, which was a Gothic archway, about two feet shorter than Mr. Crummles, through which that gentleman was to make his first entrance, and now listening to a couple of people who were cracking nuts in the gallery, wondering whether they made the whole audience, when the manager himself walked familiarly up and accosted him.

"Been in front to-night?" said Mr. Crummles.

"No," replied Nicholas, "not yet. I am going to see the play."

"We've had a pretty good let," said Mr. Crummles. "Four front places in the centre, and the whole of the stage-box."

"Oh, indeed!" said Nicholas; "a family, I suppose?"

"Yes," replied Mr. Crummles, "yes. It's an affecting thing. There are six children. and they never come unless the pheonomenon plays."

It would have been difficult for any party, family or otherwise, to have visited the theatre on a night when the phenomenon did *not* play, inasmuch as she always sustained one, and not uncommonly two or three characters every night; but Nicholas, sympathising with the feelings of a father, refrained from hinting at this trifling circumstance, and Mr. Crummles continued to talk uninterrupted by him.

"Six," said that gentleman; "pa and ma eight, aunt nine, governess ten, grandfather and grandmother twelve. Then there's the footman, who stands outside with a bag of oranges and a jug of toast-and-water, and sees the play for nothing through the little pane of glass in the box-door — it's cheap at a guinea; they gain by taking a box."

"I wonder you allow so many," observed Nicholas.

"There's no help for it," replied Mr. Crummles; "it's always expected in the country. If there are six children, six people come to hold them in their laps. A family-box carries double always. Ring in the orchestra, Grudden."

That useful lady did as she was requested, and shortly afterwards the tuning of three fiddles was heard. Which process having been protracted as long as it was supposed that the patience of the audience could possibly bear it, was put a stop to by another jerk of the bell, which, being the signal to begin in earnest, set the orchestra playing a variety of popular airs with involuntary variations.

If Nicholas had been astonished at the alteration for the better which the gentlemen displayed, the transformation of the ladies was still more extraordinary. When, from a snug corner of the manager's box, he beheld Miss Snevellicci in all the glories of white muslin with a gold hem, and Mrs. Crummles in all the dignity of the outlaw's wife, and Miss Bravassa in all the sweetness of Miss Snevellicci's confidential friend, and Miss Belvawney in the white silks of a page doing duty everywhere, and swearing to live and die in the service of everybody, he could scarcely contain his admiration, which testified itself in great applause, and the closest possible attention to the business of the scene. The plot was most interesting. It belonged to no particular age, people, or country, and was, perhaps, the more delightful on that account, as nobody's previous information could afford the remotest glimmering of what would ever come of it. An outlaw had been very successful in doing something somewhere, and came home in triumph, to the sound of shouts and fiddles, to greet his wife — a lady of masculine mind, who talked a good deal about her father's bones, which it seemed were unburied, though whether from a peculiar taste on the part of the old gentleman himself, or the reprehensible neglect of his relations, did not appear. This outlaw's wife was, somehow or other, mixed up with a patriarch living in a castle a long way off, and this patriarch was the father of several of the characters, but he didn't exactly know which, and was uncertain whether he had brought up the right ones in his castle, or the wrong ones, but rather inclined to the latter opinion, and, being uneasy, relieved his mind with a banquet, during which solemnity somebody in a cloak said, "Beware," which somebody was known by nobody (except the audience) to be the outlaw himself, who had come there for reasons unexplained, but possibly with an eye to the spoons. There was an agreeable surprise in the way of certain love-passages between the despairing captive and Miss Snevellicci, and the comic fighting-man and Miss Bravassa; besides which, Mr. Lenville had several very tragic scenes in the dark, while on throat-cutting expeditions, which were all baffled by the skill and bravery of the comic fighting-man (who overheard whatever was said all through the piece) and the intrepidity of Miss Snevellicci, who adopted tights, and therein repaired to the prison of her captive lover, with a small basket of refreshments and a dark lantern. At last, it came out that the patriarch was the man who had treated the bones of the outlaw's father-in-law with so much disrespect, for which cause and reason the outlaw's wife repaired to his castle to kill him, and so got into a dark room, where, after a good deal of groping in the dark, everybody got hold of everybody else, and took them for somebody besides, which occasioned a vast quantity of confusion, with some pistolling, loss of life, and torchlight; after which the patriarch came forward, and observing, with a knowing look, that he knew all about his children now, and would tell them when they got inside, said that there could not be a more appropriate occasion for marrying the young people than that, and, therefore, he joined their hands, with the full consent of the indefatigable page, who (being the only other person surviving) pointed with his cap into the clouds, and his right hand to the ground; thereby invoking a blessing, and giving the cue for the curtain to come down, which it did, amidst general applause.

"What did you think of that?" asked Mr. Crummles, when Nicholas went round to the stage again. Mr. Crummles was very red and hot, for your outlaws are desperate fellows to shout.

"I think it was very capital indeed," replied Nicholas; "Miss Snevellicci, in particular, was uncommonly good."

"She's a genius," said Mr. Crummles; "quite a genius, that girl. By the bye, I've been thinking of bringing out that piece of yours on her bespeak night."

"When?" asked Nicholas.

"The night of her bespeak. Her benefit night, when her friends and patrons bespeak the play," said Mr. Crummles.

"Oh, I understand," replied Nicholas.

"You see," said Mr. Crummles, "it's sure to go on such an occasion, and even if it should not work up quite as well as we expect, why, it will be her risk, you know, and not ours."

"Yours, you mean," said Nicholas.

"I said mine, didn't I?" returned Mr. Crummles. "Next Monday week. What do you say now? You'll have done it, and are sure to be up in the lover's part long before that time."

"I don't know about, 'long before,'" replied Nicholas; "but *by* that time I think I can undertake to be ready."

"Very good," pursued Mr. Crummles; "then we'll call that settled. Now, I want to ask you something else. There's a little — what shall I call it — a little canvassing takes place on these occasions."

"Among the patrons, I suppose?" said Nicholas.

"Among the patrons; and the fact is that Snevellicci has had so many bespeaks in this place, that she wants an attraction. She had a bespeak when her mother-in-law died, and a bespeak when her uncle died; and Mrs. Crummles and myself have had bespeaks on the anniversary of the phenomenon's birthday, and our wedding-day, and occasions of that description, so that, in fact, there's some difficulty in getting a good one. Now, won't you help this poor girl, Mr. Johnson?" said Crummles, sitting himself down on a drum, and taking a great pinch of snuff, as he looked him steadily in the face.

"How do you mean?" rejoined Nicholas.

"Don't you think you could spare half an hour tomorrow morning, to call with her at the houses of one or two of the principal people?" murmured the manager, in a persuasive tone.

"Oh, dear me!" said Nicholas, with an air of very strong objection, "I shouldn't like to do that."

"The infant will accompany her," said Mr. Crummles. "The moment it was suggested to me, I gave permission for the infant to go. There will not be the smallest impropriety—Miss Snevellicci, sir, is the very soul of honour. It would be of material service — the gentleman from London — author of the new piece — actor in the new piece — first appearance on any boards — it would lead to a great bespeak, Mr. Johnson."

"I am very sorry to throw a damp upon the prospects of anybody, and more especially a lady," replied Nicholas; "but really I must decidedly object to making one of the canvassing party."

"What does Mr. Johnson say, Vincent?" inquired a voice close to his ear; and, looking round, he found Mrs. Crummles and Miss Snevellicci herself standing behind him.

"He has some objection, my dear," replied Mr. Crummles, looking at Nicholas.

"Objection!" exclaimed Mrs. Crummles. "Can it be possible?"

"Oh, I hope not!" cried Miss Snevellicci. "You surely are not so cruel — oh, dear me! — Well, I — To think of that now, after all one's looking forward to it!"

"Mr. Johnson will not persist, my dear," said Mrs. Crummles. "Think better of him than to suppose it. Gallantry, humanity, all the best feelings of his nature, must be enlisted in this interesting cause."

"Which moves even a manager," said Mr. Crummles, smiling.

"And a manager's wife," added Mrs. Crummles, in her accustomed tragedy tones. "Come, come, you will relent, I know you will."

"It is not in my nature," said Nicholas, moved by these appeals, "to resist any entreaty, unless it is to do something positively wrong; and, beyond a feeling of pride, I know nothing which should prevent my doing this. I know nobody here, and nobody knows me. So be it, then. I yield."

Miss Snevellicci was at once overwhelmed with blushes and expressions of gratitude, of which latter commodity neither Mr. nor Mrs. Crummles was by any means sparing. It was arranged that Nicholas should call upon her, at her lodgings, at eleven next morning, and soon after they parted: he to return home to his authorship; Miss Snevellicci to dress for the after-piece; and the disinterested manager and his wife to discuss the probable gains of the forthcoming bespeak, of which they were to have two-thirds of the profits by solemn treaty of agreement.

At the stipulated hour next morning, Nicholas repaired to the lodgings of Miss Snevellicci, which were in a place called Lombard Street, at the house of a tailor. A strong smell of ironing pervaded the little passage, and the tailor's daughter, who opened the door, appeared in that flutter of spirit which is so often attendant upon the periodical getting up of a family's linen.

"Miss Snevellicci lives here, I believe?" said Nicholas, when the door was opened.

The tailor's daughter replied in the affirmative.

"Will you have the goodness to let her know that Mr. Johnson is here?" said Nicholas.

"Oh, if you please, you're to come upstairs," replied the tailor's daughter, with a smile.

Nicholas followed the young lady, and was shown into a small apartment on the first floor, communicating with a back room; in which, as he judged from a certain half-subdued clinking sound, as of cups and saucers, Miss Snevellicci was then taking her breakfast in bed.

"You're to wait, if you please," said the tailor's daughter, after a short period of absence, during which the clinking in the back room had ceased, and been succeeded by whispering — "she won't be long."

As she spoke she pulled up the window-blind, and having by this means (as she thought) diverted Mr. Johnson's attention from the room to the street, caught up some articles which were airing on the fender, and had very much the appearance of stockings, and darted off.

As there were not many objects of interest outside the window, Nicholas looked about the room with more curiosity than he might otherwise have bestowed upon it. On the sofa lay an old guitar, several thumbed pieces of music, and a scattered litter of curl-papers; together with a confused heap of play-bills, and a pair of soiled white satin shoes with large blue rosettes. Hanging over the back of a chair was a half-finished muslin apron, with little pockets ornamented with red ribbons, such as waiting-women wear on the stage, and (by consequence) are never seen with anywhere else. In one corner stood the diminutive pair of top-boots in which Miss Snevellicci was accustomed to enact the little jockey, and, folded on a chair hard by, was a small parcel, which bore a very suspicious resemblance to the companion smalls.

But the most interesting object of all was, perhaps, the open scrap-book, displayed in the midst of some theatrical duodecimos that were strewn upon the table, and pasted into which scrap-book were various critical notices of Miss Snevellicci's acting, extracted from different provincial journals, together with one poetic address in her honour, commencing —

Sing, God of Love, and tell me in what dearth
Thrice-gifted SNEVELLICCI came on earth,
To thrill us with her smile, her tear, her eye,
Sing, God of Love, and tell me quickly why.

Besides this effusion, there were innumerable complimentary allusions, also extracted from newspapers, such as — "We observe from an advertisement in another part of our paper of to-day, that the charming and highly-talented Miss Snevellicci takes her benefit on Wednesday, for which occasion she has put forth a bill of fare that might kindle exhilaration in the breast of a misanthrope. In the confidence that our fellow-townsmen have not lost that high appreciation of public ability and private worth, for which they have long been so pre-eminently distinguished, we predict that this charming actress will be greeted with a bumper." "To correspondents. — J. S. is misinformed when he supposes that the highly-gifted and beautiful Miss Snevellicci, nightly captivating all hearts at our pretty and commodious little theatre, is *not* the same lady to whom the young gentleman of immense fortune, residing within a hundred miles of the good city of York, lately made honourable proposals. We have reason to know that Miss Snevellicci *is* the lady who was implicated in that mysterious and romantic affair, and whose conduct on that occasion did no less honour to her head and heart than do her histrionic triumphs to her brilliant genius." A copious assortment of such paragraphs as these, with long bills of benefits, all ending with "Come Early," in large capitals, formed the principal contents of Miss Snevellicci's scrap-book.

Nicholas had read a great many of these scraps, and was absorbed in a circumstantial and melancholy account of the train of events which had led to Miss Snevellicci's spraining her ankle by slipping on a piece of orange-peel flung by a monster in human form (so the paper said) upon the stage at Winchester — when that young lady herself, attired in the coal-scuttle bonnet and walking-dress complete, tripped into the room, with a thousand apologies for having detained him so long after the appointed time.

"But really," said Miss Snevellicci, "my darling Led, who lives with me here, was taken so very ill in the night that I thought she would have expired in my arms."

"Such a fate is almost to be envied," returned Nicholas; "but I am very sorry to hear it, nevertheless."

"What a creature you are to flatter!" said Miss Snevellicci, buttoning her glove in much confusion.

"If it be flattery to admire your charms and accomplishments," rejoined Nicholas, laying his hand upon the scrapbook, "you have better specimens of it here."

"Oh, you cruel creature, to read such things as those! I'm almost ashamed to look you in the face afterwards, positively I am," said Miss Snevellicci, seizing the book, and putting it away in a closet. "How careless of Led. How could she be so naughty?"

"I thought you had kindly left it here on purpose for me to read," said Nicholas. And really it did seem possible.

"I wouldn't have had you see it for the world!" rejoined Miss Snevellicci. "I never was so vexed—never! But she is such a careless thing, there's no trusting her."

The conversation was here interrupted by the entrance of the phenomenon, who had discreetly remained in the bedroom up to this moment, and now presented herself, with much grace and lightness, bearing in her hand a very little green parasol, with a broad fringe border, and no handle. After a few words, of course, they sallied into the street.

The phenomenon was rather a troublesome companion, for first the right sandal came down, and then the left, and these mischances being repaired, one leg of the little white trousers was discovered to be longer than the other; besides these accidents, the green parasol was dropped down an iron grating, and only fished up again with great difficulty, and by dint of much exertion. However, it was impossible to scold her, as she was the manager's daughter, so Nicholas took it all in perfect good-humour, and walked on, with Miss Snevelicci, arm-in-arm on one side, and the offending infant on the other.

The first house to which they bent their steps was situated in a terrace of respectable appearance. Miss Snevellicci's modest double knock was answered by a footboy, who, in reply to her inquiry whether Mrs. Curdle was at home, opened his eyes very wide, grinned very much, and said he didn't know, but he'd inquire. With this, he showed them into a parlour, where he kept them waiting, until the two women-servants had repaired thither, under false pretences, to see the play-actors; and having compared notes with them in the passage, and joined in a vast quantity of whispering and giggling, he at length went upstairs with Miss Snevellicci's name.

Now, Mrs. Curdle was supposed, by those who were best informed on such points, to possess quite the London taste in matters relating to literature and the drama; and as to Mr. Curdle, he had written a pamphlet of sixty-four pages, post octavo, on the character of the Nurse's deceased husband in "Romeo and Juliet," with an inquiry whether he really had been a "merry man" in his lifetime, or whether it was merely his widow's affectionate partiality that induced her so to report him. He had likewise proved, that by altering the received mode of punctuation, any one of Shakespeare's plays could be made quite different, and the sense completely changed; it is needless to say, therefore, that he was a great critic, and a very profound and most original thinker.

"Well, Miss Snevellicci," said Mrs. Curdle, entering the parlour, "and how do *you* do?"

Miss Snevellicci made a graceful obeisance, and hoped Mrs. Curdle was well, as also Mr. Curdle, who at the same time appeared. Mrs. Curdle was dressed in a morning wrapper, with a little cap stuck upon the top of her head. Mr. Curdle wore a loose robe on his back, and his right forefinger on his forehead, after the portraits of Sterne, to whom somebody or other had once said he bore a striking resemblance.

"I ventured to call for the purpose of asking whether you would put your name to my bespeak, ma'am," said Miss Snevellicci, producing documents.

"Oh! I really don't know what to say," replied Mrs. Curdle. "It's not as if the theatre was in its high and palmy days—you needn't stand, Miss Snevellicci—the drama is gone, perfectly gone."

"As an exquisite embodiment of the poet's visions, and a realisation of human intellectuality, gilding with refulgent light our dreamy moments, and laying open a new and magic world before the mental eye, the drama is gone, perfectly gone," said Mr. Curdle.

"What man is there, now living, who can present before us all those changing and prismatic colours with which the character of Hamlet is invested?" exclaimed Mrs. Curdle.

"What man indeed — upon the stage?" said Mr. Curdle, with a

small reservation in favour of himself. "Hamlet! Pooh! ridiculous! Hamlet is gone, perfectly gone."

Quite overcome by these dismal reflections, Mr. and Mrs. Curdle sighed, and sat for some short time without speaking. At length the lady, turning to Miss Snevellicci, inquired what play she proposed to have.

"Quite a new one," said Miss Snevellicci, "of which this gentleman is the author, and in which he plays; being his first appearance on any stage. Mr. Johnson is the gentleman's name."

"I hope you have preserved the unities, sir?" said Mr. Curdle.

"The original piece is a French one," said Nicholas. "There is abundance of incident, sprightly dialogue, strongly-marked characters—"

"All unavailing without a strict observance of the unities, sir," returned Mr. Curdle. "The unities of the drama before everything."

"Might I ask you," said Nicholas, hesitating between the respect he ought to assume and his love of the whimsical—"might I ask you what the unities are?"

Mr. Curdle coughed and considered. "The unities, sir," he said, "are a completeness—a kind of a universal dovetailedness with regard to place and time—a sort of a general oneness, if I may be allowed to use so strong an expression. I take those to be the dramatic unities, so far as I have been enabled to bestow attention upon them, and I have read much upon the subject, and thought much. I find, running through the performances of this child," said Mr. Curdle, turning to the phenomenon, "a unity of feeling, a breadth, a light and shade, a warmth of colouring, a tone, a harmony, a glow, an artistical development of original conceptions, which I look for in vain among older performers—I don't know whether I make myself understood?"

"Perfectly," replied Nicholas.

"Just so," said Mr. Curdle, pulling up his neckcloth. "That is my definition of the unities of the drama."

Mrs. Curdle had sat listening to this lucid explanation with great complacency. It being finished, she inquired what Mr. Curdle thought about putting down their names.

"I don't know, my dear; upon my word I don't know," said Mr. Curdle. "If we do, it must be distinctly understood that we do not pledge ourselves to the quality of the performances. Let it go forth to the world, that we do not give *them* the sanction of our names, but that we confer the distinction merely upon Miss Snevellicci. That being clearly stated, I take it to be, as it were, a duty, that we should extend our patronage to a degraded stage, even for the sake of the associations with which it is entwined. Have you got two-and-six-pence for half-a-crown, Miss Snevellicci?" said Mr. Curdle, turning over four of those pieces of money.

Miss Snevellicci felt in all the corners of the pink reticule, but there was nothing in any of them. Nicholas murmured a jest about his being an author, and thought it best not to go through the form of feeling in his pockets at all.

"Let me see," said Mr. Curdle; "twice four's eight—four shillings a piece to the boxes, Miss Snevellicci, is exceedingly dear in the present state of the drama — three half-crowns is seven-and-six; we shall not differ about sixpence, I suppose? Sixpence will not part us, Miss Snevellicci?"

Poor Miss Snevellicci took the three half-crowns, with many smiles and bends, and Mrs. Curdle, adding several supplementary directions relative to keeping the places for them, and dusting the seat, and sending two clean bills as soon as they came out, rang the bell as a signal for breaking up the conference.

"Odd people those," said Nicholas, when they got clear of the house.

"I assure you," said Miss Snevellicci, taking his arm, "that I think myself very lucky they did not owe all the money instead of being sixpence short. Now, if you were to succeed, they would give people to understand that they had always patronised you; and, if you were to fail, they would have been quite certain of that from the very beginning."

At the next house they visited, they were in great glory; for there resided the six children who were so enraptured with the public actions of the phenomenon, and who, being called down from the nursery to be treated with a private view of that young lady, proceeded to poke their fingers into her eyes, and tread upon her toes, and show her many other little attentions peculiar to their time of life.

"I shall certainly persuade Mr. Borum to take a private box," said the lady of the house, after a most gracious reception. "I shall only take two of the children, and will make up the rest of the party, of gentlemen—your admirers, Miss Snevellicci. Augustus, you naughty boy, leave the little girl alone."

This was addressed to a young gentleman who was pinching the phenomenon behind, apparently with the view of ascertaining whether she was real.

"I am sure you must be very tired," said the mamma, turning to Miss Snevellicci. "I cannot think of allowing you to go without first taking a glass of wine! Fie, Charlotte, I am ashamed of you. Miss Lane, my dear, pray see to the children."

Miss Lane was the governess, and this entreaty was rendered necessary by the abrupt behaviour of the youngest Miss Borum, who, having filched the phenomenon's little green parasol, was now carrying it bodily off, while the distracted infant looked helplessly on.

"I am sure, where you ever learned to act as you do," said good-natured Mrs. Borum, turning again to Miss Snevellicci, "I cannot understand (Emma, don't stare so); laughing in one piece, and crying in the next, and so natural in all—oh, dear!"

"I am very happy to hear you express so favourable an opinion," said Miss Snevellicci. "It's quite delightful to think you like it."

"Like it!" cried Mrs. Borum. "Who can help liking it? I would go to the play twice a week if I could: I dote upon it—only you're too affecting sometimes. You do put me in such a state—into such fits of crying! Good gracious me, Miss Lane, how can you let them torment that poor child so!"

The phenomenon was really in a fair way of being torn limb from limb; for two strong little boys, one holding on by each of her hands, were dragging her in different directions as a trial of strength. However, Miss Lane (who had herself been too much occupied in contemplating the grown-up actors, to pay the necessary attention to these proceedings) rescued the unhappy infant at this juncture, who, being recruited with a glass of wine, was shortly afterwards taken away by her friends, after sustaining no more serious damage than a flattening of the pink gauze bonnet, and a rather extensive creasing of the white frock and trousers.

It was a trying morning; for there were a great many calls to make, and everybody wanted a different thing. Some wanted tragedies, and others comedies; some objected to dancing; some wanted scarcely anything else. Some thought the comic singer decidedly low, and others hoped he would have more to do than he usually had. Some people wouldn't promise to go, because other people wouldn't promise to go; and other people wouldn't go at all because other people went. At length, and by little and little, omitting something in this place, and adding something in that, Miss Snevellicci pledged herself to a bill of fare which was comprehensive enough, if it had no other merit (it included among other trifles, four pieces, divers songs, a few combats, and several dances); and they returned home, pretty well exhausted with the business of the day.

Nicholas worked away at the piece, which was speedily put into rehearsal, and then worked away at his own part, which he studied with great perseverance, and acted—as the whole company said—to perfection. And at length the great day arrived. The crier was sent round in the morning to proclaim the entertainments with sound of bell in all the thoroughfares; extra bills of three feet long by nine inches wide were dispersed in all directions, flung down all the areas, thrust under all the knockers, and developed in all the shops. They were placarded on all the walls too, though not with complete success, for an illiterate person having undertaken this office during the indisposition of the regular bill-sticker, a part were posted sideways, and the remainder upside down.

At half-past five there was a rush of four people to the gallery door; at a quarter before six there were at least a dozen; at six o'clock the kicks were terrific; and when the elder Master Crummles opened the door, he was obliged to run behind it for his life. Fifteen shillings were taken by Mrs. Grudden in the first ten minutes.

Behind the scenes the same unwonted excitement prevailed. Miss Snevellicci was in such a perspiration that the paint would scarcely stay on her face. Mrs. Crummles was so nervous that she could hardly remember her part. Miss Bravassa's ringlets came out of curl with the heat and anxiety; even Mr. Crummles himself kept peeping through the hole in the curtain, and running back every now and then to announce that another man had come into the pit.

At last the orchestra left off, and the curtain rose upon the new piece. The first scene, in which there was nobody particular, passed off calmly enough, but when Miss Snevellicci went on in the second, accompanied by the phenomenon as child, what a roar of applause broke out! The people in the Borum box rose as one man, waving their hats and handkerchiefs, and uttering shouts of "Bravo!" Mrs. Borum and the governess cast wreaths upon the stage, of which, some fluttered into the lamps, and one crowned the temples of a fat gentleman in the pit, who, looking eagerly towards the scene, remained unconscious of the honour; the tailor and his family kicked at the panels of the upper boxes till they threatened to come out altogether; the very ginger-beer boy remained transfixed in the centre of the house; a young officer, supposed to entertain a passion for Miss Snevellicci, stuck his glass in his eye as though to hide a tear. Again and again Miss Snevellicci curtsied lower and lower, and again and again the applause came down louder and louder. At length, when the phenomenon picked up one of the smoking wreaths and put it on, sideways, over Miss Snevellicci's eye, it reached its climax, and the play proceeded.

But when Nicholas came on for his crack scene with Mrs. Crummles, what a clapping of hands there was! When Mrs. Crummles (who was his unworthy mother) sneered, and called him "presumptuous boy," and he defied her, what a tumult of applause came on! When he quarrelled with the other gentleman about the young lady, and producing a case of pistols, said, that if he *was* a gentleman, he would fight him in that drawing-room, until the furniture was sprinkled with the blood of one, if not of two — how boxes, pit, and gallery joined in one most vigorous cheer! When he called his mother names, because she wouldn't give up the young lady's property, and she relenting, caused him to relent likewise, and fall down on one knee and ask her blessing, how the ladies in the audience sobbed! When he was hid behind the curtain in the dark, and the wicked relation poked a sharp sword in every direction, save where his legs were plainly visible, what a thrill of anxious fear ran through the house! His air, his figure, his walk, his look, everything he said or did, was the subject of commendation. There was a round of applause every time he spoke. And when, at last, in the pump-and-tub scene, Mrs. Grudden lighted the blue fire, and all the unemployed members of the company came in, and tumbled down in various directions — because that had anything to do with the plot, but in order to finish off with a tableau — the audience (who had by this time increased considerably) gave vent to such a shout of enthusiasm as had not been heard in those walls for many and many a day.

In short, the success of both new piece and new actor was complete, and when Miss Snevellicci was called for at the end of the play, Nicholas led her on, and divided the applause.

CONCERNING A YOUNG LADY FROM LONDON, WHO JOINS THE
COMPANY, AND AN ELDERLY ADMIRER WHO FOLLOWS IN
HER TRAIN; WITH AN AFFECTING CEREMONY
CONSEQUENT ON THEIR ARRIVAL

The new piece being a decided hit, was announced for every evening of performance until further notice, and the evenings when the theatre was closed were reduced from three in the week to two. Nor were these the only tokens of extraordinary success; for, on the succeeding Saturday, Nicholas received, by favour of the indefatigable Mrs. Grudden, no less a sum than thirty shillings; besides which substantial reward, he enjoyed considerable fame and honour, having a presentation copy of Mr. Curdle's pamphlet forwarded to the theatre, with that gentleman's own autograph (in itself an inestimable treasure) on the flyleaf, accompanied with a note, containing many expressions of approval, and an unsolicited assurance that Mr. Curdle would be very happy to read Shakespeare to him for three hours every morning before breakfast during his stay in the town.

"I've got another novelty, Johnson," said Mr. Crummles, one morning, in great glee.

"What's that?" rejoined Nicholas. "The pony?"

"No, no, we never come to the pony till everything else has failed," said Mr. Crummles. "I don't think we shall come to the pony at all this season. No, no, not the pony."

"A boy phenomenon, perhaps?" suggested Nicholas.

"There is only one phenomenon, sir," replied Mr. Crummles impressively, "and that's a girl."

"Very true," said Nicholas. "I beg your pardon. Then I don't know what it is, I am sure."

"What should you say to a young lady from London?" inquired

Mr. Crummles. "Miss So-and-so, of the Theatre Royal, Drury Lane?"

"I should say she would look very well in the bills," said Nicholas.

"You're about right there," said Mr. Crummles; "and if you had said she would look very well upon the stage, too, you wouldn't have been far out. Look here; what do you think of this?"

With this inquiry Mr. Crummles severally unfolded a red poster, and a blue poster, and a yellow poster, at the top of each of which public notification was inscribed in enormous characters — "First appearance of the unrivalled Miss Petowker, of the Theatre Royal, Drury Lane!"

"Dear me!" said Nicholas, "I know that lady."

"Then you are acquainted with as much talent as ever was compressed into one young person's body," retorted Mr. Crummles, rolling up the bills again; "that is, talent of a certain sort — of a certain sort. 'The Blood-drinker,'" added Mr. Crummles, with a prophetic sigh — "'The Blood-drinker' will die with that girl; and she's the only sylph *I* ever saw who could stand upon one leg and play the tambourine on her other knee, *like* a sylph."

"When does she come down?" asked Nicholas.

"We expect her to-day," replied Mr. Crummles. "She is an old friend of Mrs. Crummles's. Mrs. Crummles saw what she could do — always knew it from the first. She taught her, indeed, nearly all she knows. Mrs. Crummles was the original Blood-drinker."

"Was she, indeed?"

"Yes. She was obliged to give it up though."

"Did it disagree with her?" asked Nicholas, smiling.

"Not so much with her as with her audiences," replied Mr. Crummles. "Nobody could stand it. It was too tremendous. You don't quite know what Mrs. Crummles is yet."

Nicholas ventured to insinuate that he thought he did.

"No, no, you don't," said Mr. Crummles; "you don't, indeed. *I* don't, and that's a fact. I don't think her country will, till she is dead. Some new proof of talent bursts from that astonishing woman every year of her life. Look at her — mother of six children — three of 'em alive, and all upon the stage!"

"Extraordinary!" cried Nicholas.

"Ah! extraordinary, indeed," rejoined Mr. Crummles, taking a complacent pinch of snuff, and shaking his head gravely. "I pledge you my professional word I didn't even know she could dance till her last benefit, and then she played Juliet, and Helen Macgregor, and did the skipping-rope hornpipe between the pieces. The very first time I saw that admirable woman, Johnson," said Mr. Crummles, drawing a little nearer, and speaking in the tone of confidential friendship, "she stood upon her head on the butt-end of a spear, surrounded with blazing fireworks."

"You astonish me!" said Nicholas.

"*She* astonished *me!*" returned Mr. Crummles, with a very serious countenance. "Such grace, coupled with such dignity! I adored her from that moment."

The arrival of the gifted subject of these remarks put an abrupt termination to Mr. Crummles's eulogium and almost immediately afterwards Master Percy Crummles entered with a letter, which had arrived by the general post, and was directed to his gracious mother; at sight of the superscription whereof, Mrs. Crummles exclaimed, "From Henrietta Petowker, I do declare!" and instantly became absorbed in the contents.

"Is it —?" inquired Mr. Crummles, hesitating.

"Oh, yes, it's all right," replied Mrs. Crummles, anticipating the question. "What an excellent thing for her, to be sure!"

"It's the best thing, altogether, that I ever heard of, I think," said Mr. Crummles; and then Mr. Crummles, Mrs. Crummles, and Master Percy Crummles, all fell to laughing violently. Nicholas left them to enjoy their mirth together, and walked to his lodgings, wondering very much what mystery connected with Miss Petowker could provoke such merriment, and pondering still more on the extreme surprise with which that lady would regard his sudden enlistment in a profession of which she was such a distinguished and brilliant ornament.

But, in this latter respect he was mistaken; for — whether Mr. Vincent Crummles had paved the way, or Miss Petowker had some special reason for treating him with even more than her usual amiability — their meeting at the theatre next day was more like that of two dear friends who had been inseparable from infancy, than a recognition passing between a lady and gentleman who had only met some half-dozen times, and then by mere chance. Nay, Miss Petowker even whispered that she had wholly dropped the Kenwigses in her conversations with the manager's family, and had represented herself as having encountered Mr. Johnson in the very first and most fashionable circles; and on Nicholas receiving this intelligence with unfeigned surprise, she added, with a sweet glance, that she had a claim on his good-nature now, and might tax it before long.

Nicholas had the honour of playing in a slight piece with Miss Petowker that night, and could not but observe that the warmth of her reception was mainly attributable to a most persevering umbrella in the upper boxes; he saw, too, that the enchanting actress cast many sweet looks towards the quarter whence these sounds proceeded; and that every time she did so the umbrella broke out afresh. Once he thought that a peculiarly shaped hat in the same corner was not wholly unknown to him; but being occupied with his share of the stage business he bestowed no great attention upon this circumstance, and it had quite vanished from his memory by the time he reached home.

He had just sat down to supper with Smike, when one of the people of the house came outside the door, and announced that a gentleman below stairs wished to speak to Mr. Johnson.

"Well, if he does, you must tell him to come up; that's all I know," replied Nicholas. "One of our hungry brethren, I suppose, Smike."

His fellow-lodger looked at the cold meat, in silent calculation of the quantity that would be left for dinner next day, and put back a slice he had cut for himself, in order that the visitor's encroachments might be less formidable in their effects.

"It is not anybody who has been here before," said Nicholas, "for he is tumbling up every stair. Come in, come in. In the name of wonder — Mr. Lillyvick!"

It was, indeed, the collector of water-rates, who, regarding Nichols with a fixed look and immovable countenance, shook hands with most portentous solemnity, and sat himself down in a seat by the chimney corner.

"Why, when did you come here?" asked Nicholas.

"This morning, sir," replied Mr. Lillyvick.

"Oh! I see; then you were at the theatre to-night, and it was your umb —"

"This umbrella," said Mr. Lillyvick, producing a fat green cotton

one with a battered ferrule. "What did you think of that performance?"

"So far as I could judge, being on the stage," replied Nicholas, "I
thought it very agreeable."

"Agreeable!" cried the collector. "I mean to say, sir, that it was delicious."

Mr. Lillyvick bent forward to pronounce the last word with great
emphasis; and having done so, drew himself up, and frowned and
nodded a great many times.

"I say delicious," repeated Mr. Lillyvick, "Absorbing, fairy-like
toomultuous." And again Mr. Lillyvick drew himself up, and again
he frowned and nodded.

"Ah!" said Nicholas, a little surprised at these symptoms of ecstatic
approbation. "Yes — she is a clever girl."

"She is a divinity," returned Mr. Lillyvick, giving a collector's
double knock on the ground with the umbrella before mentioned. "I
have known divine actresses before now, sir; I used to collect — at
least I used to *call for* — and very often call for — the water-rate at
the house of a divine actress, who lived in my beat for upwards of
four year, but never — no, never, sir — of all divine creatures, actresses
or no actresses, did I see a diviner one than is Henrietta Petowker."

Nicholas had much ado to prevent himself from laughing; not
trusting himself to speak, he merely nodded in accordance with Mr.
Lillyvick's nods, and remained silent.

"Let me speak a word with you in private," said Mr. Lillyvick.

Nicholas looked good-humouredly at Smike, who, taking the hint
disappeared.

"A bachelor is a miserable wretch, sir," said Mr. Lillyvick,

"Is he?" asked Nicholas.

"He is," rejoined the collector. "I have lived in the world for nigh
sixty year, and I ought to know what it is."

"You *ought* to know, certainly," thought Nicholas; "but whether
you do or not, is another question."

"If a bachelor happens to have saved a little matter of money,"
said Mr. Lillyvick, "his sisters and brothers, and nephews and nieces,
look *to* that money, and not to him; even if, by being a public character, he is the head of the family, or, as it may be, the main from

which all the other little branches are turned on, they still wish him
dead all the while, and get low-spirited every time they see him looking in good health, because they want to come into his little property. You see that?"

"Oh, yes," replied Nicholas; "it's very true, no doubt."

"The great reason for not being married," resumed Mr. Lillyvick,
"is the expense; that's what's kept me off, or else — Lord!" said Mr.
Lillyvick, snapping his fingers, "I might have had fifty women."

"Fine women?" asked Nicholas.

"Fine women, sir!" replied the collector; "aye! — not so fine as
Henrietta Petowker, for she is an uncommon specimen, but such
women as don't fall into every man's way, I can tell you. Now suppose a man can get a fortune *in* a wife instead of with her — eh?"

"Why, then, he's a lucky fellow," replied Nicholas.

"That's what I say," retorted the collector, patting him benig-
nantly on the side of the head with his umbrella; "just what I say.
Henrietta Petowker, the talented Henrietta Petowker, has a fortune
in herself, and I am going to —"

"To make her Mrs. Lillyvick?" suggested Nicholas.

"No, sir, not to make her Mrs. Lillyvick," replied the collector.
"Actresses, sir, always keep their maiden names — that's the regular
thing — but I'm going to marry her; and the day after to-morrow,
too."

"I congratulate you, sir," said Nicholas.

"Thank you, sir," replied the collector, buttoning his waistcoat. "I
shall draw her salary, of course, and I hope after all that it's nearly as
cheap to keep two as it is to keep one; that's a consolation."

"Surely you don't want any consolation at such a moment?" observed Nicholas.

"No," replied Mr. Lillyvick, shaking his head nervously; "no — of
course not."

"But how came you both here, if you're going to be married, Mr.
Lillyvick?" asked Nicholas.

"Why, that's what I came to explain to you," replied the collector
of water-rate. "The fact is, we have thought it best to keep it secret
from the family!"

"Family!" said Nicholas. "What family?"

"The Kenwigses, of course," rejoined Mr. Lillyvick. "If my niece and the children had known a word about it before I came away, they'd have gone into fits at my feet, and never have come out of 'em till I took an oath not to marry anybody — or they'd have got out a commission of lunacy, or some dreadful thing," said the collector, quite trembling as he spoke.

"To be sure," said Nicholas, "yes; they would have been jealous, no doubt."

"To prevent which," said Mr. Lillyvick, "Henrietta Petowker, it was settled between us, should come down here to her friends, the Crummleses, under pretence of this engagement, and I should go down to Guildford, the day before, and join her on the coach there, which I did, and we came down from Guildford yesterday together. Now, for fear you should be writing to Mr. Noggs, and to let you into the secret. We shall be married from the Crummleses lodgings and shall be delighted to see you — either before church or at break-fast-time, which you like. It won't be expensive, you know," said the collector, highly anxious to prevent any misunderstanding on this point; "just muffins and coffee, with perhaps a shrimp or something of that sort for a relish, you know."

"Yes, yes, I understand," replied Nicholas. "Oh, I shall be most happy to come; it will give me the greatest pleasure. Where's the lady stopping — with Mrs. Crummles?"

"Why no," said the collector; "they couldn't very well dispose of her at night, and so she is staying with an acquaintance of hers, and another young lady; they both belong to the theatre."

"Miss Snevellicci, I suppose?" said Nicholas.

"Yes, that's the name."

"And they'll be bride's-maids, I presume?" said Nicholas.

"Why," said the collector, with a rueful face, "they *will* have four bride's-maids; I'm afraid they'll make it rather theatrical."

"Oh, no, not at all," replied Nicholas, with an awkward attempt to convert a laugh into a cough. "Who may the four be? Miss Snevellicci of course — Miss Ledrook —"

"The — the phenomenon," groaned the collector.

"Ha, ha!" cried Nicholas. "I beg your pardon, I don't know what I'm laughing at — yes, that'll be very pretty — the phenomenon — who else?"

"Some young woman or other," replied the collector, rising; "some other friend of Henrietta Petowker's. Well, you'll be careful not to say anything about it, will you?"

"You may safely depend upon me," replied Nicholas. "Won't you take anything to eat or drink?"

"No," said the collector; "I haven't any appetite. I should think it was a very pleasant life, the married one — eh?"

"I have not the least doubt of it," rejoined Nicholas.

"Yes," said the collector; "certainly. Oh, yes. No doubt. Goodnight."

With these words, Mr. Lillyvick, whose manner had exhibited through the whole of this interview a most extraordinary compound of precipitation, hesitation, confidence, and doubt; fondness, misgiving, meanness, and self-importance, turned his back upon the room, and left Nicholas to enjoy a laugh by himself, if he felt so disposed.

Without stopping to inquire whether the intervening day appeared to Nicholas to consist of the usual number of hours of the ordinary length, it may be remarked that, to the parties more directly interested in the forthcoming ceremony, it passed with great rapidity, insomuch that when Miss Petowker awoke on the succeeding morning in the chamber of Miss Snevellicci, she declared that nothing should ever persuade her that that really was the day which was to behold a change in her condition.

"I never will believe it," said Miss Petowker; "I cannot really. It's of no use talking, I never can make up my mind to go through with such a trial!"

On hearing this, Miss Snevellicci and Miss Ledrook, who knew perfectly well that their fair friend's mind had been made up for three or four years, at any period of which time she would have cheerfully undergone the desperate trial now approaching if she could have found any eligible gentleman disposed for the venture, began to preach comfort and firmness, and to say how very proud she ought to feel that it was in her power to confer lasting bliss on a deserving object, and how necessary it was for the happiness of mankind in general that women should possess fortitude and resignation on such occasions; and that although for their parts they held true happiness to consist in a single life which they would not willingly exchange — no, not for any worldly consideration — still (thank God) if ever the time *should* come, they hoped they knew their duty too well to repine, but would the rather submit with meekness and humility of spirit to a fate for which Providence had clearly designed them with a view to the contentment and reward of their fellow-creatures.

"I might feel it was a great blow," said Miss Snevellicci, "to break up old associations and what-do-you-callems of that kind, but I would submit, my dear, I would, indeed."

"So would I," said Miss Ledrook; "I would rather court the yoke than shun it. I have broken hearts before now, and I'm very sorry for it; for it's a terrible thing to reflect upon."

"It is indeed," said Miss Snevellicci. "Now, Led, my dear, we must positively get her ready, or we shall be too late, we shall indeed."

This pious reasoning, and perhaps the fear of being too late, supported the bride through the ceremony of robing, after which strong tea and brandy were administered in alternate doses as a means of strengthening her feeble limbs and causing her to walk steadier.

"How do you feel now, my love?" inquired Miss Snevellicci.

"Oh, Lillyvick!" cried the bride, "if you knew what I am undergoing for you!"

"Of course he knows it, love, and will never forget it," said Miss Ledrook.

"Do you think he won't?" cried Miss Petowker, really showing great capability for the stage. "Oh, do you think he won't? Do you think Lillyvick will always remember it — always, always, always?"

There is no knowing in what this burst of feeling might have ended, if Miss Snevellicci had not at that moment proclaimed the arrival of the fly, which so astounded the bride that she shook off divers alarming symptoms which were coming on very strong, and running to the glass adjusted her dress, and calmly declared that she was ready for the sacrifice.

She was accordingly supported into the coach, and there "kept up" (as Miss Snevellicci said) with perpetual sniffs of sal-volatile and sips of brandy and other gentle stimulants, until they reached the manager's door, which was already opened by the two Masters Crummles, who wore white cockades, and were decorated with the choicest and most resplendent waistcoats in the theatrical wardrobe. By the combined exertions of these young gentlemen and the bride's-maids, assisted by the coachman, Miss Petowker was at length supported in a condition of much exhaustion to the first floor, where she no sooner encountered the youthful bridegroom than she fainted with great decorum.

"Henrietta Petowker!" said the collector; "cheer up, my lovely one."

Miss Petowker grasped the collector's hand, but emotion choked her utterance.

"Is the sight of me so dreadful, Henrietta Petowker?" said the collector.

"Oh, no, no, no," rejoined the bride; "but all the friends — the darling friends — of my youthful days — to leave them all — it is such a shock!"

With such expressions of sorrow, Miss Petowker went on to enumerate the dear friends of her youthful days one by one, and to call upon such of them as were present to come and embrace her. This done, she remembered that Mrs. Crummles had been more than a mother to her, and after that, that Mr. Crummles had been more than a father to her, and after that, that the Masters Crummles and Miss Ninetta Crummles had been more than brothers and sisters to her. These various remembrances being each accompanied with a series of hugs, occupied a long time, and they were obliged to drive to church very fast, for fear they should be too late.

The procession consisted of two flys; in the first of which were Miss Bravassa (the fourth bride's-maid), Mrs. Crummles, the collector, and Mr. Folair, who had been chosen as his second on the occasion. In the other were the bride, Mr. Crummles, Miss Snevellicci, Miss Ledrook, and the phenomenon. The costumes were beautiful. The bride's-maids were quite covered with artificial flowers, and the phenomenon, in particular, was rendered almost invisible by the portable arbour in which she was enshrined. Miss Ledrook, who was of a romantic turn, wore in her breast the miniature of some field-officer unknown, which she had purchased, a great bargain, not very long before; the other ladies displayed several dazzling articles of imitative jewellery, almost equal to real; and Mrs. Crummles came out in a stern and gloomy majesty, which attracted the admiration of all beholders.

But perhaps the appearance of Mr. Crummles was more striking and appropriate than that of any member of the party. This gentleman, who personated the bride's father, had, in pursuance of a happy and original conception, "made up" for the part by arraying himself in a theatrical wig, of a style and pattern commonly known as a brown George, and moreover, assuming a snuff-coloured suit, of the previous century, with gray silk stockings, and buckles to his shoes. The better to support his assumed character, he had determined to be greatly overcome, and, consequently, when they entered the church, the sobs of the affectionate parent were so heartrending that the pew-opener suggested the propriety of his retiring to the vestry, and comforting himself with a glass of water before the ceremony began.

The procession up the aisle was beautiful. The bride, with the four bride's-maids, forming a group previously arranged and rehearsed; the collector, followed by his second, imitating his walk and gestures, to the indescribable amusement of some theatrical friends in the gallery; Mr. Crummles, with an infirm and feeble gait; Mrs. Crummles advancing with that stage walk, which consists of a stride and a stop alternately — it was the completest thing ever witnessed. The ceremony was very quickly disposed of, and all parties present having signed the register (for which purpose, when it came to his turn, Mr. Crummles carefully wiped and put on an immense pair of spectacles), they went back to breakfast in high spirits. And here they found Nicholas awaiting their arrival.

"Now, then," said Crummles, who had been assisting Mrs. Grudden in the preparations, which were on a more extensive scale than was quite agreeable to the collector, "breakfast, breakfast."

No second invitation was required. The company crowded and squeezed themselves at the table as well as they could, and fell to immediately; Miss Petowker blushing very much when anybody was looking, and eating very much when anybody was *not* looking; and Mr. Lillyvick going to work as though with the cool resolve, that since the good things must be paid for by him, he would leave as little as possible for the Crummleses to eat up afterwards.

"It's very soon done, sir, isn't it?" inquired Mr. Folair of the collector, leaning over the table to address him.

"What is soon done, sir?" returned Mr. Lillyvick.

"The tying up — the fixing one's self with a wife," replied Mr. Folair. "It don't take long, does it?"

"No, sir," replied Mr. Lillyvick, colouring; "it does not take long. And what then, sir?"

"Oh, nothing," said the actor. "It don't take a man long to hang himself either, eh? ha, ha!"

Mr. Lillyvick laid down his knife and fork, and looked round the table with indignant astonishment.

"To hang himself!" repeated Mr. Lillyvick.

A profound silence came upon all, for Mr. Lillyvick was dignified beyond expression.

"To hang himself!" cried Mr. Lillyvick again. "Is any parallel attempted to be drawn in this company between matrimony and hanging?"

"The noose, you know," said Mr. Folair, a little crestfallen.

"The noose, sir?" retorted Mr. Lillyvick. "Does any man dare to speak to me of a noose and Henrietta Pe ——"

"Lillyvick," suggested Mr. Crummles.

"And Henrietta Lillyvick in the same breath?" said the collector. "In this house, in the presence of Mr. and Mrs. Crummles, who have brought up a talented and virtuous family to be blessings and phenomenons, and what not, are we to hear talk of nooses?"

"Folair," said Mr. Crummles, deeming it a matter of decency to be affected by this allusion to himself and partner, "I'm astonished at you."

"What are you going on in this way at me for?" urged the unfortunate actor. "What have I done?"

"Done, sir!" cried Mr. Lillyvick, "aimed a blow at the whole framework of society —"

"And the best and tenderest feelings," added Crummles, relapsing into the old man.

"And the highest and most estimable of social ties," said the collector. "Noose! As if one was caught, trapped into the married state, pinned by the leg, instead of going into it of one's own accord, and glorying in the act!"

"I didn't mean to make it out that you were caught and trapped, and pinned by the leg," replied the actor. "I'm sorry for it; I can't say any more."

"So you ought to be, sir," returned Mr. Lillyvick; "and I am glad to hear that you have enough of feeling left to be so."

The quarrel appearing to terminate with this reply, Mrs. Lillyvick considered that the fittest occasion (the attention of the company being no longer distracted) to burst into tears, and require the assistance of all four bride's-maids, which was immediately rendered, though not without some confusion, for the room being small, and the table-cloth long, a whole detachment of plates were swept off the board at the very first move. Regardless of this circumstance, however, Mrs. Lillyvick refused to be comforted until the belligerents had passed their words that the dispute should be carried no further, which, after a sufficient show of reluctance, they did, and from that time Mr. Folair sat in moody silence, contenting himself with pinching Nicholas's leg when anything was said, and so expressing his contempt both for the speaker and the sentiments to which he gave utterance.

There were a great number of speeches made, some by Nicholas, and some by Crummles, and some by the collector; two by the Masters Crummles in returning thanks for themselves, and one by the phenomenon on behalf of the bride's-maids, at which Mrs. Crummles shed tears. There was some singing, too, from Miss Ledrook and Miss Bravassa, and very likely there might have been more if the fly-driver, who stopped to drive the happy pair to the spot where they proposed to take steamboat to Ryde, had not sent in a peremptory message, intimating that if they didn't come directly he should infallibly demand eighteen pence over and above his agreement.

This desperate threat effectually broke up the party. After a most pathetic leave-taking, Mr. Lillyvick and his bride departed for Ryde, where they were to spend the next two days in profound retirement, and whither they were accompanied by the infant, who had been appointed travelling bride's-maid on Mr. Lillyvick's express stipulation, as the steamboat people, deceived by her size, would (he had previously ascertained) transport her at half-price.

As there was no performance that night, Mr. Crummles declared his intention of keeping it up till everything to drink was disposed of; but Nicholas, having to play Romeo for the first time on the ensuing evening, contrived to slip away in the midst of a temporary confusion, occasioned by the unexpected development of strong symptoms of inebriety in the conduct of Mrs. Grudden.

To this act of desertion he was led, not only by his own inclinations, but by his anxiety on account of Smike, who, having to sustain the character of the Apothecary, had been as yet wholly unable to get any more of the part into his head than the general idea that he was very hungry, which — perhaps from old recollections — he had acquired with great aptitude.

"I don't know what's to be done, Smike," said Nicholas, laying down the book. "I am afraid you can't learn it, my poor fellow."

"I am afraid not," said Smike, shaking his head. "I think if you — But that would give you so much trouble."

"What?" inquired Nicholas. "Never mind me."

"I think," said Smike, "if you were to keep saying it to me in little bits, over and over again, I should be able to recollect it from hearing you."

"Do you think so?" exclaimed Nicholas. "Well said. Let us see who tires first. Not I, Smike, trust me. Now then. 'Who calls so loud?' "

" 'Who calls so loud?' " said Smike.

" 'Who calls so loud?' " repeated Nicholas.

" 'Who calls so loud?' " cried Smike.

Thus they continued to ask each other who called so loud, over and over again; and when Smike had that by heart, Nicholas went to another sentence, and then to two at a time, and then to three, and so on, until at midnight poor Smike found to his unspeakable joy that he really began to remember something about the text.

Early in the morning they went to it again, and Smike, rendered more confident by the progress he had already made, got on faster and with better heart. As soon as he began to acquire the words pretty freely, Nicholas showed him how he must come in with both hands spread out upon his stomach, and how he must occasionally rub it, in compliance with the established form by which people on the stage always denote that they want something to eat. After the morning's rehearsal they went to work again, nor did they stop, except for a hasty dinner, until it was time to repair to the theatre at night.

Never had master a more anxious, humble, docile pupil. Never had pupil a more patient, unwearying, considerate, kind-hearted master.

As soon as they were dressed, and at every interval when he was not upon the stage, Nicholas renewed his instructions. They pros-

pered well. The Romeo was received with hearty plaudits and unbounded favour, and Smike was pronounced unanimously, alike by
audience and actors, the very prince and prodigy of Apothecaries.

OF THE PROCEEDINGS OF NICHOLAS, AND CERTAIN INTERNAL
DIVISIONS IN THE COMPANY OF MR. VINCENT CRUMMLES

The unexpected success and favour with which his experiment at
Portsmouth had been received, induced Mr. Crummles to prolong
his stay in that town for a fortnight beyond the period he had originally assigned for the duration of his visit, during which time Nicholas personated a vast variety of characters with undiminished success,
and attracted so many people to the theatre who had never been
seen there before, that a benefit was considered by the manager a
very promising speculation. Nicholas assenting to the terms proposed, the benefit was had, and by it he realised no less a sum than
twenty pounds.

Possessed of this unexpected wealth, his first act was to inclose to
honest John Browdie the amount of his friendly loan, which he accompanied with many expressions of gratitude and esteem, and many
cordial wishes for his matrimonial happiness. To Newman Noggs he
forwarded one half ot the sum he had realised, entreating him to
take an opportunity of handing it to Kate in secret, and conveying
to her the warmest assurances of his love and affection. He made no
mention of the way in which he had employed himself; merely informing Newman that a letter addressed to him under his assumed
name at the Post Office, Portsmouth, would readily find him, and
entreating that worthy friend to write full particulars of all the grand
things that Ralph Nickleby had done for them since his departure
from London.

"You are out of spirits," said Smike, on the night after the letter
had been despatched.

"Not I!" rejoined Nicholas, with assumed gaiety, for the confession
would have made the boy miserable all night; "I was thinking about
my sister, Smike."

"Sister!"

"Aye."

"Is she like you?" inquired Smike.

"Why, so they say," replied Nicholas, laughing, "only a great deal handsomer."

"She must be *very* beautiful," said Smike, after thinking a little while with his hands folded together, and his eyes bent upon his friend.

"Anybody who didn't know you as well as I do, my dear fellow, would say you were an accomplished courtier," said Nicholas.

"I don't even know what that is," replied Smike, shaking his head. "Shall I ever see your sister?"

"To be sure," cried Nicholas; "we shall all be together one of these days — when we are rich, Smike."

"How is it that you, who are so kind and good to me, have nobody to be kind to you?" asked Smike. "I cannot make that out."

"Why, it is a long story," replied Nicholas, "and one you would have some difficulty in comprehending, I fear. I have an enemy — you understand what that is?"

"Oh, yes, I understand that," said Smike.

"Well, it is owing to him," returned Nicholas. "He is rich, and not so easily punished as *your* old enemy, Mr. Squeers. He is my uncle, but he is a villain, and has done me wrong."

"Has he though?" asked Smike, bending eagerly forward. "What is his name? Tell me his name."

"Ralph — Ralph Nickleby."

"Ralph Nickleby," repeated Smike. "Ralph. I'll get that name by heart."

He had muttered it over to himself some twenty times, when a loud knock at the door disturbed him from his occupation. Before he could open it, Mr. Folair, the pantomimist, thrust in his head.

Mr. Folair's head was usually decorated with a very round hat, unusually high in the crown, and curled up quite tight in the brims. On the present occasion he wore it very much on one side, with the back part forward, in consequence of its being the least rusty; round his neck he wore a flaming red worsted comforter, whereof the straggling ends peeped out beneath his threadbare Newmarket coat, which was very tight and buttoned all the way up. He carried in his hand one dirty glove, and a cheap dress cane with a glass handle; in short, his whole appearance was unusually dashing, and demonstrated a far more scrupulous attention to his toilet than he was in the habit of bestowing upon it.

"Good-evening, sir," said Mr. Folair, taking off the tall hat, and running his fingers through his hair. "I bring a communication. Hem!"

"From whom, and what about?" inquired Nicholas, "You are unusually mysterious to-night."

"Cold, perhaps," returned Mr. Folair; "cold, perhaps. That is the fault of my position — not of myself, Mr. Johnson. My position as a mutual friend requires it, sir." Mr. Folair paused with a most impressive look, and diving into the hat before noticed, drew thence a small piece of whity-brown paper, curiously folded, whence he brought forth a note, which it had served to keep clean, and handing it over to Nicholas, said —

"Have the goodness to read that, sir."

Nicholas, in a state of much amazement, took the note and broke the seal, glancing at Mr. Folair as he did so, who, knitting his brow, and pursing up his mouth with great dignity, was sitting with his eyes steadily fixed upon the ceiling.

It was directed to blank Johnson, Esq., by favour of Augustus Folair, Esq.; and the astonishment of Nicholas was in no degree lessened when he found it to be couched in the following laconic terms: —

"Mr. Lenville presents his kind regards to Mr. Johnson, and will feel obliged if he will inform him at what hour to-morrow morning it will be most convenient to him to meet Mr. L. at the theatre, for the purpose of having his nose pulled in the presence of the company.

"Mr. Lenville requests Mr. Johnson not to neglect making an appointment, as he has invited two or three professional friends to witness the ceremony, and cannot disappoint them upon any account whatever.

"*Portsmouth, Tuesday night.*"

Indignant as he was at this impertinence, there was something so exquisitely absurd in such a cartel of defiance, that Nicholas was obliged to bite his lip and read the note over two or three times before he could muster sufficient gravity and sternness to address the hostile messenger, who had not taken his eyes from the ceiling, nor altered the expression of his face in the slightest degree.

"Do you know the contents of this note, sir?" he asked, at length.

"Yes," rejoined Mr. Folair, looking round for an instant, and immediately carrying his eyes back again to the ceiling.

"And how dare you bring it here, sir?" asked Nicholas, tearing it into very little pieces, and jerking it in a shower towards the messenger. "Had you no fear of being kicked downstairs, sir?"

Mr. Folair turned his head — now ornamented with several fragments of the note — towards Nicholas, and with the same imperturbable dignity, briefly replied, "No."

"Then," said Nicholas, taking up the tall hat, and tossing it towards the door, "you had better follow that article of your dress, sir, or you may find yourself very disagreeably deceived, and that within a dozen seconds."

"I say, Johnson," remonstrated Mr. Folair, suddenly losing all his dignity, "none of that, you know. No tricks with a gentleman's wardrobe."

"Leave the room," returned Nicholas. "How could you presume to come here on such an errand, you scoundrel?"

"Pooh! pooh!" said Mr. Folair, unwinding his comforter, and gradually getting himself out of it. "There — that's enough."

"Enough!" cried Nicholas, advancing towards him. "Take yourself off, sir."

"Pooh! pooh! I tell you," returned Mr. Folair, waving his hand in deprecation of any further wrath; "I wasn't in earnest. I only brought it in joke."

"You had better be careful how you indulge in such jokes again," said Nicholas, "or you may find an allusion to pulling noses rather a dangerous reminder for the subject of your facetiousness. Was it written in joke too, pray?"

"No, no, that's the best of it," returned the actor; "right down earnest — honour bright."

Nicholas could not repress a smile at the odd figure before him, which, at all times more calculated to provoke mirth than anger, was especially so at that moment, when, with one knee upon the ground, Mr. Folair twirled his old hat round upon his hand, and affected the extremest agony lest any of the nap should have been knocked off —

an ornament which, it is almost superfluous to say, it had not boasted for many months.

"Come, sir," said Nicholas, laughing in spite of himself, "have the goodness to explain."

"Why, I'll tell you how it is," said Mr. Folair, sitting himself down in a chair, with great coolness. "Since you came here, Lenville has done nothing but second business, and, instead of having a reception every night, as he used to have, they have let him come on as if he was nobody."

"What do you mean by a reception?" asked Nicholas.

"Jupiter!" exclaimed Mr. Folair, "what an unsophisticated shepherd you are, Johnson! Why, applause from the house when you first come on. So he has gone on night after night, never getting a hand and you getting a couple of rounds at least, and sometimes three, till at length he got quite desperate, and had half a mind last night to play Tybalt with a real sword, and pink you — not dangerously, but just enough to lay you up for a month or two."

"Very considerate," remarked Nicholas.

"Yes, I think it was, under the circumstances; his professional reputation being at stake," said Mr. Folair, quite seriously. "But his heart failed him, and he cast about for some other way of annoying you, and making himself popular at the same time — for that's the point. Notoriety, notoriety is the thing. Bless you, if he had pinked you," said Mr. Folair, stopping to make a calculation in his mind, "it would have been worth — ah, it would have been worth eight or ten shillings a week to him. All the town would have come to see the actor who nearly killed a man by mistake; I shouldn't wonder if it had got him an engagement in London. However, he was obliged to try some other mode of getting popular, and this one occurred to him. It's a clever idea, really. If you had shown the white feather, and let him pull your nose, he'd have got it into the paper; if you had sworn the peace against him, it would have been in the paper too, and he'd have been just as much talked about as you — don't you see?"

"Oh, certainly," rejoined Nicholas; "but suppose I were to turn the tables and pull *his* nose, what then? Would that make his fortune?"

"Why, I don't think it would," replied Mr. Folair, scratching his head, "because there wouldn't be any romance about it, and he wouldn't be favourably known. To tell you the truth, though, he didn't calculate much upon that, for you're always so mild spoken, and are so popular among the women, that we didn't suspect you of showing fight. If you did, however, he has a way of getting out of it easily, depend upon that."

"Has he?" rejoined Nicholas. "We will try, to-morrow morning. In the meantime, you can give whatever account of our interview you like best. Good-night."

As Mr. Folair was pretty well known among his fellow-actors for a man who delighted in mischief, and was by no means scrupulous, Nicholas had not much doubt but that he had secretly prompted the tragedian in the course he had taken, and, moreover, that he would have carried his mission with a very high hand if he had not been disconcerted by the very unexpected demonstrations with which it had been received. It was not worth his while to be serious with him, however, so he dismissed the pantomimist, with a gentle hint that if he offended again it would be under the penalty of a broken head; and Mr. Folair, taking the caution in exceeding good part, walked away to confer with his principal, and give such an account of his proceedings as he might think best calculated to carry on the joke.

He had no doubt reported that Nicholas was in a state of extreme bodily fear; for when that young gentleman walked with much deliberation down to the theatre next morning at the usual hour, he found all the company assembled in evident expectation, and Mr. Lenville, with his severest stage face, sitting majestically on a table, whistling defiance.

Now, the ladies were on the side of Nicholas, and the gentlemen (being jealous) were on the side of the disappointed tragedian; so that the latter formed a little group about the redoubtable Mr. Lenville, and the former looked on at a little instance in some trepidation and anxiety. On Nicholas stopping to salute them, Mr. Lenville laughed a scornful laugh, and made some general remark touching the natural history of puppies.

"Oh!" said Nicholas, looking quietly round, "are you there?"

"Slave!" returned Mr. Lenville, flourishing his right arm, and approaching Nicholas with a theatrical stride. But somehow he appeared just at that moment a little startled, as if Nicholas did not look quite so frightened as he had expected, and came all at once to an awkward halt, at which the assembled ladies burst into a shrill laugh.

"Object of my scorn and hatred!" said Mr. Lenville, "I told ye in contempt."

Nicholas laughed in very unexpected enjoyment of this performance; and the ladies, by way of encouragement, laughed louder than before; whereat Mr. Lenville assumed his bitterest smile, and expressed his opinion that they were "minions."

"But they shall not protect ye!" said the tragedian, taking an upward look at Nicholas, beginning at his boots and ending at the crown of his head, and then a downward one, beginning at the crown of his head, and ending at his boots — which two looks, as everybody knows, express defiance on the stage. "They shall not protect ye — boy!"

Thus speaking, Mr. Lenville folded his arms, and treated Nicholas to that expression of face with which, in melodramatic performances, he was in the habit of regarding the tyrannical kings when they said, "Away with him to the deepest dungeon beneath the castle moat;" and which, accompanied with a little jingling of fetters, had been known to produce great effects in its time.

Whether it was the absence of the fetters or not, it made no very deep impression on Mr. Lenville's adversary, however, but rather seemed to incearse the good-humour expressed in his countenance; in which stage of the contest, one or two gentlemen, who had come out expressly to witness the pulling of Nicholas's nose, grew impatient, murmuring that if it were to be done at all it had better be done at once, and that if Mr. Lenville didn't mean to do it he had better say so, and not keep them waiting there. Thus urged, the tragedian adjusted the cuff of his right coat sleeve for the performance of the operation, and walked in a very stately manner up to Nicholas, who suffered him to approach to within the requisite distance, and then, without the smallest discomposure, knocked him down.

Before the discomfited tragedian could raise his head from the boards, Mrs. Lenville (who, as has before been hinted, was in an interesting state) rushed from the rear rank of ladies, and uttering a piercing scream threw herself upon the body.

"Do you see this, monster? Do you see *this?*" cried Mr. Lenville, sitting up, and pointing to his prostrate lady, who was holding him very tight round the waist.

"Come," said Nicholas, nodding his head, "apologise for the insolent note you wrote to me last night, and waste no more time in talking."

"Never!" cried Mr. Lenville.

"Yes — yes — yes," screamed his wife. "For my sake — for mine, Lenville — forego all idle forms, unless you would see me a blighted corse at your feet."

"This is affecting!" said Mr. Lenville, looking round him, and drawing the back of his hand across his eyes. "The ties of nature are strong. The weak husband and the father — the father that is yet to be — relents. I apologise."

"Humbly and submissively?" said Nicholas.

"Humbly and submissively," returned the tragedian, scowling upwards. "But only to save her — for a time will come —"

"Very good," said Nicholas; "I hope Mrs. Lenville may have a good one; and when it does come, and you are a father, you shall retract it if you have the courage. There. Be careful, sir, to what lengths your jealousy carries you another time; and be careful, also, before you venture too far, to ascertain your rival's temper." With this parting advice, Nicholas picked up Mr. Lenville's ash stick, which had flown out of his hand, and breaking it in half, threw him the pieces and withdrew, bowing slightly to the spectators as he walked out.

The profoundest deference was paid to Nicholas that night, and the people who had been most anxious to have his nose pulled in the morning, embraced occasions of taking him aside, and telling him, with great feeling, how very friendly they took it that he should have treated that Lenville so properly, who was a most unbearable fellow, and on whom they had all, by a remarkable coincidence, at one time or other contemplated the infliction of condign punishment, which they had only been restrained from administering by considerations of mercy; indeed, to judge from the invariable termination of all these stories, there never was such a charitable and kind-hearted set of people as the male members of Mr. Crummles's company.

Nicholas bore his triumph, as he had his success in the little world of the theatre, with the utmost moderation and good-humour. The crestfallen Mr. Lenville made an expiring effort to obtain revenge by sending a boy into the gallery to hiss, but he fell a sacrifice to popular indignation, and was promptly turned out without having his money back.

"Well, Smike," said Nicholas, when the first piece was over, and he had almost finished dressing to go home, "is there any letter yet?"

"Yes," replied Smike, "I got this one from the post-office."

"From Newman Noggs," said Nicholas, casting his eye upon the cramped direction; "it's no easy matter to make his writing out. Let me see — let me see."

By dint of poring over the letter for half an hour, he contrived to make himself master of the contents, which were certainly not of a nature to set his mind at ease. Newman took upon himself to send back the ten pounds, observing that he had ascertained that neither Mrs. Nickleby nor Kate was in actual want of money at the moment, and that a time might shortly come when Nicholas might want it more. He entreated him not to be alarmed at what he was about to say; there was no bad news — they were in good health — but he thought circumstances might occur, or were occurring, which would render it absolutely necessary that Kate should have her brother's protection; and if so, Newman said, he would write to him to that effect, either by the next post or the next but one.

Nicholas read this passage very often, and the more he thought of it the more he began to fear some treachery upon the part of Ralph. Once or twice he felt tempted to repair to London at all hazards without an hour's delay, but a little reflection assured him that if such a step were necessary, Newman would have spoken out and told him so at once.

"At all events I should prepare them here for the possibility of my going away suddenly," said Nicholas; "I should lose no time in doing that." As the thought occurred to him, he took up his hat and hurried to the green-room.

"Well, Mr. Johnson," said Mrs. Crummles, who was seated there in full regal costume, with the phenomenon as the Maiden in her maternal arms, "next week for Ryde, then for Winchester, then for —"

"I have some reason to fear," interrupted Nicholas, "that before you leave here my career with you will have closed."

"Closed!" cried Mrs. Crummles, raising her hands in astonishment.

"Closed!" cried Miss Snevellicci. Trembling so much in her tights that she actually laid her hand upon the shoulder of the manageress for support.

"Why, he don't mean to say he's going!" exclaimed Mrs. Grudden, making her way towards Mrs. Crummles. "Hoity, toity! nonsense."

The phenomenon, being of an affectionate nature, and, moreover, excitable, raised a loud cry, and Miss Belvawney and Miss Bravassa actually shed tears. Even the male performers stopped in their conversation, and echoed the word "Going!" although some among them (and they had been the loudest in their congratulations that day) winked at each other as though they would not be sorry to lose such a favoured rival; an opinion, indeed, which the honest Mr. Folair, who was ready dressed for the Savage, openly stated in so many words to a demon with whom he was sharing a pot of porter.

Nicholas briefly said that he feared it would be so, although he could not yet speak with any degree of certainty; and getting away as soon as he could, went home to con Newman's letter once more, and speculate upon it afresh.

How trifling all that had been occupying his time and thoughts for many weeks seemed to him during that sleepless night, and how constantly and incessantly present to his imagination was the one idea that Kate, in the midst of some great trouble and distress, might even then be looking — and vainly, too — for him.

FESTIVITIES ARE HELD IN HONOUR OF NICHOLAS, WHO SUDDENLY
WITHDRAWS HIMSELF FROM THE SOCIETY OF MR. VINCENT
CRUMMLES AND HIS THEATRICAL COMPANIONS

Mr. Vincent Crummles was no sooner acquainted with the public announcement which Nicholas had made relative to the probability of his shortly ceasing to be a member of the company, than he evinced many tokens of grief and consternation; and, in the extremity of his despair, even held out certain vague promises of a speedy improvement not only in the amount of his regular salary, but also in the contingent emoluments appertaining to his authorship. Finding Nicholas bent upon quitting the society — for he had now determined that, even if no further tidings came from Newman, he would, at all hazards, ease his mind by repairing to London and ascertaining the exact position of his sister — Mr. Crummles was fain to content himself by calculating the chances of his coming back again, and taking prompt and energetic measures to make the most of him before he went away.

"Let me see," said Mr. Crummles, taking off his outlaw's wig, the better to arrive at a cool-headed view of the whole case. "Let me see. This is Wednesday night. We'll have posters out the first thing in the morning, announcing positively your last appearance for to-morrow."

"But perhaps it may not be my last appearance, you know," said Nicholas. "Unless I am summoned away, I should be sorry to inconvenience you by leaving before the end of the week."

"So much the better," returned Mr. Crummles. "We can have positively your last appearance, on Thursday — re-engagement for one night more, on Friday — and, yielding to the wishes of numerous influential patrons, who were disappointed in obtaining seats, on Saturday. That ought to bring three very decent houses."

"Then I am to make three last appearances, am I?" inquired Nicholas, smiling.

"Yes," rejoined the manager, scratching his head with an air of some vexation; "three is not enough, and it's very bungling and irregular not to have more, but if we can't help it we can't, so there's no use in talking. A novelty would be very desirable. You couldn't sing a comic song on the pony's back, could you?"

"No," replied Nicholas, "I couldn't, indeed."

"It has drawn money before now," said Mr. Crummles, with a look of disappointment. "What do you think of a brilliant display of fireworks?"

"That it would be rather expensive," replied Nicholas drily.

"Eighteenpence would do it," said Mr. Crummles. "You on the top of a pair of steps with the phenomenon in an attitude; 'Farewell' on a transparency behind; and nine people at the wings with a squib in each hand — all the dozen and a half going off at once — it would be very grand — awful from the front, quite awful."

As Nicholas appeared by no means impressed with the solemnity of the proposed effect, but, on the contrary, received the proposition in a most irreverent manner, and laughed at it very heartily, Mr. Crummles abandoned the project in its birth, and gloomily observed that they must make up the best bill they could with combats and horn-pipes, and so stick to the legitimate drama.

For the purpose of carrying this object into instant execution, the manager at once repaired to a small dressing-room adjacent, where Mrs. Crummles was then occupied in exchanging the habiliments of a melodramatic empress for the ordinary attire of matrons in the nineteenth century. And with the assistance of this lady and the accomplished Mrs. Grudden (who had quite a genius for making out bills, being a great hand at throwing in the notes of admiration, and knowing from long experience exactly where the largest capitals ought to go), he seriously applied himself to the composition of the poster.

"Heigho!" sighed Nicholas, as he threw himself back in the prompter's chair, after telegraphing the needful directions to Smike, who had been playing a meagre tailor in the interlude, with one skirt to his coat, and a little pocket-handkerchief with a large hole in it, and a woollen nightcap, and a red nose, and other distinctive marks peculiar to tailors on the stage. "Heigho! I wish all this were over."

"Over, Mr. Johnson?" repeated a female voice behind him, in a kind of plaintive surprise.

"It was an ungallant speech, certainly," said Nicholas, looking up to see who the speaker was and recognising Miss Snevellicci. "I would not have made it if I had known you had been within hearing."

"What a dear that Mr. Digby is!" said Miss Snevellicci, as the tailor went off on the opposite side, at the end of the piece, with great applause. (Smike's theatrical name was Digby.)

"I'll tell him presently, for his gratification, that you said so," returned Nicholas.

"Oh, you naughty thing!" rejoined Miss Snevellicci. "I don't know, though, that I should much mind *his* knowing my opinion of him; with some other people, indeed, it might be —" Here Miss Snevellicci stopped, as though waiting to be questioned, but no questioning came, for Nicholas was thinking about more serious matters.

"How kind it is of you," resumed Miss Snevellicci, after a short silence, "to sit waiting here for him night after night, night after night, no matter how tired you are; and taking so much pains with him, and doing it all with as much delight and readiness as if you were coining gold by it!"

"He well deserves all the kindness I can show him, and a great deal more," said Nicholas. "He is the most grateful, single-hearted, affectionate creature that ever breathed."

"So odd, too," remarked Miss Snevellicci, "isn't he?"

"God help him, and those who have made him so, he is indeed," rejoined Nicholas, shaking his head.

"He is such a devilish close chap," said Mr. Folair, who had come up a little before, and now joined in the conversation. "Nobody can ever get anything out of him."

"What *should* they get out of him?" asked Nicholas, turning round with some abruptness.

"Zooks! what a fire-eater you are, Johnson!" returned Mr. Folair, pulling up the heel of his dancing-shoe. "I'm only talking of the natural curiosity of the people here, to know what he has been about all his life."

"Poor fellow! it is pretty plain, I should think, that he has not the intellect to have been about anything of much importance to them or anybody else," said Nicholas.

"Ay," rejoined the actor, contemplating the effect of his face in a lamp-reflector, "but that involves the whole question, you know."

"What question?" asked Nicholas.

"Why, the who he is and what he is, and how you two, who are so different, came to be such close companions," replied Mr. Folair, delighted with the opportunity of saying something disagreeable. "That's in everybody's mouth."

"The 'everybody' of the theatre, I suppose?" said Nicholas contemptuously.

"In it and out of it, too," replied the actor. "Why you know, Lenville says —"

"I thought I had silenced him effectually," interrupted Nicholas, reddening.

"Perhaps you have," rejoined the immovable Mr. Folair; "if you have, he said this before he was silenced: Lenville says that you're a regular stick of an actor, and that it's only the mystery about you that has caused you to go down with the people here, and that Crummles keeps it up for his own sake; though Lenville says he don't believe there's anything at all in it, except your having got into a scrape and run away from somewhere, for doing something or other."

"Oh!" said Nicholas, forcing a smile.

"That's a part of what he says," added Mr. Folair. "I mention it as the friend of both parties, and in strict confidence. I don't agree with him, you know. He says he takes Digby to be more knave than fool; and old Fluggers, who does the heavy business, you know, *he* says that when he delivered messages at Covent Garden the season before last, there used to be a pickpocket hovering about the coach-stand, who had exactly the face of Digby; though, as he very properly says, Digby may not be the same, but only his brother, or some near relation."

"Oh!" cried Nicholas again.

"Yes," said Mr. Folair, with undisturbed calmness, "that's what they say. I thought I'd tell you, because really you ought to know. Oh, here's this blessed phenomenon at last. Ugh, you little imposition, I should like to — Quite ready, my darling — humbug. — Ring up Mrs. G., and let the favourite wake 'em."

Uttering in a loud voice such of the latter allusions as were complimentary to the unconscious phenomenon, and giving the rest in a confidential "aside" to Nicholas, Mr. Folair followed the ascent of the curtain with his eyes, regarded with a sneer the reception of Miss Crummles as the Maiden, and, falling back a step or two to advance with the better effect, uttered a preliminary howl, and "went on" chattering his teeth and brandishing his tin tomahawk as the Indian Savage.

"So these are some of the stories they invent about us, and bandy from mouth to mouth!" thought Nicholas. "If a man would commit an inexpiable offence against any society, large or small, let him be successful. They will forgive him any crime but that."

"You surely don't mind what that malicious creature says, Mr. Johnson?" observed Miss Snevellicci, in her most winning tones.

"Not I," replied Nicholas. "If I were going to remain here, I might think it worth my while to embroil myself. As it is, let them talk till they are hoarse. But here," added Nicholas, as Smike approached — "here comes the subject of a portion of their good-nature, so let he and I say good-night together."

"No, I will not let either of you say anything of the kind," said Miss Snevellicci. "You must come home and see mamma, who only came to Portsmouth to-day, and is dying to behold you. Led, my dear, persuade Mr. Johnson."

"Oh, I'm sure," returned Miss Ledrook, with considerable vivacity, "if *you* can't persuade him —" Miss Ledrook said no more, but intimated, by a dexterous playfulness, that if Miss Snevellicci couldn't persuade him, nobody could.

"Mr. and Mrs. Lillyvick have taken lodgings in our house, and share our sitting-room for the present," said Miss Snevellicci. "Won't that induce you?"

"Surely," returned Nicholas, "I can require no possible inducement beyond your invitation."

"Oh, no! I dare say," rejoined Miss Snevellicci. And Miss Ledrook said, "Upon my word!" Upon which Miss Snevellicci said that Miss Ledrook was a giddy thing; and Miss Ledrook said that Miss Snevellicci beat Miss Ledrook, and Miss Ledrook beat Miss Snevellicci.

"Come," said Miss Ledrook, "it's high time we were there, or we shall have poor Mrs. Snevellicci thinking that you've run away with her daughter, Mr. Johnson; and then we should have a pretty to-do."

"My dear Led," remonstrated Miss Snevellicci, "how you do talk!"

Miss Ledrook made no answer, but taking Smike's arm in hers, left her friend and Nicholas to follow at their pleasure; which it pleased them, or rather pleased Nicholas, who had no great fancy for a tête-à-tête under the circumstances, to do at once.

There were not wanting matters of conversation when they reached the street, for it turned out that Miss Snevellicci had a small basket to carry home, and Miss Ledrook a small bandbox, both containing such minor articles of theatrical costume as the lady performers usually carried to and fro every evening. Nicholas would insist upon carrying the basket, and Miss Snevellicci would insist upon carrying it herself, which gave rise to a struggle, in which Nicholas captured the basket and bandbox likewise. Then Nicholas said, that he wondered what could possibly be inside the basket, and attempted to peep in, whereat Miss Snevellicci screamed, and declared that if she thought he had seen, she was sure she should faint away. This declaration was followed by a similar attempt on the bandbox, and similar demonstrations on the part of Miss Ledrook, and then both

ladies vowed that they wouldn't move a step farther until Nicholas
had promised that he wouldn't offer to peep again. At last Nicholas
pledged himself to betray no further curiosity, and they walked on;
both ladies giggling very much, and declaring that they never had
seen such a wicked creature in all their born days — never.

Lightening the way with such pleasantry as this, they arrived at the
tailor's house in no time; and here they made quite a little party,
there being present, besides Mr. Lillyvick and Mrs. Lillyvick, not
only Miss Snevellicci's mamma, but her papa also. And an uncommonly fine man Miss Snevellicci's papa was, with a hook nose, and
a white forehead, and curly black hair, and high cheekbones, and altogether quite a handsome face, only a little pimply, as though with
drinking. He had a very broad chest had Miss Snevellicci's papa, and
he wore a threadbare blue dress-coat, tuttoned with gilt buttons
tight across it; and he no sooner saw Nicholas come into the room
than he whipped the two forefingers of his right hand in between the
two centre buttons, and sticking his other arm gracefully akimbo,
seemed to say, "Now, here I am, my buck, and what have you got to
say to me?"

Such was, and in such an attitude sat, Miss Snevellicci's papa, who
had been in the profession ever since he had first played the ten-year-
old imps in the Christmas pantomimes; who could sing a little, dance
a little, fence a little, act a little, and do everything a little, but not
much; who had been sometimes in the ballet, and sometimes in the
chorus, at every theatre in London; who was always selected in virtue
of his figure to play the military visitors and the speechless noblemen;
who always wore a smart dress and came on arm-in-arm with a smart
lady in short petticoats — and always did it too with such an air that
people in the pit had been several times known to cry out "Bravo!"
under the impression that he was somebody. Such was Miss Snevellicci's papa, upon whom some envious persons cast the imputation
that he occasionally beat Miss Snevellicci's mamma, who was still a
dancer, with a neat little figure, and some remains of good looks; and
who now sat, as she danced — being rather too old for the full glare
of the footlights — in the background.

To these good people Nicholas was presented with much formality. The introduction being completed, Miss Snevellicci's papa (who
was scented with rum and water) said that he was delighted to make

the acquaintance of a gentleman so highly talented; and furthermore remarked that there hadn't been such a hit made — no, not since the first appearance of his friend Mr. Glavormelly, at the Coburg.

"You have seen him, sir?" said Miss Snevellicci's papa.

"No, really I never did," replied Nicholas.

"You never saw my friend Glavormelly, sir!" said Miss Snevellicci's papa. "Then you have never seen acting yet. If he had lived —"

"Oh, he is dead, is he?" interrupted Nicholas.

"He is," said Mr. Snevellicci, "but he isn't in Westminster Abbey, more's the shame. He was a — Well, no matter. He is gone to that bourne from whence no traveller returns. I hope he is appreciated *there*."

So saying, Miss Snevellicci's papa rubbed the tip of his nose with a very yellow silk handkerchief, and gave the company to understand that these recollections overcame him.

"Well, Mr. Lillyvick," said Nicholas, "and how are you?"

"Quite well, sir," replied the collector. "There is nothing like the married state, sir, depend upon it."

"Indeed!" said Nicholas, laughing.

"Ah! nothing like it, sir," replied Mr. Lillyvick solemnly. "How do you think," whispered the collector, drawing him aside — "how do you think she looks to-night?"

"As handsome as ever," replied Nicholas, glancing at the late Miss Petowker.

"Why, there's a air about her, sir," whispered the collector, "that I never saw in anybody. Look at her now she moves to put the kettle on. There! Isn't it fascination, sir?"

"You're a lucky man," said Nicholas.

"Ha, ha, ha!" rejoined the collector. "No. Do you think I am, though, eh? Perhaps I may be, perhaps I may be. I say, I couldn't have done much better if I had been a young man, could I? You couldn't have done much better yourself, could you — eh — could you?" With such inquiries, and many more such, Mr. Lillyvick jerked his elbow into Nicholas's side, and chuckled till his face became quite purple in the attempt to keep down his satisfaction.

By this time the cloth had been laid under the joint superintendence of all the ladies, upon two tables put together, one being high and narrow, and the other low and broad. There were oysters at the top, sausages at the bottom, a pair of snuffers in the centre, and baked potatoes wherever it was most convenient to put them. Two additional chairs were brought in from the bedroom; Miss Snevellicci sat at the head of the table, and Mr. Lillyvick at the foot; and Nicholas had not only the honour of sitting next Miss Snevellicci, but of having Miss Snevellicci's mamma on his right hand, and Miss Snevellicci's papa over the way. In short, he was the hero of the feast; and when the table was cleared and something warm introduced, Miss Snevellicci's papa got up and proposed his health in a speech containing such affecting allusions to his coming departure that Miss Snevellicci wept, and was compelled to retire into the bedroom.

"Hush! Don't take any notice of it," said Miss Ledrook, peeping in from the bedroom. "Say, when she comes back, that she exerts herself too much."

Miss Ledrook eked out this speech with so many mysterious nods and frowns before she shut the door again, that a profound silence came upon all the company, during which Miss Snevellicci's papa looked very big indeed — several sizes larger than life — at everybody in turn, but particularly at Nicholas, and kept on perpetually emptying his tumbler, and filling it again, until the ladies returned in a cluster, with Miss Snevellicci among them.

"You needn't alarm yourself a bit, Mr. Snevellicci," said Mrs. Lillyvick. "She is only a little weak and nervous; she has been so ever since the morning."

"Oh," said Mr. Snevellicci, "that's all, is it?"

"Oh, yes, that's all. Don't make a fuss about it," cried all the ladies together.

Now, this was not exactly the kind of reply suited to Mr. Snevellicci's importance as a man and a father, so he picked out the unfortunate Mrs. Snevellicci, and asked her what the devil she meant by talking to him in that way.

"Dear me, my dear —" said Mrs. Snevellicci.

"Don't call me your dear, ma'am," said Mr. Snevellicci, "if you please."

"Pray, pa, don't," interposed Miss Snevellicci.

"Don't what, my child?"

"Talk in that way."

"Why not?" said Mr. Snevellicci. "I hope you don't suppose there's anybody here who is to prevent my talking as I like?"

"Nobody wants to, pa," rejoined his daughter.

"Nobody would if they did want to," said Snevellicci. "I am not ashamed of myself. Snevellicci is my name; I'm to be found in Broad Court, Bow Street, when I'm in town. If I'm not at home, let any man ask for me at the stage door. Damme, they know me at the stage door, I suppose. Most men have seen my portrait at the cigar shop round the corner. I've been mentioned in the newspapers before now, haven't I? Talk! I'll tell you what; if I found out that any man had been tampering with the affections of my daughter, I wouldn't talk. I'd astonish him without talking — that's my way."

So saying, Mr. Snevellicci struck the palm of his left hand three smart blows with his clenched fist, pulled a phantom nose with his right thumb and forefinger, and swallowed another glassful at a draught. "That's my way," repeated Mr. Snevellicci.

Most public characters have their failings; and the truth is, that Mr. Snevellicci was a little addicted to drinking; or, if the whole truth must be told, that he was scarcely ever sober. He knew in his cups three distinct stages of intoxication — the dignified — the quarrelsome — the amorous. When professionally engaged he never got beyond the dignified; in private circles he went through all three, passing from one to another with a rapidity of transition often rather perplexing to those who had not the honour of his acquaintance.

Thus Mr. Snevellicci had no sooner swallowed another glassful than he smiled upon all present, in happy forgetfulness of having exhibited symptoms of pugnacity, and proposed "The ladies — bless their hearts!" in a most vivacious manner.

"I love 'em," said Mr. Snevellicci, looking round the table. "I love 'em, every one."

"Not every one," reasoned Mr. Lillyvick mildly.

"Yes, every one," repeated Mr. Snevellicci.

"That would include the married ladies, you know," said Mr. Lillyvick.

"I love them too, sir," said Mr. Snevellicci.

The collector looked into the surrounding faces with an aspect of grave astonishment, seeming to say, "This is a nice man!" and appeared a little surprised that Mrs. Lillyvick's manner yielded no evidence of horror and indignation.

"One good turn deserves another," said Mr. Snevellicci. "I love them and they love me." And as if this avowal were not made in sufficient disregard and defiance of all moral obligations, what did Mr. Snevellicci do? He winked — winked openly and undisguisedly; winked with his right eye — upon Henrietta Lillyvick!

The collector fell back in his chair in the intensity of his astonishment. If anybody had winked at her as Henrietta Petowker, it would have been indecorous in the last degree; but as Mrs. Lillyvick! While he thought of it in a cold perspiration, and wondered whether it was possible that he could be dreaming, Mr. Snevellicci repeated the wink, and drinking to Mrs. Lillyvick in dumb show, actually blew her a kiss! Mr. Lillyvick left his chair, walked straight up to the other end of the table, and fell upon him — literally fell upon him — instantaneously. Mr. Lillyvick was no light weight, and consequently when he fell upon Mr. Snevellicci, Mr. Snevellicci fell under the table. Mr. Lillyvick followed him, and the ladies screamed.

"What is the matter with the men — are they mad?" cried Nicholas, diving under the table, dragging up the collector by main force, and thrusting him, all doubled up, into a chair, as if he had been a stuffed figure. "What do you mean to do? what do you want to do? what is the matter with you?"

While Nicholas raised up the collector, Smike had performed the same office for Snevellicci, who now regarded his late adversary in tipsy amazement.

"Look here, sir," replied Mr. Lillyvick, pointing to his astonished wife, "here is purity and elegance combined, whose feelings have been outraged — violated, sir!"

"Lor, what nonsense he talks!" exclaimed Mrs. Lillyvick, in answer to the inquiring look of Nicholas. "Nobody has said anything to me."

"Said, Henrietta!" cried the collector. "Didn't I see him —" Mr. Lillyvick couldn't bring himself to utter the word, but he counterfeited the motion of the eye.

"Well!" cried Mrs. Lillyvick, "do you suppose nobody is ever to look at me? A pretty thing to be married, indeed, if that was law!"

"You didn't mind it?" cried the collector.

"Mind it!" repeated Mrs. Lillyvick contemptuously. "You ought to go down on your knees and beg everybody's pardon, that you ought."

"Pardon, my dear?" said the dismayed collector.

"Yes, and mine first," replied Mrs. Lillyvick. "Do you suppose *I* ain't the best judge of what's proper and what's improper?"

"To be sure," cried all the ladies. "Do you suppose *we* shouldn't be the first to speak, if there was anything that ought to be taken notice of?"

"Do you suppose *they* don't know, sir?" said Miss Snevellicci's papa, pulling up his collar, and muttering something about a punching of heads, and being only withheld by considerations of age. With which Miss Snevellicci's papa looked steadily and sternly at Mr. Lillyvick for some seconds, and then rising deliberately from his chair, kissed the ladies all round, beginning with Mrs. Lillyvick.

The unhappy collector looked piteously at his wife, as if to see whether there was any one trait of Miss Petowker left in Mrs. Lillyvick, and finding too surely that there was not, begged pardon of all the company with great humility, and sat down such a crestfallen, dispirited, disenchanted man that, despite all his selfishness and dotage, he was quite an object of compassion.

Miss Snevellicci's papa being greatly exalted by this triumph and incontestible proof of his popularity with the fair sex, quickly grew convivial, not to say uproarious; volunteering more than one song of no inconsiderable length, and regaling the social circle between whiles with recollections of divers splendid women who had been supposed to entertain a passion for himself, several of whom he toasted by name, taking occasion to remark at the same time that if he had been a little more alive to his own interest, he might have been rolling at that moment in his chariot-and-four. These reminiscences appeared to awaken no very torturing pangs in the breast of Mrs. Snevellicci, who was sufficiently occupied in descanting to Nicholas upon the manifold accomplishments and merits of her daughter. Nor was the young lady herself at all behind-hand in displaying her choicest allurements; but these, heightened as they were by the artifices of Miss Ledrook, had no effect whatever in increasing the attentions of Nicholas, who, with the precedent of Miss Squeers still fresh in his memory, steadily resisted every fascination, and placed so strict a guard upon his behaviour, that when he had taken his leave the ladies were unanimous in pronouncing him quite a monster of insensibility.

Next day the posters appeared in due course, and the public were informed, in all the colours of the rainbow, and in letters afflicted with every possible variation of spinal deformity, how that Mr. Johnson would have the honour of making his last appearance that evening, and how that an early application for places was requested, in consequence of the extraordinary overflow attendant on his performances — it being a remarkable fact in theatrical history, but one long since established beyond dispute, that it is a hopeless endeavour to attract people to a theatre unless they can be first brought to believe that they will never get into it.

Nicholas was somewhat at a loss, on entering the theatre at night, to account for the unusual perturbation and excitement visible in the countenances of all the company, but he was not long in doubt as to the cause, for before he could make any inquiry respecting it, Mr. Crummles approached, and, in an agitated tone of voice, informed him that there was a London manager in the boxes.

"It's the phenomenon, depend upon it, sir," said Crummles, dragging Nicholas to the little hole in the curtain that he might look through at the London manager. "I have not the smallest doubt it's the fame of the phenomenon — that's the man! him in the great-coat and no shirt-collar. She shall have ten pound a week, Johnson; she shall not appear on the London boards for a farthing less. They shan't engage her either, unless they engage Mrs. Crummles too — twenty pound a week for the pair; or I'll tell you what, I'll throw in myself and the two boys, and they shall have the family for thirty. I can't say fairer than that. They must take us all, if none of us will go without the others. That's the way some of the London people do, and it always answers. Thirty pound a week. It's too cheap, Johnson. It's dirt cheap."

Nicholas replied that it certainly was; and Mr. Vincent Crummles, taking several huge pinches of snuff to compose his feelings, hurried away to tell Mrs. Crummles that he had quite settled the only terms that could be accepted, and had resolved not to abate one single farthing.

When everybody was dressed and the curtain went up, the excitement occasioned by the presence of the London manager increased

a thousandfold. Everybody happened to know that the London manager had come down specially to witness his or her own performance,
and all were in a flutter of anxiety and expectation. Some of those
who were not on in the first scene hurried to the wings, and there
stretched their necks to have a peep at him; others stole up into the
two little private boxes over the stage doors, and from that position
reconnoitred the London manager. Once the London manager was
seen to smile — he smiled at the comic countryman's pretending to
catch a blue-bottle, while Mrs. Crummles was making her greatest
effect. "Very good, my fine fellow," said Mr. Crummles, shaking his
fist at the countryman when he came off, "you leave this company
next Saturday night."

In the same way, everybody who was on the stage beheld no audience but one individual; everybody played to the London manager.
When Mr. Lenville, in a sudden burst of passion, called the emperor a
miscreant, and then biting his glove said, "But I must dissemble," instead of looking gloomily at the boards, and so waiting for his cue, as
is proper in such cases, he kept his eye fixed upon the London manager. When Miss Bravassa sang her song at her lover, who according
to custom stood ready to shake hands with her between the verses,
they looked, not at each other, but at the London manager. Mr.
Crummles died point blank at him; and when the two guards came in
to take the body off after a very hard death, it was seen to open its eyes
and glance at the London manager. At length the London manager
was discovered to be asleep, and shortly after that he woke up and
went away; whereupon all the company fell foul of the unhappy
comic countryman, declaring that his buffoonery was the sole cause;
and Mr. Crummles said that he had put up with it for a long time, but
that he really couldn't stand it any longer, and therefore would feel
obliged by his looking out for another engagement.

All this was the occasion of much amusement to Nicholas, whose
only feeling upon the subject was one of sincere satisfaction that the
great man went away before he appeared. He went through his part
in the two last pieces as briskly as he could, and having been received
with unbounded favour and unprecedented applause — so said the
bills for next day, which had been printed an hour or two before —
he took Smike's arm, and walked home to bed.

With the post next morning came a letter from Newman Noggs,

very inky, very short, very dirty, very small, and very mysterious, urging Nicholas to return to London instantly; not to lose an instant; to be there that night if possible.

"I will," said Nicholas. "Heaven knows I have remained here for the best, and sorely against my own will; but even now I may have dallied too long. What can have happened; Smike, my good fellow, here — take my purse. Put our things together, and pay what little debts we owe — quick, and we shall be in time for the morning coach. I will only tell them that we are going, and will return to you immediately."

So saying, he took his hat, and hurrying away to the lodgings of Mr. Crummles, applied his hand to the knocker with such hearty good-will, that he awakened that gentleman, who was still in bed, and caused Mr. Bulph the pilot to take his morning's pipe very nearly out of his mouth in the extremity of his surprise.

The door being opened, Nicholas ran upstairs without any ceremony, and bursting into the darkened sitting-room of the one-pair front, found that the two Masters Crummles had sprung out of the sofa-bedstead, and were putting on their clothes with great rapidity, under the impression that it was the middle of the night, and the next house was on fire.

Before he could undeceive them, Mr. Crummles came down in a flannel gown and nightcap; and to him Nicholas briefly explained that circumstances had occurred which rendered it necessary for him to repair to London immediately.

"So, good-bye," said Nicholas; "good-bye, good-bye."

He was half-way downstairs before Mr. Crummles had sufficiently recovered his surprise to be able to gasp out something about the posters.

"I can't help it," replied Nicholas. "Set whatever I may have earned this week against them, or if it will not repay you, say at once what will. Quick, quick."

"We'll cry quits about that," returned Crummles. "But can't we have one last night more?"

"Not an hour — not a minute," replied Nicholas impatiently.

"Won't you stop to say something to Mrs. Crummles?" asked the manager, following him down to the door.

"I couldn't stop if it were to prolong my life a score of years," rejoined Nicholas. "Here, take my hand, and with it my hearty thanks. Oh, that I should have been fooling here!"

Accompanying these words with an impatient stamp on the ground, he tore himself from the manager's detaining grasp, and darting rapidly down the street was out of sight in an instant.

"Dear me, dear me," said Mr. Crummles, looking wistfully towards the point at which he had just disappeared; "if he only acted like that, what a deal of money he'd draw! He should have kept upon this circuit; he'd have been very useful to me. But he don't know what's good for him. He is an impetuous youth. Young men are rash, very rash."

Mr. Crummles being in a moralising mood, might possibly have moralised for some minutes longer if he had not mechanically put his hand towards his waistcoat pocket, where he was accustomed to keep his snuff. The absence of any pocket at all in the usual direction suddenly recalled to his recollection that fact that he had no waistcoat on; and this leading him to a contemplation of the extreme scantiness of his attire, he shut the door abruptly, and retired upstairs with great precipitation.

Smike had made good speed while Nicholas was absent, and with his help everything was soon ready for their departure. They scarcely stopped to take a morsel of breakfast, and in less than half an hour arrived at the coach-office, quite out of breath with the haste they had made to reach it in time. There were yet a few minutes to spare, so, having secured the places, Nicholas hurried into a slopseller's hard by, and bought Smike a great-coat. It would have been rather large for a substantial yeoman, but the shopman averring (and with considerable truth) that it was a most uncommon fit, Nicholas would have purchased it in his impatience if it had been twice the size.

As they hurried up to the coach, which was now in the open street and all ready for starting, Nicholas was not a little astonished to find himself suddenly clutched in a close and violent embrace, which nearly took him off his legs; nor was his amazement at all lessened by hearing the voice of Mr. Crummles exclaim, "It is he — my friend, my friend!"

"Bless my heart," cried Nicholas, struggling in the manager's arms, "what are you about?"

The manager made no reply, but strained him to his breast again, exclaiming as he did so, "Farewell, my noble, my lion-hearted boy!"

In fact, Mr. Crummles, who could never lose any opportunity for professional display, had turned out for the express purpose of taking a public farewell of Nicholas; and to render it the more imposing, he was now, to that young gentleman's most profound annoyance, inflicting upon him a rapid succession of stage embraces, which, as everybody knows, are performed by the embracer's laying his or her chin on the shoulder of the object of affection, and looking over it. This Mr. Crummles did in the highest style of melodrama, pouring forth at the same time all the most dismal forms of farewell he could think of, out of the stock pieces. Nor was this all, for the elder Master Crummles was going through a similar ceremony with Smike; while Master Percy Crummles, with a very little second-hand camlet cloak, worn theatrically over his left shoulder, stood by, in the attitude of an attendant officer, waiting to convey the two victims to the scaffold.

The lookers-on laughed very heartily, and as it was as well to put a good face upon the matter, Nicholas laughed too when he had succeeded in disengaging himself; and, rescuing the astonished Smike, climbed up to the coach after him, and kissed his hand in honour of the absent Mrs. Crummles as they rolled away.

BEING FOR THE BENEFIT OF MR. VINCENT CRUMMLES, AND
POSITIVELY HIS LAST APPEARANCE ON THIS STAGE

[Nicholas has now rejoined his sister Kate in London.]

Nicholas found himself poring with the utmost interest over a large playbill hanging outside a minor theatre which he had to pass on his way home, and reading a list of the actors and actresses who had promised to do honour to some approaching benefit, with as much gravity as if it had been a catalogue of the names of those ladies and gentlemen who stood highest upon the Book of Fate, and he had been looking anxiously for his own. He glanced at the top of the bill, with a smile at his own dulness, as he prepared to resume his walk, and there saw announced in large letters, with a large space between each of them, "Positively the last appearance of Mr. Vincent Crummles of Provincial Celebrity! ! !"

"Nonsense!" said Nicholas, turning back again. "It can't be."

But there it was. In one line by itself was an announcement of the first night of a new melodrama; in another line by itself was an announcement of the last six nights of an old one; a third line was devoted to the re-engagement of the unrivalled African Knife-swallower, who had kindly suffered himself to be prevailed upon to forego his country engagements for one week longer; a fourth line announced that Mr. Snittle Timberry, having recovered from his late severe indisposition, would have the honour of appearing that evening; a fifth line said that there were "Cheers, Tears, and Laughter!" every night; a sixth, that that was positively the last appearance of Mr. Vincent Crummles of Provincial Celebrity.

"Surely it must be the same man," thought Nicholas. "There can't be two Vincent Crummleses."

The better to settle this question he referred to the bill again, and finding that there was a Baron in the first piece, and that Roberto (his son) was enacted by one Master Crummles, and Spaletro (his nephew) by one Master Percy Crummles — *their* last appearances — and that, incidental to the piece, was a characteristic dance by the characters, and a castanet *pas seul* by the Infant Phenomenon — *her* last appearance — he no longer entertained any doubt; and, presenting himself at the stage door, and sending in a scrap of paper with "Mr. Johnson" written thereon in pencil, was presently conducted by a Robber, with a very large belt and buckle round his waist, and very large leather gauntlets on his hands, into the presence of his former manager.

Mr. Crummles was unfeignedly glad to see him, and starting up from before a small dressing-glass, with one very bushy eyebrow stuck on crooked over his left eye, and the fellow eyebrow and the calf of one of his legs in his hand, embraced him cordially; at the same time observing that it would do Mrs. Crummles's heart good to bid him good-bye before they went.

"You were always a favourite of hers, Johnson," said Crummles, "always were from the first. I was quite easy in my mind about you from the first day you dined with us. One that Mrs. Crummles took a fancy to was sure to turn out right. Ah! Johnson, what a woman that is!"

"I am sincerely obliged to her for her kindness in this and all other respects," said Nicholas. "But where are you going, that you talk about bidding good-bye?"

"Haven't you seen it in the papers?" said Crummles, with some dignity.

"No," replied Nicholas.

"I wonder at that," said the manager. "It was among the varieties. I had the paragraph here somewhere — but I don't know — oh, yes, here it is!"

So saying, Mr. Crummles, after pretending that he thought he must have lost it, produced a square inch of newspaper from the pocket of the pantaloons he wore in private life (which, together with the plain clothes of several other gentlemen, lay scattered about on a kind of dresser in the room), and gave it to Nicholas to read.

"The talented Vincent Crummles, long favourably known to fame as a country manager and actor of no ordinary pretensions, is about to cross the Atlantic on a histrionic expedition. Crummles is to be accompanied, we hear, by his lady and gifted family. We know no man superior to Crummles in his particular line of character, or one who, whether as a public or private individual, could carry with him the best wishes of a larger circle of friends. Crummles is certain to succeed."

"Here's another bit," said Mr. Crummles, handing over a still smaller scrap. "This is from the notices to correspondents, this one."

Nicholas read it aloud. " 'Philo Dramaticus. — Crummles, the country manager and actor, cannot be more than forty-three or forty-four years of age. Crummles is NOT a Prussian, having been born at Chelsea.' Humph!" said Nicholas, "that's an odd paragraph."

"Very," returned Crummles, scratching the side of his nose, and looking at Nicholas with an assumption of great unconcern. "I can't think who puts these things in. I didn't."

Still keeping his eye on Nicholas, Mr. Crummles shook his head twice or thrice with profound gravity, and remarking that he could not for the life of him imagine how the newspapers found out the things they did, folded up the extracts and put them in his pocket again.

"I am astonished to hear this news," said Nicholas. "Going to America! You had no such thing in contemplation when I was with you."

"No," replied Crummles, "I hadn't then. The fact is that Mrs. Crummles — most extraordinary woman, Johnson" — here he broke off and whispered something in his ear.

"Oh!" said Nicholas, smiling. "The prospect of an addition to your family?"

"The seventh addition, Johnson," returned Mr. Crummles solemnly. "I thought such a child as the phenomenon must have been a closer; but it seems we are to have another. She is a very remarkable woman."

"I congratulate you," said Nicholas, "and I hope this may prove a phenomenon too."

"Why, it's pretty sure to be something uncommon, I suppose," rejoined Mr. Crummles. "The talent of the other three is principally in combat and serious pantomime. I should like this one to have a turn for juvenile tragedy; I understand they want something of that sort in America very much. However, we must take it as it comes. Perhaps it may have a genius for the tightrope. It may have any sort of genius, in short, if it takes after its mother, Johnson, for she is an universal genius; but, whatever its genius is, that genius shall be developed."

Expressing himself after these terms, Mr. Crummles put on his other eyebrow, and the calves of his legs, and then put on his legs, which were of a yellowish flesh-colour, and rather soiled about the knees, from frequent going down upon those joints, in curses, prayers, last struggles, and other strong passages.

While the ex-manager completed his toilet, he informed Nicholas that as he should have a fair start in America, from the proceeds of a tolerably good engagement which he had been fortunate enough to obtain, and as he and Mrs. Crummles could scarcely hope to act for ever — not being immortal, except in the breath of Fame and in a figurative sense — he had made up his mind to settle there permanently, in the hope of acquiring some land of his own which would support them in their old age, and which they could afterwards bequeath to their children. Nicholas, having highly commended this resolution, Mr. Crummles went on to impart such further intelligence relative to their mutual friends as he thought might prove interesting; informing Nicholas, among other things, that Miss Snevellicci was happily married to an affluent young wax-chandler who had supplied the theatre with candles, and that Mr. Lillyvick didn't dare say his soul was his own, such was the tyrannical sway of Mrs. Lillyvick, who reigned paramount and supreme.

Nicholas responded to this confidence on the part of Mr. Crummles by confiding to him his own name, situation, and prospects, and informing him in as few general words as he could, of the circumstances which had led to their first acquaintance. After congratulating him with great heartiness on the improved state of his fortunes, Mr. Crummles gave him to understand that next morning he and his were to start for Liverpool, where the vessel lay which was to carry them from the shores of England, and that if Nicholas wished to take a last adieu of Mrs. Crummles, he must repair with him that night to a farewell supper, given in honour of the family at a neighbouring tavern; at which Mr. Snittle Timberry would preside, while the honours of the vice-chair would be sustained by the African Swallower.

The room being by this time very warm and somewhat crowded, in consequence of the influx of four gentlemen, who had just killed each other in the piece under representation, Nicholas accepted the invitation, and promised to return at the conclusion of the performances; preferring the cool air and twilight out of doors to the mingled perfume of gas, orange-peel, and gunpowder, which pervaded the hot and glaring theatre.

He availed himself of this interval to buy a silver snuffbox — the best of his funds would afford — as a token of remembrance for Mr. Crummles, and having purchased, besides, a pair of earrings for Mrs. Crummles, a necklace for the phenomenon, and a flaming shirt-pin for each of the young gentlemen, he refreshed himself with a walk, and returning a little after the appointed time, found the lights out, the theatre empty, the curtain raised for the night, and Mr. Crummles walking up and down the stage expecting his arrival.

"Timberry won't be long," said Mr. Crummles. "He played the audience out to-night. He does a faithful black in the last piece, and it takes him a little longer to wash himself."

"A very unpleasant line of character, I should think?" said Nicholas.

"No, I don't know," replied Mr. Crummles; "it comes off easily enough, and there's only the face and neck. We had a first-tragedy man in our company once, who, when he played Othello, used to black himself all over. But that's feeling a part and going into it as if you meant it; it isn't usual — more's the pity."

Mr. Snittle Timberry now appeared, arm-in-arm with the African Swallower, and, being introduced to Nicholas, raised his hat half a foot, and said he was proud to know him. The Swallower said the same, and looked and spoke remarkably like an Irishman.

"I see by the bills that you have been ill, sir," said Nicholas to Mr. Timberry. "I hope you are none the worse for your exertions to-night!"

Mr. Timberry, in reply, shook his head with a gloomy air, tapped his chest several times with great significancy, and drawing his cloak more closely about him, said, "But no matter — no matter. Come!"

It is observable that when people upon the stage are in any strait involving the very last extremity of weakness and exhaustion, they invariably perform feats of strength requiring great ingenuity and muscular power. Thus, a wounded prince or bandit chief, who is bleeding to death and too faint to move, except to the softest music (and then only upon his hands and knees), shall be seen to approach a cottage door for aid, in such a series of writhings and twistings, and with such curlings up of the legs, and such rollings over and over, and such gettings up and tumblings down again, as could never be achieved save by a very strong man skilled in posture-making. And so natural did this sort of performance come to Mr. Snittle Timberry, that on their way out of the theatre and towards the tavern where the supper was to be holden, he testified the severity of his recent indisposition and its wasting effects upon the nervous system, by a series of gymnastic performances, which were the admiration of all witnesses.

"Why, this is indeed a joy I had not looked for!" said Mrs. Crummles, when Nicholas was presented.

"Nor I," replied Nicholas. "It is by a mere chance that I have this opportunity of seeing you, although I would have made a great exertion to have availed myself of it."

"Here is one whom you know," said Mrs. Crummles, thrusting forward the phenomenon in a blue gauze frock, extensively flounced, and trousers of the same; "and here another — and another," presenting the Masters Crummles. "And how is your friend, the faithful Digby?"

"Digby!" said Nicholas, forgetting at the instant that this had been

Smike's theatrical name. "Oh, yes. He's quite — what am I saying? — he is very far from well."

"How!" exclaimed Mrs. Crummles, with a tragic recoil.

"I fear," said Nicholas, shaking his head, and making an attempt to smile, "that your better-half would be more struck with him now than ever."

"What mean you?" rejoined Mrs. Crummles, in her most popular manner. "Whence comes this altered tone?"

"I mean that a dastardly enemy of mine has struck at me through him, and that while he thinks to torture me, he inflicts on him such agonies of terror and suspense as — You will excuse me, I am sure," said Nicholas, checking himself. "I should never speak of this, and never do, except to those who know the facts, but for a moment I forgot myself."

With this hasty apology, Nicholas stooped down to salute the phenomenon, and changed the subject; inwardly cursing his precipitation, and very much wondering what Mrs. Crummles must think of so sudden an explosion.

That lady seemed to think very little about it, for the supper being by this time on the table, she gave her hand to Nicholas, and repaired with a stately step to the left hand of Mr. Snittle Timberry. Nicholas had the honour to support her, and Mr. Crummles was placed upon the chairman's right; the phenomenon and the Masters Crummles sustained the vice.

The company amounted in number to some twenty-five or thirty, being composed of such members of the theatrical profession, then engaged or disengaged in London, as were numbered among the most intimate friends of Mr. and Mrs. Crummles. The ladies and gentlemen were pretty equally balanced, the expenses of the entertainment being defrayed by the latter, each of whom had the privilege of inviting one of the former as his guest.

It was, upon the whole, a very distinguished party, for independently of the lesser theatrical lights who clustered on this occasion round Mr. Snittle Timberry, there was a literary gentleman present who had dramatised in his time two hundred and forty-seven novels, as fast as they had come out — some of them faster than they had come out — and *was* a literary gentleman in consequence.

This gentleman sat on the left hand of Nicholas, to whom he was introduced by his friend the African Swallower, from the bottom of the table, with a high eulogium upon his fame and reputation.

"I am happy to know a gentleman of such great distinction," said Nicholas politely.

"Sir," replied the wit, "you're very welcome, I'm sure. The honour is reciprocal, sir, as I usually say when I dramatise a book. Did you ever hear a definition of fame, sir?"

"I have heard several," replied Nicholas, with a smile. "What is yours?"

"When I dramatise a book, sir," said the literary gentleman, "*that's* fame for its author."

"Oh, indeed!" rejoined Nicholas.

"That's fame, sir," said the literary gentleman.

"So Richard Turpin, Tom King, and Jerry Abershaw have handed down to fame the names of those on whom they committed their most impudent robberies?" said Nicholas.

"I don't know anything about that, sir," answered the literary gentleman.

"Shakespeare dramatised stories which had previously appeared in print, it is true," observed Nicholas.

"Meaning Bill, sir?" said the literary gentleman. "So he did. Bill was an adapter, certainly, so he was — and very well he adapted, too — considering."

"I was about to say," rejoined Nicholas, "that Shakespeare derived some of his plots from old tales and legends in general circulation; but it seems to me that some of the gentlemen of your craft at the present day have shot very far beyond him — "

"You're quite right, sir," interrupted the literary gentleman, leaning back in his chair, and exercising his toothpick. "Human intellect, sir, has progressed since his time — is progressing — will progress —"

"Shot beyond him, I mean," resumed Nicholas, "in quite another respect, for whereas he brought within the magic circle of his genius traditions peculiarly adapted for his purpose, and turned familiar things into constellations which should enlighten the world for ages, you drag within the magic circle of your dulness subjects not at all adapted to the purposes of the stage, and debase as he exalted. For instance, you take the uncompleted books of living authors, fresh from their hands, wet from the press, cut, hack, and carve them to the powers and capacities of your actors, and the capability of your theatres, finish unfinished works, hastily and crudely vamp up ideas not yet worked out by their original projector, but which have doubtless cost him many thoughtful days and sleepless nights; by a comparison of incidents and dialogue, down to the very last word he may have written a fortnight before, do your utmost to anticipate his plot — all this without his permission, and against his will; and then, to crown the whole proceeding, publish in some mean pamphlet, an unmeaning farrago of garbled extracts from his work, to which you put your name as author, with the honourable distinction annexed, of having perpetrated a hundred other outrages of the same description. Now, show me the distinction between such pilfering as this, and picking a man's pocket in the street; unless, indeed, it be that the legislature has a regard for pocket-handkerchiefs, and leaves men's brains, except when they are knocked out by violence, to take care of themselves."

"Men must live, sir," said the literary gentleman, shrugging his shoulders.

"That would be an equally fair plea in both cases," replied Nicholas; "but if you put it upon that ground, I have nothing more to say than that if I were a writer of books, and you a thirsty dramatist, I would rather pay your tavern score for six months — large as it might be — than have a niche in the Temple of Fame with you for the humblest corner of my pedestal, through six hundred generations."

The conversation threatened to take a somewhat angry tone when it had arrived thus far, but Mrs. Crummles opportunely interposed to prevent its leading to any violent outbreak, by making some inquiries of the literary gentleman relative to the plots of the six new pieces which he had written by contract to introduce the African Knife-swallower in his various unrivalled performances. This speedily engaged him in an animated conversation with that lady, in the interest of which all recollection of his recent discussion with Nicholas very quickly evaporated.

The board being now clear of the more substantial articles of food, and punch, wine, and spirits being placed upon it and handed about, the guests, who had been previously conversing in little groups of three or four, gradually fell off into a dead silence, while the majority of those present glanced from time to time at Mr. Snittle Timberry, and the bolder spirits did not even hesitate to strike the table with their knuckles, and plainly intimate their expectations by uttering such encouragements as, "Now, Tim," "Wake up, Mr. Chairman," "All charged, sir, and waiting for a toast," and so forth.

To these remonstrances, Mr. Timberry deigned no other rejoinder than striking his chest and gasping for breath, and giving many other indications of being still the victim of indisposition — for a man must not make himself too cheap either on the stage or off — while Mr. Crummles, who knew full well that he would be the subject of the forthcoming toast, sat gracefully in his chair, with his arm thrown carelessly over the back, and now and then lifted his glass to his mouth, and drank a little punch, with the same air with which he was accustomed to take long draughts of nothing out of the pasteboard goblets in banquet scenes.

At length Mr. Snittle Timberry rose in the most approved attitude, with one hand in the breast of his waistcoat and the other on the nearest snuff-box, and having been received with great enthusiasm, proposed, with abundance of quotations, his friend Mr. Vincent Crummles: ending a pretty long speech by extending his right hand on one side and his left on the other, and severally calling upon Mr. and Mrs. Crummles to grasp the same. This done, Mr. Vincent Crummles returned thanks, and that done, the African Swallower proposed Mrs. Vincent Crummles, in affecting terms. Then were heard loud moans and sobs from Mrs. Crummles and the ladies, despite of which that heroic woman insisted upon returning thanks herself, which she did, in a manner and in a speech which has never been surpassed and seldom equalled. It then became the duty of Mr. Snittle Timberry to give the young Crummleses, which he did; after which Mr. Vincent Crummles, as their father, addressed the company in a supplementary speech, enlarging on their virtues, amiabilities, and excellences, and wishing that they were the sons and daughter of every lady and gentleman present. These solemnities having been succeeded by a decent interval, enlivened by musical and other entertainments, Mr. Crummles proposed that ornament of the profession, Mr. Snittle Timberry; and at a little later period of the evening the health of that other ornament of the profession, the African Swallower — his very dear friend, if he would allow him to call him so; which liberty (there being no particular reason why he should not allow it) the African Swallower graciously permitted. The literary gentleman was then about to be drunk, but it being discovered that he had been drunk for some time in another acceptation of the term, and was then asleep on the stairs, the intention was abandoned, and the honour transferred to the ladies. Finally, after a very long sitting, Mr. Snittle Timberry vacated the chair, and the company with many adieus and embraces dispersed.

Nicholas waited to the last to give his little presents when he had said good-bye all round and came to Mr. Crummles, he could not but mark the difference between their present separation and their parting at Portsmouth. Not a jot of his theatrical manner remained; he put out his hand with an air which, if he could have summoned it at will, would have made him the best actor of his day in homely parts, and when Nicholas shook it with the warmth he honestly felt, appeared thoroughly melted.

"We were a very happy little company, Johnson," said poor Crummles. "You and I never had a word. I shall be very glad to-morrow morning to think that I saw you again, but now I almost wish you hadn't come."

Nicholas was about to return a cheerful reply, when he was greatly disconcerted by the sudden apparition of Mrs. Grudden, who it seemed had declined to attend the supper, in order that she might rise earlier in the morning, and who now burst out of an adjoining bedroom, habited in very extraordinary white robes; and throwing her arms about his neck, hugged him with great affection.

"What! Are you going too?" said Nicholas, submitting with as good a grace as if she had been the finest young creature in the world.

"Going?" returned Mrs. Grudden. "Lord ha' mercy, what do you think they'd do without me?"

Nicholas submitted to another hug with even a better grace than before, if that were possible, and waving his hat as cheerfully as he could, took farewell of the Vincent Crummleses.

The Restoration of Shakespeare's
Lear to the Stage

[*This article was published in* The Examiner, *February 4, 1838.*]

What we ventured to anticipate when Mr. Macready assumed the management of Covent Garden Theatre, has been every way realised. But the last of his well-directed efforts to vindicate the higher objects and uses of the drama has proved the most brilliant and the most successful. He has restored to the stage Shakespeare's true *Lear*, banished from it, by impudent ignorance, for upwards of a hundred and fifty years.

A person of the name of Boteler has the infamous repute of having recommended to a notorious poet-laureate, Mr. Nahum Tate, the "new modelling" of *Lear*. "I found the whole," quoth Mr. Tate, addressing the aforesaid Boteler in his dedication, "to answer your account of it; a heap of jewels unstrung and unpolished, yet so dazzling in their disorder, that I soon perceived I had seized a treasure." And accordingly to work set Nahum very busily indeed: strung the jewels and polished them with a vengeance; omitted the grandest things, the *Fool* among them; polished all that remained into commonplace; interlarded love-scenes; sent *Cordelia* into a comfortable cave with her lover, to dry her clothes and get warm, while her distracted and homeless old father was still left wandering without, amid all the pelting of the pitiless storm; and finally, rewarded the poor old man in his turn, and repaid him for all his suffering, by giving him back again his gilt robes and tinsel sceptre!

Betterton was the last great actor who played *Lear* before the commission of this outrage. His performances of it between the years 1663 and 1671 are recorded to have been the greatest efforts of his genius. Ten years after the latter date, Mr. Tate published his disgusting version, and this was adopted successively by Boheme, Quin, Booth, Barry, Garrick, Henderson, Kemble, Kean. Mr. Macready has now, to his lasting honour, restored the text of Shakespeare, and we shall be glad to hear of the actor foolhardy enough to attempt another restoration of the text of Mr. Tate! Mr. Macready's success has banished that disgrace from the stage for ever.

The *Fool* in the tragedy of *Lear* is one of the most wonderful creations of Shakespeare's genius. The picture of his quick and pregnant sarcasm, of his loving devotion, of his acute sensibility, of his despairing mirth, of his heartbroken silence — contrasted with the rigid sublimity of *Lear's* suffering, with the huge desolation of *Lear's* sorrow, with the vast and outraged image of *Lear's* madness — is the noblest thought that ever entered into the heart and mind of man. Nor is it a noble thought alone. Three crowded houses in Covent Garden Theatre have now proved by something better than even the deepest attention that it is for action, for representation; that it is necessary to an audience as tears are to an overcharged heart; and necessary to *Lear* himself as the recollections of his kingdom, or as the worn and faded garments of his power. We predicted some years since that this would be felt, and we have the better right to repeat it now. We take leave again to say that Shakespeare would have as soon consented to the banishment of *Lear* from the tragedy as to the banishment of his *Fool*. We may fancy him, while planning his immortal work, feeling suddenly, with an instinct of divinest genius, that its gigantic sorrows could never be presented on the stage without a suffering too frightful, a sublimity too remote, a grandeur too terrible — unless relieved by quiet pathos, and in some way brought home to the apprehensions of the audience by homely and familiar illustration. At such a moment that *Fool* rose to his mind, and not till then could he have contemplated his marvellous work in the greatness and beauty of its final completion.

The *Fool* in *Lear* is the solitary instance of such a character, in all the writings of Shakespeare, being identified with the pathos and passion of the scene. He is interwoven with *Lear*, he is the link that still associates him with *Cordelia's* love, and the presence of the regal estate he has surrendered. The rage of the wolf *Goneril* is first stirred by a report that her favourite gentleman had been struck by her father "for chiding of his fool," — and the first impatient questions we hear from the dethroned old man are: "Where's my knave — my fool? Go you and call my fool hither." — "Where's my fool? Ho! I think the world's asleep." — "But where's my fool? I have not seen him these two days." — "Go you and call hither my fool," — all which prepare us for that affecting answer stammered forth at last by the knight in attendance: "Since my young lady's going into France, sir, the fool hath much pined away." Mr. Macready's manner of turning off at this with an expression of half impatience, half ill-repressed emotion — "No more of that, *I have noted it well*" — was inexpressibly touching. We saw him, in the secret corner of his heart, still clinging to the memory of her who was used to be his best object, the argument of his praise, balm of his age, "most best, most dearest." And in the same noble and affecting spirit was his manner of fondling the *Fool* when he sees him first, and asks him with earnest care, "How now, my pretty knave? *How dost thou?*" Can there be a doubt, after this, that his love for the *Fool* is associated with *Cordelia*, who had been kind to the poor boy, and for the loss of whom he pines away? And are we not even then prepared for the sublime pathos of the close, when *Lear*, bending over the dead body of all he had left to love upon the earth, connects with her the memory of that other gentle, faithful, and loving being who had passed from his side — unites, in that moment of final agony, the two hearts that had been broken in his service, and exclaims, "And my poor fool is hanged!"

Mr. Macready's *Lear*, remarkable before for a masterly completeness of conception, is heightened by this introduction of the *Fool* to a surprising degree. It accords exactly with the view he seeks to present of *Lear's* character. The passages we have named, for instance, had even received illustration in the first scene, where something beyond the turbulent greatness or royal impatience of *Lear* had been presented — something to redeem him from his treatment of *Cordelia*. The bewildered pause after giving his "father's heart" away — the hurry yet hesitation of his manner as he orders *France* to be called — "Who stirs? Call *Burgundy*" — had told us at once how much consideration he needed, how much pity, of how little of himself he was indeed the master, how crushing and irrepressible was the strength of his sharp impatience. We saw no material change in his style of playing the first great scene with *Goneril*, which fills the stage with true and appalling touches of nature. In that scene he ascends indeed with the heights of *Lear's* passion; through all its changes of agony, of anger, of impatience, of turbulent assertion, of despair, and mighty grief, till on his knees, with arms upraised and head thrown back, the tremendous Curse bursts from him amid heaving and reluctant throes of suffering and anguish. The great scene of the second act had also its great passages of power and beauty: his self-persuading utterance of "hysterias passio" — his anxious and fearful tenderness to *Regan* — the elevated grandeur of his appeal to the heavens — his terrible suppressed efforts, his pauses, his reluctant pangs of passion, in the speech "I will not trouble thee, my child," — and surpassing the whole, as we think, in deep simplicity as well as agony of pathos, that noble conception of shame as he *hides his face* on the arm of *Goneril* and says —

> "I'll go with thee;
> Thy fifty yet doth double five and twenty,
> And thou art twice her love"

The *Fool's* presence then enabled him to give an effect, unattempted before, to those little words which close the scene, when, in the effort of bewildering passion with which he strives to burst through the phalanx of amazed horrors that have closed him round, he feels that his intellect is shaking, and suddenly exclaims, "O *Fool!* I shall go mad!" This is better than hitting the forehead and ranting out a self-reproach.

But the presence of the *Fool* in the storm-scene! The reader must witness this to judge its power and observe the deep impression with which it affects the audience. Every resource that the art of the painter and the mechanist can afford is called in aid of this scene — every illustration is thrown on it of which the great actor of *Lear* is capable, but these are nothing to that simple presence of the *Fool!* He has changed his character there. So long as hope existed he had sought by his hectic merriment and sarcasms to win *Lear* back to love and reason, but that half of his work is now over, and all that remains for him is to soothe and lessen the certainty of the worst. *Kent* asks who is with *Lear* in the storm, and is answered —

> "None but the *Fool*, who labours to outjest
> His heart-struck injuries!"

When all his attempts have failed, either to soothe or to outjest these injuries, he sings, in the shivering cold, about the necessity of "going to bed at noon." He leaves the stage to die in his youth, and we hear of him no more till we hear the sublime touch of pathos over the dead body of the hanged *Cordelia*.

The finest passage of Mr. Macready's scenes upon the heath is his remembrance of the "poor naked wretches," wherein a new world seems indeed to have broken upon his mind. Other parts of these scenes wanted more of tumultuous extravagance, more of a preternatural cast of wildness. We should always be made to feel something beyond physical distress predominant here. His colloquy with *Mad Tom*, however, was touching in the last degree, and so were the two last scenes, the recognition of *Cordelia* and the death, which elicited from the audience the truest and best of all tributes to their beauty and pathos. Mr. Macready's representation of the father at the end, broken down to his last despairing struggle, his heart swelling gradually upwards till it bursts in its closing sigh, completed the only perfect picture that we have had of *Lear* since the age of Betterton.

The Nubbles Family at Astley's Circus

[The Old Curiosity Shop *appeared in the weekly numbers of* Master Humphrey's Clock *between April 4, 1840, and February 6, 1841. The visit to Astley's is from Chapter 39; Nell's adventures among the strolling entertainers — Punch-and-Judy shows, giants and dwarfs, performing dogs, and Mrs. Jarley's Wax-work — are from Chapters 16-18 and 27-28.*

Kit Nubbles is a London boy doing odd jobs in a suburban household, his mother a widowed washerwoman. He is treating his family, together with a neighbor and her daughter Barbara, to a night at the theater, followed by supper at an oyster-shop.]

However, it was high time now to be thinking of the play; for which great preparation was required in the way of shawls and bonnets, not to mention one handkerchief full of oranges and another of apples, which took some time tying up, in consequence of the fruit having a tendency to roll out at the corners. At length every thing was ready, and they went off very fast; Kit's mother carrying the baby, who was dreadfully wide awake, and Kit holding little Jacob in one hand, and escorting Barbara with the other — a state of things which occasioned the two mothers, who walked behind, to declare that they looked quite family folks, and caused Barbara to blush and say, "Now don't, mother!" But Kit said she had no call to mind what they said; and indeed she need not have had, if she had known how very far from Kit's thoughts any love-making was. Poor Barbara!

At last they got to the theatre, which was Astley's: and in some two minutes after they had reached the yet unopened door, little Jacob was squeezed flat, and the baby had received divers concussions, and Barbara's mother's umbrella had been carried several yards off and passed back to her over the shoulders of the people, and Kit had hit a man on the head with the handkerchief of apples for "scrowdging" his parent with unnecessary violence, and there was a great uproar. But when they were once past the pay-place, and tearing away for very life with their checks in their hands, and, above all, when they were fairly in the theatre, and seated in such places that they couldn't have had better if they had picked them out and taken them beforehand, all this was looked upon as quite a capital joke, and an essential part of the entertainment.

Dear, dear, what a place it looked, that Astley's; with all the paint, gilding, and looking-glass; the vague smell of horses suggestive of coming wonders; the curtain that hid such gorgeous mysteries; the clean white sawdust down in the circus; the company coming in and taking their places; the fiddlers looking carelessly up at them while they tuned their instruments, as if they didn't want the play to begin, and knew it all beforehand! What a glow was that, which burst upon them all, when that long, clear, brilliant row of lights came slowly up; and what the feverish excitement when the little bell rang and the music began in good earnest, with strong parts for the drums, and sweet effects for the triangles! Well might Barbara's mother say to Kit's mother that the gallery was the place to see from, and wonder it wasn't much dearer than the boxes, well might Barbara feel doubtful whether to laugh or cry, in her flutter of delight.

Then the play itself! the horses, which little Jacob believed from the first to be alive, and the ladies and gentlemen of whose reality he could be by no means persuaded, having never seen or heard any thing at all like them — the firing, which made Barbara wink — the forlorn lady, who made her cry — the tyrant, who made her tremble — the man who sang the song with the lady's-maid and danced the chorus, who made her laugh — the pony who reared up on his hind legs when he saw the murderer, and wouldn't hear of walking on all fours again until he was taken into custody — the clown who ventured on such familiarities with the military man in boots — the lady who jumped over the nine-and-twenty ribbons and came down safe upon the horse's back — every thing was delightful, splendid, and surprising! Little Jacob applauded till his hands were sore; Kit cried "an-kor" at the end of every thing, the three-act piece included; and Barbara's mother beat her umbrella on the floor, in her ecstasies, until it was nearly worn down to the gingham.

What was all this, though — even all this — to the extraordinary dissipation that ensued, when Kit, walking into an oyster-shop as bold as if he lived there, and not so much as looking at the counter or the man behind it, led his party into a box — a private box, fitted up with red curtains, white tablecloth, and cruet-stand complete — and ordered a fierce gentleman with whiskers, who acted as waiter and called him, him Christopher Nubbles, "sir," to bring three dozen of his largest-sized oysters, and to look sharp about it! Yes, Kit told this gentleman to look sharp, and he not only said he would look sharp, but he actually did, and presently came running back with the newest loaves, and the freshest butter, and the largest oysters, ever seen. Then said Kit to this gentleman, "a pot of beer" — just so — and the gentleman, instead of replying, "Sir, did you address that language to me?" only said, "Pot o' beer, sir? Yes, sir," and went off and fetched it, and put it on the table in a small decanter-stand, like those which blind-men's dogs carry about the streets in their mouths to catch the half-pence in; and both Kit's mother and Barbara's mother declared, as he turned away, that he was one of the slimmest and gracefullest young men she had ever looked upon.

Then they fell to work upon the supper in earnest; and there was Barbara, that foolish Barbara, declaring that she could not eat more than two, and wanting more pressing than you would believe before she would eat four: though her mother and Kit's mother made up for it pretty well, and ate and laughed and enjoyed themselves so thoroughly that it did Kit good to see them, and made him laugh and eat likewise from strong sympathy. But the greatest miracle of the night was little Jacob, who ate oysters as if he had been born and bred to the business — sprinkled the pepper and the vinegar with a discretion beyond his years — and afterward built a grotto on the table with the shells. There was the baby too, who had never closed an eye all night, but had sat as good as gold, trying to force a large orange into his mouth, and gazing intently at the lights in the chandelier — there he was, sitting up in his mother's lap, staring at the gas without winking, and making indentations in his soft visage with an oyster-shell, to that degree that a heart of iron must have loved him! In short, there never was a more successful supper; and when Kit ordered in a glass of something hot to finish with, and proposed Mr. and Mrs. Garland before sending it round, there were not six happier people in all the world.

NELL AMONG THE STROLLERS

[*Nell and her grandfather have left London almost penniless, and are making their way through rural England. In a churchyard, they meet the two Punch-and-Judy men introduced below.*]

The old man and the child quitted the gravel path, and strayed among the tombs; for there the ground was soft, and easy to their tired feet. As they passed behind the church, they heard voices near at hand, and presently came on those who had spoken.

They were two men who were seated in easy attitudes upon the grass, and so busily engaged as to be at first unconscious of intruders. It was not difficult to divine that they were of a class of itinerant showmen — exhibiters of the freaks of Punch — for, perched cross-legged upon a tombstone behind them, was a figure of that hero himself, his nose and chin as hooked and his face as beaming as usual. Perhaps his imperturbable character was never more strikingly developed, for he preserved his usual equable smile notwithstanding that his body was dangling in a most uncomfortable position, all loose and limp and shapeless, while his long peaked cap, unequally balanced against his exceedingly slight legs, threatened every instant to bring him toppling down.

In part scattered upon the ground at the feet of the two men, and in part jumbled together in a long flat box, were the other persons of the Drama. The hero's wife and one child, the hobby-horse, the doctor, the foreign gentleman who, not being familiar with the language, is unable in the representation to express his ideas otherwise than by the utterance of the word "Shallabalah" three distinct times, the radical neighbor who will by no means admit that a tin bell is an organ, the executioner, and the devil, were all here. Their owners had evidently come to that spot to make some needful repairs in the stage arrangements, for one of them was engaged in binding together a small gallows with thread, while the other was intent upon fixing a new black wig, with the aid of a small hammer and some tacks, upon the head of the radical neighbor, who had been beaten bald.

They raised their eyes when the old man and his young companion were close upon them, and pausing in their work, returned their looks of curiosity. One of them, the actual exhibiter, no doubt, was a little merry faced man with a twinkling eye and a red nose, who seemed to have unconsciously imbibed something of his hero's character. The other — that was he who took the money — had rather a careful and cautious look, which was perhaps inseparable from his occupation also.

The merry man was the first to greet the strangers with a nod; and following the old man's eyes, he observed that perhaps that was the first time he had ever seen a Punch off the stage. (Punch, it may be remarked, seemed to be pointing with the tip of his cap to a most flourishing epitaph, and to be chuckling over it with all his heart.)

"Why do you come here to do this?" said the old man, sitting down beside them, and looking at the figures with extreme delight.

"Why you see," rejoined the little man, "we're putting up for to-night at the public-house yonder, and it wouldn't do to let 'em see the present company undergoing repair."

"No!" cried the old man, making signs to Nell to listen, "why not, eh? why not?"

"Because it would destroy all the delusion, and take away all the interest, wouldn't it?" replied the little man. "Would you care a ha'penny for the Lord Chancellor if you know'd him in private and without his wig? — certainly not."

"Good!" said the old man, venturing to touch one of the puppets, and drawing away his hand with a shrill laugh. "Are you going to show 'em to-night? are you?"

"That is the intention, governor," replied the other, "and unless I'm much mistaken, Tommy Codlin is a-calculating at this minute what we've lost through your coming upon us. Cheer up, Tommy, it can't be much."

The little man accompanied these latter words with a wink, expressive of the estimate he had formed of the travelers' finances.

To this Mr. Codlin, who had a surly, grumbling manner, replied, as he twitched Punch off the tombstone and flung him into the box, "I don't care if we haven't lost a farden, but you're too free. If you stood in front of the curtain and see the public's faces as I do, you'd know human natur' better."

"Ah! it's been the spoiling of you, Tommy, your taking to that branch," rejoined his companion. "When you played the ghost in the reg'lar drama in the fairs, you believed in every thing — except ghosts. But now you're a universal mistruster. *I* never see a man so changed."

"Never mind," said Mr. Codlin, with the air of a discontented philosopher. "I know better now, and p'raps I'm sorry for it."

Turning over the figures in the box like one who knew and despised them, Mr. Codlin drew one forth and held it up for the inspection of his friend:

"Look here; here's all this Judy's clothes falling to pieces again. You haven't got a needle and thread, I suppose?"

The little man shook his head, and scratched it ruefully as he contemplated this severe indisposition of a principal performer. Seeing that they were at a loss, the child said, timidly:

"I have a needle, sir, in my basket, and thread too. Will you let me try to mend it for you? I think I could do it neater than you could."

Even Mr. Codlin had nothing to urge against a proposal so seasonable. Nelly, kneeling down beside the box, was soon busily engaged in her task, and accomplishing it to a miracle.

They had stopped to rest beneath a finger-post where four roads met, and Mr. Codlin in his deep misanthropy had let down the drapery and seated himself in the bottom of the show, invisible to mortal eyes and disdainful of the company of his fellow-creatures, when two monstrous shadows were seen stalking toward them from a turning in the road by which they had come. The child was at first quite terrified by the sight of these gaunt giants — for such they looked as they advanced with lofty strides beneath the shadow of the trees — but Short, telling her there was nothing to fear, blew a blast upon the trumpet, which was answered by a cheerful shout.

"It's Grinder's lot, ain't it?" cried Mr. Short, in a loud key.

"Yes," replied a couple of shrill voices.

"Come on, then," said Short. "Let's have a look at you. I thought it was you."

Thus invited, "Grinder's lot" approached with redoubled speed, and soon came up with the little party.

Mr. Grinder's company, familiarly termed a lot, consisted of a young gentleman and a young lady on stilts, and Mr. Grinder himself, who used his natural legs for pedestrian purposes and carried at his back a drum. The public costume of the young people was of the Highland kind, but the night being damp and cold, the young gentleman wore over his kilt a man's pea-jacket reaching to his ankles, and a glazed hat; the young lady too was muffled in an old cloth pelisse, and had a handkerchief tied about her head. Their Scotch bonnets, ornamented with plumes of jet-black feathers, Mr. Grinder carried on his instrument.

"Bound for the races, I see," said Mr. Grinder, coming up out of breath. "So are we. How are you, Short?" With that they shook hands in a very friendly manner. The young people being too high up for the ordinary salutations, saluted Short after their own fashion. The young gentleman twisted up his right stilt and patted him on the shoulder, and the young lady rattled her tambourine.

"Practice?" said Short, pointing to the stilts.

"No," returned Grinder. "It comes either to walkin' in 'em or carryin' of 'em, and they like walkin' in 'em best."

The Jolly Sandboys was a small road-side inn of pretty ancient date, with a sign, representing three Sandboys increasing their jollity with as many jugs of ale and bags of gold, creaking and swinging on its post on the opposite side of the road. As the travelers had observed that day many indications of their drawing nearer and nearer to the race-town, such as gypsy camps, carts laden with gambling booths and their appurtenances, itinerant showmen of various kinds, and beggars and trampers of every degree, all wending their way in the same direction, Mr. Codlin was fearful of finding the accommodations forestalled; this fear increasing as he diminished the distance between himself and the hostelry, he quickened his pace, and notwithstanding the burden he had to carry, maintained a round trot until he reached the threshold. Here he had the gratification of finding that his fears were without foundation, for the landlord was leaning against the door-post looking lazily at the rain, which had by this time begun to descend heavily, and no tinkling of cracked bell, nor boisterous shout, nor noisy chorus, gave note of company within.

A mighty fire was blazing on the hearth and roaring up the wide chimney with a cheerful sound, which a large iron caldron, bubbling and simmering in the heat, lent its pleasant aid to swell. There was a deep red ruddy blush upon the room, and when the landlord stirred the fire, sending the flames skipping and leaping up — when he took off the lid of the iron pot and there rushed out a savory smell, while the bubbling sound grew deeper and more rich, and an unctuous steam came floating out, hanging in a delicious mist above their heads — when he did this, Mr. Codlin's heart was touched. He sat down in the chimney-corner and smiled.

Mr. Codlin sat smiling in the chimney-corner, eying the landlord as with a roguish look he held the cover in his hand, and, feigning that his doing so was needful to the welfare of the cookery, suffered the delightful steam to tickle the nostrils of his guest. The glow of the fire was upon the landlord's bald head, and upon his twinkling eye, and upon his watering mouth, and upon his pimpled face, and upon his round, fat figure. Mr. Codlin drew his sleeve across his lips, and said, in a murmuring voice, "What is it?"

"It's a stew of tripe," said the landlord, smacking his lips, "and cow-heel," smacking them again, "and bacon," smacking them once more, "and steak," smacking them for the fourth time, "and peas, cauliflowers, new potatoes, and sparrow-grass, all working up together in one delicious gravy." . . . [Suddenly] strange footsteps were heard without, and fresh company entered.

These were no other than four very dismal dogs, who came pattering in one after the other, headed by an old bandy dog of particularly mournful aspect, who stopping when the last of his followers had got as far as the door, erected himself upon his hind legs and looked round at his companions, who immediately stood upon their hind legs, in a grave and melancholy row. Nor was this the only remarkable circumstance about these dogs, for each of them wore a kind of little coat of some gaudy color trimmed with tarnished spangles, and one of them had a cap upon his head, tied very carefully under his chin, which had fallen down upon his nose and completely obscured one eye; add to this, that the gaudy coats were all wet through and discolored with rain, and that the wearers were splashed and dirty, and some idea may be formed of the unusual appearance of these new visitors to the Jolly Sandboys.

Neither Short nor the landlord nor Thomas Codlin, however, was in the least surprised, merely remarking that these were Jerry's dogs, and that Jerry could not be far behind. So there the dogs stood, patiently winking and gaping and looking extremely hard at the boiling pot, until Jerry himself appeared, when they all dropped down at once and walked about the room in their natural manner. This posture it must be confessed did not much improve their appearance, as their own personal tails and their coat tails — both capital things in their way — did not agree together.

Jerry, the manager of these dancing dogs, was a tall black-whiskered man in a velveteen coat, who seemed well known to the landlord and his guests, and accosted them with great cordiality. Disencumbering himself of a barrel organ which he placed upon a chair, and retaining in his hand a small whip wherewith to awe his company of comedians, he came up to the fire to dry himself, and entered into conversation.

"Your people don't usually travel in character, do they?" said Short, pointing to the dresses of the dogs. "It must come expensive if they do?"

"No," replied Jerry, "no, it's not the custom with us. But we've been playing a little on the road today, and we come out with a new wardrobe at the races, so I didn't think it worth while to stop to undress. Down, Pedro!"

This was addressed to the dog with the cap on, who being a new member of the company, and not quite certain of his duty, kept his unobscured eye anxiously on his master, and was perpetually starting upon his hind legs when there was no occasion, and falling down again.

"I've got a animal here," said Jerry, putting his hand into the capacious pocket of his coat, and diving into one corner as if he were feeling for a small orange or an apple or some such article, "a animal here, wot I think you know something of, Short."

"Ah!" cried Short, "let's have a look at him."

"Here he is," said Jerry, producing a little terrier from his pocket. "He was once a Toby of yours, warn't he!"

In some versions of the great drama of Punch there is a small dog
— a modern innovation — supposed to be the private property of
that gentleman, whose name is always Toby. This Toby has been
stolen in youth from another gentleman, and fraudulently sold to the
confiding hero, who having no guile himself has no suspicion that it
lurks in others; but Toby, entertaining a grateful recollection of his
old master, and scorning to attach himself to any new patrons, not
only refuses to smoke a pipe at the bidding of Punch, but, to mark
his old fidelity more strongly, seizes him by the nose and wrings the
same with violence, at which instance of canine attachment the spectators are deeply affected. This was the character which the little terrier in question had once sustained; if there had been any doubt
upon the subject he would speedily have resolved it by his conduct;
for not only did he, on seeing Short, give the strongest tokens of
recognition, but catching sight of the flat box he barked so furiously
at the pasteboard nose which he knew was inside, that his master was
obliged to gather him up and put him into his pocket again, to the
great relief of the whole company.

The landlord now busied himself in laying the cloth, in which
process Mr. Codlin obligingly assisted by setting forth his own knife
and fork in the most convenient place and establishing himself behind them. When every thing was ready, the landlord took off the
cover for the last time, and then indeed there burst forth such a
goodly promise of supper, that if he had offered to put it on again
or had hinted at postponement, he would certainly have been sacri-
ficed on his own hearth.

However, he did nothing of the kind, but instead thereof assisted a
stout servant girl in turning the contents of the caldron into a large
tureen; a proceeding which the dogs, proof against various hot
splashes which fell upon their noses, watched with terrible eagerness.
At length the dish was lifted on the table, and mugs of ale having
been previously set round, little Nell ventured to say grace, and supper began.

At this juncture the poor dogs were standing on their hind legs
quite surprisingly; the child, having pity on them, was about to cast
some morsels of food to them before she tasted it herself, hungry
though she was, when their master interposed.

"No, my dear, no, not an atom from any body's hand but mine if you please. That dog," said Jerry, pointing out the old leader of the troop, and speaking in a terrible voice, "lost a half-penny to-day. *He* goes without his supper."

The unfortunate creature dropped upon his fore legs directly, wagged his tail, and looked imploringly at his master.

"You must be more careful, sir," said Jerry, walking coolly to the chair where he had placed the organ, and setting the stop. "Come here. Now, sir, you play away at that while we have supper, and leave off if you dare."

The dog immediately began to grind most mournful music. His master having shown him the whip, resumed his seat and called up the others, who, at his directions, formed in a row, standing upright as a file of soldiers.

"Now, gentlemen," said Jerry, looking at them attentively. "The dog whose name's called, eats. The dogs whose names ain't called, keep quiet. Carlo!"

The lucky individual whose name was called snapped up the morsel thrown toward him, but none of the others moved a muscle. In this manner they were fed at the discretion of their master. Meanwhile the dog in disgrace ground hard at the organ, sometimes in quick time, sometimes in slow, but never leaving off for an instant. When the knives and forks rattled very much, or any of his fellows got an unusually large piece of fat, he accompanied the music with a short howl, but he immediately checked it on his master looking round, and applied himself with increased diligence to the Old Hundredth.

[*In the course of their journey the old man and the child have met Mrs. Jarley, the kind-hearted proprietress of a traveling wax-work, who has offered to let them ride on with her in her caravan.*]

When they had traveled slowly forward for some short distance, Nell ventured to steal a look round the caravan and observe it more closely. One half of it — that moiety in which the comfortable proprietress was then seated — was carpeted, and so partitioned off at the farther end as to accommodate a sleeping-place, constructed after the fashion of a berth on board ship, which was shaded, like the little windows, with fair white curtains, and looked comfortable enough, though by what kind of gymnastic exercise the lady of the caravan ever contrived to get into it, was an unfathomable mystery. The other half served for a kitchen, and was fitted up with a stove whose small chimney passed through the roof. It held also a closet or larder, several chests, a great pitcher of water, and a few cooking utensils and articles of crockery. These latter necessaries hung upon the walls, which, in that portion of the establishment devoted to the lady of the caravan, were ornamented with such gayer and lighter decorations as a triangle and a couple of well-thumbed tambourines.

The lady of the caravan sat at one window in all the pride and poetry of the musical instruments, and little Nell and her grandfather sat at the other in all the humility of the kettle and saucepans, while the machine jogged on and shifted the darkening prospect very slowly. At first the two travelers spoke little, and only in whispers, but as they grew more familiar with the place they ventured to converse with greater freedom, and talked about the country through which they were passing, and the different objects that presented themselves, until the old man fell asleep; which the lady of the caravan observing, invited Nell to come and sit beside her.

"Well, child," she said, "how do you like this way of traveling?"

Nell replied that she thought it was very pleasant indeed, to which the lady assented in the case of people who had their spirits. For herself, she said, she was troubled with a lowness in that respect which required a constant stimulant; though whether the aforesaid stimulated was derived from the suspicious bottle of which mention has been already made or from other sources, she did not say.

"That's the happiness of you young people," she continued. "You don't know what it is to be low in your feelings. You always have your appetites too, and what a comfort that is."

Nell thought that she could sometimes dispense with her own appetite very conveniently; and thought, moreover, that there was nothing either in the lady's personal appearance or in her manner of taking tea, to lead to the conclusion that her natural relish for meat and drink had at all failed her. She silently assented, however, as in duty bound, to what the lady had said, and waited until she should speak again.

Instead of speaking, however, she sat looking at the child for a long time in silence, and then getting up, brought out from a corner a

large roll of canvas about a yard in width, which she laid upon the
floor and spread open with her foot until it nearly reached from one
end of the caravan to the other.

"There, child," she said, "read that."

Nell walked down it, and read aloud, in enormous black letters,
the inscription, "JARLEY'S WAX-WORK."

"Read it again," said the lady, complacently.

"Jarley's Wax-work," repeated Nell.

"That's me," said the lady. "I am Mrs. Jarley."

Giving the child an encouraging look, intended to reassure her,
and let her know that, although she stood in the presence of the
original Jarley, she must not allow herself to be utterly overwhelmed
and borne down, the lady of the caravan unfolded another scroll,
whereon was the inscription, "One hundred figures the full size of
life"; and then another scroll, on which was written, "The only stupendous collection of real wax-work in the world"; and then several
smaller scrolls, with such inscriptions as "Now exhibiting within" —
"The genuine and only Jarley" — "Jarley's unrivaled collection" —
"Jarley is the delight of the Nobility and Gentry" — "The Royal
Family are the patrons of Jarley." When she had exhibited these
leviathans of public announcement to the astonished child, she
brought forth specimens of the lesser fry in the shape of handbills,
some of which were couched in the form of parodies on popular
melodies, as "Believe me if all Jarley's wax-work so rare" — "I saw
thy show in youthful prime" — "Over the water to Jarley"; while, to
consult all tastes, others were composed with a view to the lighter and
more facetious spirits, as a parody on the favorite air of "If I had a
donkey," beginning

> If I know'd a donkey wot wouldn't go
> To see Mrs. JARLEY's wax-work show,
> Do you think I'd acknowledge him?
> Oh no, no!
> Then run to Jarley's —

besides several compositions in prose, purporting to be dialogues between the Emperor of China and an oyster, or the Archbishop of
Canterbury and a Dissenter on the subject of church-rates, but all
having the same moral, namely, that the reader must make haste to

Jarley's, and that children and servants were admitted at half-price. When she had brought all these testimonials of her important position in society to bear upon her young companion, Mrs. Jarley rolled them up, and having put them carefully away, sat down again, and looked at the child in triumph.

"Never go into the company of a filthy Punch any more," said Mrs. Jarley, "after this."

"I never saw any wax-work, ma'am," said Nell. "Is it funnier than Punch?"

"Funnier!" said Mrs. Jarley, in a shrill voice. "It is not funny at all."

"Oh!" said Nell, with all possible humility.

"It isn't funny at all," repeated Mrs. Jarley. "It's calm and — what's that word again — critical? — no — classical, that's it — it's calm and classical. No low beatings and knockings about, no jokings and squeakings like your precious Punches, but always the same, with a constantly unchanging air of coldness and gentility; and so like life, that if wax-work only spoke and walked about, you'd hardly know the difference. I won't go so far as to say that, as it is, I've seen wax-work quite like life, but I've certainly seen some life that was exactly like wax-work."

"Is it here, ma'am?" asked Nell, whose curiosity was awakened by this description.

"Is what here, child?"

"The wax-work, ma'am."

"Why, bless you, child, what are you thinking of? How could such a collection be here, where you see every thing except the inside of one little cupboard and a few boxes? It's gone on in the other wans to the assembly-rooms, and there it'll be exhibited the day after tomorrow. You are going to the same town, and you'll see it, I dare say. It's natural to expect that you'll see it, and I've no doubt you will. I suppose you couldn't stop away if you was to try ever so much."

Rumbling along with most unwonted noise, the caravan stopped at last at the place of exhibition, where Nell dismounted amidst an admiring group of children, who evidently supposed her to be an important item of the curiosities, and were fully impressed with the belief that her grandfather was a cunning device in wax. The chests

were taken out with all convenient dispatch, and taken in to be un-
locked by Mrs. Jarley, who, attended by George and another man in
velveteen shorts and a drab hat ornamented with turnpike tickets,
were waiting to dispose their contents (consisting of red festoons
and other ornamental devices in upholstery work) to the best advantage in the decoration of the room.

They all got to work without loss of time, and very busy they were.
As the stupendous collection were yet concealed by cloths, lest the
envious dust should injure their complexions, Nell bestirred herself to
assist in the embellishment of the room, in which her grandfather
also was of great service. The two men being well used to it, did a
great deal in a short time; and Mrs. Jarley served out the tin tacks
from a linen pocket like a toll-collector's which she wore for the purpose, and encouraged her assistants to renewed exertion.

When the festoons were all put up as tastily as they might be, the
stupendous collection was uncovered, and there were displayed, on a
raised platform some two feet from the floor, running round the
room and parted from the rude public by a crimson rope breast high,
divers sprightly effigies of celebrated characters, singly and in groups,
clad in glittering dresses of various climes and times, and standing
more or less unsteadily upon their legs, with their eyes very wide open,
and their nostrils very much inflated, and the muscles of their legs
and arms very strongly developed, and all their countenances expressing great surprise. All the gentlemen were very pigeon-breasted and
very blue about the beards; and all the ladies were miraculous figures;
and all the ladies and all the gentlemen were looking intensely nowhere, and staring with extraordinary earnestness at nothing.

When Nell had exhausted her first raptures at this glorious sight,
Mrs. Jarley ordered the room to be cleared of all but herself and the
child, and, sitting herself down in an arm-chair in the centre, formally
invested Nell with a willow wand, long used by herself for pointing
out the characters, and was at great pains to instruct her in her duty.

"That," said Mrs. Jarley, in her exhibition tone, as Nell touched a
figure at the beginning of the platform, "is an unfortunate Maid of
Honor in the Time of Queen Elizabeth, who died from pricking her
finger in consequence of working upon a Sunday. Observe the blood

which is trickling from her finger; also the gold-eyed needle of the period, with which she is at work."

All this Nell repeated twice or thrice — pointing to the finger and the needle at the right times; and then passed on to the next.

"That, ladies and gentlemen," said Mrs. Jarley, "is Jasper Packle-merton, of atrocious memory, who courted and married fourteen wives, and destroyed them all, by tickling the soles of their feet when they were sleeping in the consciousness of innocence and virtue. On being brought to the scaffold and asked if he was sorry for what he had done, he replied yes, he was sorry for having let 'em off so easy, and hoped all Christian husbands would pardon him the offense. Let this be a warning to all young ladies to be particular in the character of the gentlemen of their choice. Observe that his fingers are curled as if in the act of tickling, and that his face is represented with a wink, as he appeared when committing his barbarous murders."

When Nell knew all about Mr. Packlemerton, and could say it without faltering, Mrs. Jarley passed on to the fat man, and then to the thin man, the tall man, the short man, the old lady who died of dancing at a hundred and thirty-two, the wild boy of the woods, the woman who poisoned fourteen families with pickled walnuts, and other historical characters and interesting but misguided individuals. And so well did Nell profit by her instructions, and so apt was she to remember them, that by the time they had been shut up together for a couple of hours, she was in full possession of the history of the whole establishment, and perfectly competent to the enlightenment of visitors.

Mrs. Jarley was not slow to express her admiration at this happy result, and carried her young friend and pupil to inspect the remaining arrangements within doors, by virtue of which the passage had been already converted into a grove of green-baize hung with the inscription she had already seen (Mr. Slum's productions), and a highly ornamented table placed at the upper end for Mrs. Jarley herself, at which she was to preside and take the money, in company with his Majesty King George the Third, Mr. Grimaldi as clown, Mary Queen of Scots, an anonymous gentleman of the Quaker persuasion, and Mr. Pitt holding in his hand a correct model of the bill for the imposition of the window duty. The preparations without

doors had not been neglected either; a nun of great personal attrac-
tions was telling her beads on the little portico over the door; and a
brigand with the blackest possible head of hair, and the clearest possible complexion, was at that moment going round the town in a
cart, consulting the miniature of a lady.

Unquestionably Mrs. Jarley had an inventive genius. In the midst of
the various devices for attracting visitors to the exhibition, little Nell
was not forgotten. The light cart in which the Brigand usually made
his perambulations being gayly dressed with flags and streamers, and
the Brigand placed therein, contemplating the miniature of his beloved as usual, Nell was accommodated with a seat beside him, decorated with artificial flowers, and in this state and ceremony rode
slowly through the town every morning, dispersing handbills from a
basket, to the sound of drum and trumpet. The beauty of the child,
coupled with her gentle and timid bearing, produced quite a sensation in the little country place. The Brigand, heretofore a source of
exclusive interest in the streets, became a mere secondary consideration, and to be important only as a part of the show of which she
was the chief attraction. Grown-up folks began to be interested in
the bright-eyed girl, and some score of little boys fell desperately
in love, and constantly left inclosures of nuts and apples, directed in
small-text, at the wax-work door.

This desirable impression was not lost on Mrs. Jarley, who, lest
Nell should become too cheap, soon sent the Brigand out alone
again, and kept her in the exhibition-room, where she described the
figures every half-hour to the great satisfaction of admiring audiences.
And these audiences were of a very superior description, including a
great many young ladies' boarding-schools, whose favor Mrs. Jarley
had been at great pains to conciliate, by altering the face and costume
of Mr. Grimaldi as clown to represent Mr. Lindley Murray as he appeared when engaged in the composition of his English Grammar,
and turning a murderess of great renown into Mrs. Hannah More —
both of which likenesses were admitted by Miss Monflathers, who
was at the head of the head Boarding and Day Establishment in the
town, and who condescended to take a Private View with eight
chosen young ladies, to be quite startling from their extreme correct-
ness. Mr. Pitt in a night-cap and bed-gown, and without his boots,

represented the poet Cowper with perfect exactness; and Mary Queen of Scots in a dark wig, white shirt-collar, and male attire, was such a complete image of Lord Byron that the young ladies quite screamed when they saw it. Miss Monflathers, however, rebuked this enthusiasm, and took occasion to reprove Mrs. Jarley for not keeping her collection more select: observing that His Lordship had held certain opinions quite incompatible with wax-work honors, and adding something about a Dean and Chapter, which Mrs. Jarley did not understand.

Canadian Footlights

[*Dickens and Kate, his wife, arrived in Montreal, on the last leg of their American journey in 1842, during the afternoon or evening of May 11. The benefit theatrical performance he had arranged to give for a local charity took place at the Theatre Royal, renamed, for that night only, the Queen's Theatre, on May 25, before a brilliant audience five or six hundred strong, including Sir Charles Bagot, the Governor-General; Sir Richard Jackson, the Commander of the Forces; and the officers of the garrison and their families. It was repeated publicly on the twenty-eighth. In addition to Snobbington, in* Past Two O'Clock in the Morning, *Dickens himself played Alfred Highflyer in* A Roland for an Oliver *and Gallop in* Deaf as a Post.]

To C. C. FELTON

Niagara Falls, 29th April, 1842

What do you say to my *acting* at the Montreal Theatre? I am an old hand at such matters, and am going to join the officers of the garrison in a public representation for the benefit of a local charity. We shall have a good house, they say. I am going to enact one Mr. Snobbington in a funny farce called A Good Night's Rest. I shall want a flaxen wig and eyebrows; and my nightly rest is broken by visions of there being no such commodities in Canada. I wake in the dead of night in a cold perspiration, surrounded by imaginary barbers, all denying the existence or possibility of obtaining such articles. If ——— had a flaxen head, I would certainly have it shaved and get a wig and eyebrows out of him, for a small pecuniary compensation.

To Henry Austin

Sunday, First May, 1842

I suppose you have heard that I am going to act at the Montreal theatre with the officers? Farce-books being scarce, and the choice consequently limited, I have selected Keeley's part in Two o'Clock in the Morning. I wrote yesterday to Mitchell, the actor and manager at New York, to get and send me a comic wig, light flaxen, with a small whisker halfway down the cheek; over this I mean to wear two night-caps, one with a tassel and one of flannel; a flannel wrapper, drab tights and slippers, will complete the costume.

To John Forster

Twelfth May [1842]

The Theatricals . . . are, A Roland for an Oliver; Two o'clock in the Morning; and either the Young Widow, or Deaf as a Post. Ladies (unprofessional) are going to play, for the first time. I wrote to Mitchell at New York for a wig for Mr. Snobbington, which has arrived, and is brilliant. If they had done Love, Law and Physick, as at first proposed, I was already "up" in Flexible, having played it of old, before my authorship days; but if it should be Splash in the Young Widow, you will have to do me the favor to imagine me in a smart livery-coat, shiny black hat and cockade, white knee-cords, white top-boots, blue stock, small whip, red cheeks and dark eyebrows. Conceive Topping's state of mind if I bring this dress home and put it on unexpectedly!

To C. C. Felton

Twenty-First May, 1842

The wig and whiskers are in a state of the highest preservation. The play comes off next Wednesday night, the twenty-fifth. What would I give to see you in the front row of the centre box, your spectacles gleaming not unlike those of my dear friend Pickwick, your face radiant with as broad a grin as a staid professor may indulge in, and your very coat, waistcoat, and shoulders expressive of what we should take together when the performance was over! I would give something (not so much, but still a good round sum) if you could only stumble into that very dark and dusty theatre in the daytime (at any minute between twelve and three), and see me with my coat off, the stage manager and universal director, urging impracticable ladies and impossible gentlemen on to the very confines of insanity, shouting and driving about, in my own person, to an extent which would justify any philanthropic stranger in clapping me into a strait-waistcoat without further inquiry, endeavouring to goad Putnam into some dim and faint understanding of a prompter's duties, and struggling in such a vortex of noise, dirt, bustle, confusion, and inextricable entanglement of speech and action as you would grow giddy in contemplating. We perform A Roland for an Oliver, A Good Night's Rest, and Deaf as a Post. This kind of voluntary hard labour used to be my great delight. The *furor* has come strong upon me again, and I begin to be once more of opinion that nature intended me for the lessee of a national theatre, and that pen, ink, and paper have spoiled a manager.

To John Forster

Twenty-Sixth of May [1842]

The play came off last night. The audience, between five and six hundred strong, were invited as to a party; a regular table with refreshments being spread in the lobby and saloon. We had the band of the twenty-third (one of the finest in the service) in the orchestra, the theatre was lighted with gas, the scenery was excellent, and the properties were all brought from private houses. Sir Charles Bagot, Sir Richard Jackson, and their staffs were present; and as the military portion of the audience were all in full uniform, it was really a splendid scene.

We "went" also splendidly; though with nothing very remarkable in the acting way. We had for Sir Mark Chase a genuine odd fish, with plenty of humour; but our Tristram Sappy was not up to the marvellous reputation he has somehow or other acquired here. I am not, however, let me tell you, placarded as a stage-manager for nothing. Everybody was told they would have to submit to the most iron despotism; and didn't I come Macready over them? Oh no. By no means. Certainly not. The pains I have taken with them, and the perspiration I have extended, during the last ten days, exceed in amount anything you can imagine. I had regular plots of the scenery made out, and lists of the properties wanted; and had them nailed up by the prompter's chair. Every letter that was to be delivered, was written; every piece of money that had to be given, provided; and not a single thing lost sight of. I prompted, myself, when I was not on; when I was, I made the regular prompter of the theatre my deputy; and I never saw anything so perfectly touch and go, as the first two pieces. The bedroom scene in the interlude was as well furnished as Vestris had it; with a "practicable" fireplace blazing away like mad, and everything in a concatenation accordingly. I really do believe that I was very funny: at least I know that I laughed heartily at myself, and made the part a character, such as you and I know very well: a mixture of T——, Harley, Yates, Keeley, and Jerry Sneak. It went with a roar, all through; and, as I am closing this, they have told me I was so well made up that Sir Charles Bagot, who sat in the stagebox, had no idea who played Mr. Snobbington, until the piece was over.

But only think of Kate playing! and playing devilish well, I assure! All the ladies were capital, and we had no wait or hitch for an instant. You may suppose this, when I tell you that we began at eight, and had the curtain down at eleven. It is their custom here, to prevent heartburnings in a very heartburning town, whenever they have played in private, to repeat the performances in public. So, on Saturday (substituting, of course, real actresses for the ladies), we repeat the two first pieces to a paying audience, for the manager's benefit. . . .

I have not told you half enough. But I promise you I shall make you shake your sides about this play. Wasn't it worthy of Crummles that when Lord Mulgrave and I went out to the door to receive the Governor-general, the regular prompter followed us in agony with four tall candlesticks with wax candles in them, and besought us with a bleeding heart to carry two apiece, in accordance with all the precedents?

Transcendental Symposium

[*Though not strictly theater, the following episode from* Martin Chuzzlewit, *inspired by some of Dickens's experiences in the United States, is certainly public entertainment and is so ludicrous that we have been unable to resist it. The Honorable Elijah Pogram, the two Literary Ladies, and the Mother of the Modern Gracchi, all wallowing out of their intellectual depth and piling up billows of verbiage that they imagine to be poetry and philosophy, form a hilariously outrageous spectacle. The passage is from Chapter 34 of the novel, which was published in monthly installments between January 1843 and July 1844.*

This gathering takes place at the National Hotel in an Ohio river town. The Honorable Elijah Pogram is a member of Congress, Mrs. Hominy a lady whom Martin and his servant Mark Tapley had met earlier in their journey.]

. . . It was suddenly determined to pounce upon the Honourable Elijah Pogram, and give *him* a le-vee forthwith.

As the general evening meal of the house was over before the arrival of the boat, Martin, Mark, and Pogram, were taking tea and fixings at the public table by themselves, when the deputation entered, to announce this honour: consisting of six gentlemen boarders, and a very shrill boy.

"Sir!" said the spokesman.

"Mr. Pogram!" cried the shrill boy.

The spokesman thus reminded of the shrill boy's presence, introduced him. "Doctor Ginery Dunkle, Sir. A gentleman of great poetical elements. He has recently jined us here, Sir, and is an acquisition

THE DANCING ACADEMY

Cruikshank — *Sketches by Boz*

MRS. JOSEPH PORTER

Cruikshank — *Sketches by Boz*

PRIVATE THEATRES

Cruikshank — *Sketches by Boz*

THE COUNTRY MANAGER REHEARSES A COMBAT
Phiz — *Nicholas Nickleby*

NICHOLAS INSTRUCTS SMIKE IN THE ART OF ACTING

Phiz — *Nicholas Nickleby*

THE GREAT BESPEAK FOR MISS SNEVELLICCI

Phiz — *Nicholas Nickleby*

NICHOLAS HINTS AT THE PROBABILITY OF HIS LEAVING THE COMPANY

Phiz — *Nicholas Nickleby*

THEATRICAL EMOTION OF MR. VINCENT CRUMMLES
Phiz — *Nicholas Nickleby*

THEATRE ROYAL,

MANCHESTER.

DRESS CIRCLE	SEVEN SHILLINGS.
PIT STALLS	SEVEN SHILLINGS.
UPPER CIRCLE	FIVE SHILLINGS.
PIT	THREE SHILLINGS.
GALLERY	TWO SHILLINGS.
UPPER GALLERY	ONE SHILLING.

The Performance to commence at Seven o'Clock exactly, by which time it is particularly requested that the whole of the Audience may be seated. An interval of few minutes between the close at each play and the commencement of the Overture to the next.

FOR THE BENEFIT OF
MR. LEIGH HUNT,

"Who, after years of ill health and hard struggle, is not, without this assistance, released from difficulty by a Pension granted late in life."

"It is proposed to devote a portion of the proceeds of this Benefit to the assistance of another celebrated Writer, whose literary career is at an end, and who has no provision for the decline of his life."—*Circular originally issued in London.*

On Monday Evening, July 26, 1847,

Will be presented, Ben Jonson's Comedy of

EVERY MAN
IN HIS HUMOUR.

Kitely	Mr. JOHN FORSTER.
Old Knowell	Mr. G. H. LEWES.
Young Knowell (His Son)	Mr. FREDERICK DICKENS.
Wellbred	Mr. T. J. THOMPSON.
Master Stephen	Mr. DOUGLAS JERROLD.
Master Matthew	Mr. JOHN LEACH.
Justice Clement	Mr. DUDLEY COSTELLO.
Downright	Mr. FRANK STONE.
Captain Bobadil	Mr. CHARLES DICKENS.
Cash	Mr. AUGUSTUS DICKENS.
Formal	Mr. AUGUSTUS EGG.
Cob	Mr. GEORGE CRUIKSHANK.
Brainworm	Mr. MARK LEMON.
Mrs. Kitely	Miss EMMELINE MONTAGUE.
Bridget	Mrs. A. WIGAN.
(Of the Theatre-Royal English Opera House)	
Tib	Mrs. CAULFIELD
(Of the Theatre-Royal, Haymarket.)	

Previous to the Comedy, an ADDRESS, written for the occasion by Mr. Sergeant TALFOURD, will be spoken by Mr. CHARLES DICKENS.

Prior to the Comedy, the Overture to	"Fra Diavolo."
Prior to the Interlude the Overture to	"La Gazza Ladra,"
Prior to the Farce, the Overture to	"Massaniello."

MUSICAL DIRECTOR & LEADER - MR. SEYMOUR.

After the Comedy, the Interlude called

A GOOD NIGHT'S REST;
OR, TWO O'CLOCK IN THE MORNING.

Mr. Snobbington	Mr. CHARLES DICKENS.
The Stranger	Mr. MARK LEMON.

To conclude with Mr. Poole's Farce of

TURNING THE TABLES

Mr. Knibbs	Mr. GEO. CRUIKSHANK.
Jeremiah Bumps	Mr. CHARLES DICKENS.
Edgar de Courcy	Mr. DUDLEY COSTELLO.
Tom Thornton (His Friend)	Mr. FREDERICK DICKENS.
Jack Humphries	Mr. G. H. LEWES,
Miss Knibbs (with a Song)	Miss ROMER.
Patty Larkins	Mrs. A. WIGAN.
Mrs. Humphries	Mrs. CAULFIELD.

No Seats will be reserved in the Dress Stalls or Upper Circle after the termination of the first act.

NOTICE.—The Address written by Mr Sergeant Talfourd, and spoken by Mr Charles Dickens, will be published in Manchester, on Monday Evening, by Mr. Abel Heywood, and Messrs. Simms and Dinham. It will also be on Sale at the Theatre after the first act of the Comedy. Price One Shilling; the profits in aid of the benefit.

LOWES AND Co., PRINTERS, 14, LLOYD STREET, MANCHESTER.

PLAYBILL OF THE LEIGH HUNT BENEFIT
which Dickens organized

CHARLES DICKENS AS CAPTAIN BOBADIL

in Ben Jonson's *Every Man in His Humour* — from the painting by C. R. Leslie, R.A.

Mr. Charles Dickens's Last Reading

CHARLES DICKENS EXHAUSTED
after one of his readings — from the drawing by Harry Furniss

to us, Sir, I do assure you. Yes, Sir. Mr. Jodd, Sir. Mr. Izzard, Sir. Mr. Julius Bib, Sir."

"Julius Washington Merryweather Bib," said the gentleman himself *to* himself.

"I beg your pardon, Sir. Ex-cuse me. Mr. Julius Washington Merryweather Bib, Sir; a gentleman in the lumber line, Sir, and much esteemed. Colonel Groper, Sir. Pro-fessor Piper, Sir. My own name, Sir, is Oscar Buffum."

Each man took one slide forward as he was named; butted at the Honourable Elijah Pogram with his head; shook hands, and slid back again. The introductions being completed, the spokesman resumed.

"Sir!"

"Mr. Pogram!" cried the shrill boy.

"Perhaps," said the spokesman, with a hopeless look, "you will be so good, Dr. Ginery Dunkle, as to charge yourself with the execution of our little office, Sir?"

As there was nothing the shrill boy desired more, he immediately stepped forward.

"Mr. Pogram! Sir! A handful Of your fellow citizens, Sir, hearing Of your arrival at the National Hotel; and feeling the patriotic character Of your public services; wish, Sir, to have the gratification Of beholding you; and mixing with you, Sir; and unbending with you, Sir, in those moments which —"

"Air," suggested Buffum.

"Which air so peculiarly the lot, Sir, Of our great and happy country."

"Hear!" cried Colonel Groper, in a loud voice. "Good! Hear him! Good!"

"And therefore, Sir," pursued the Doctor, "they request; as A mark Of their respect; the honour of your company at a little le-Vee, Sir, in the ladies' ordinary, at eight o'clock."

Mr. Pogram bowed, and said:

"Fellow countrymen!"

"Good!" cried the Colonel. "Hear him! Good!"

Mr. Pogram bowed to the Colonel individually, and then resumed:

"Your approbation of My labors in the common cause, goes to My heart. At all times and in all places; in the ladies' ordinary, My friends, and in the Battle Field —"

"Good, very good! Hear him! Hear him!" said the Colonel.

"The name Of Pogram will be proud to jine you. And may it, My friends, be written on My tomb, 'He was a member of the Con-gress of our common country, and was ac-Tive in his trust.' "

"The Com-mittee, Sir," said the shrill boy, "will wait upon you at five minutes afore eight. I take My leave, Sir!"

Mr. Pogram shook hands with him, and everybody else, once more; and when they came back again at five minutes before eight, they said, one by one, in a melancholy voice, "How do you do, Sir?" and shook hands with Mr. Pogram all over again, as if he had been abroad for a twelvemonth in the meantime, and they met, now, at a funeral.

But by this time Mr. Pogram had freshened himself up, and had composed his hair and features after the Pogram statue, so that any one with half an eye might cry out, "There he is! as he delivered the Defiance!" The Committee were embellished also; and when they entered the ladies' ordinary in a body, there was much clapping of hands from ladies and gentlemen, accompanied by cries of "Pogram! Pogram!" and some standing up on chairs to see him.

The object of the popular caress looked round the room as he walked up it, and smiled: at the same time observing to the shrill boy, that he knew something of the beauty of the daughters of their common country, but had never seen it in such lustre and perfection as at that moment. Which the shrill boy put in the paper next day; to Elijah Pogram's great surprise.

"We will re-quest you, Sir, if you please," said Buffum, laying hands on Mr. Pogram as if he were taking his measure for a coat, "to stand up with your back agin the wall right in the furthest corner, that there may be more room for our fellow cit-izens. If you could set your back right slap agin that curtain-peg, Sir, keeping your left leg everlastingly behind the stove, we should be fixed quite slick."

Mr. Pogram did as he was told, and wedged himself into such a little corner, that the Pogram statue wouldn't have known him.

The entertainments of the evening then began. Gentlemen brought ladies up, and brought themselves up, and brought each other up; and asked Elijah Pogram what he thought of this political question, and what he thought of that; and looked at him, and looked at one another, and seemed very unhappy indeed. The ladies on the chairs looked at Elijah Pogram through their glasses, and said audibly, "I wish he'd speak. Why don't he speak. Oh, do ask him to speak!" And Elijah Pogram looked sometimes at the ladies and sometimes elsewhere, delivering senatorial opinions, as he was asked for them. But the great end and object of the meeting seemed to be, not to let Elijah Pogram out of the corner on any account: so there they kept him, hard and fast.

A great bustle at the door, in the course of the evening, announced the arrival of some remarkable person; and immediately afterwards an elderly gentleman, much excited, was seen to precipitate himself upon the crowd, and battle his way towards the Honourable Elijah Pogram. Martin, who had found a snug place of observation in a distant corner, where he stood with Mark beside him (for he did not so often forget him now as formerly, though he still did sometimes), thought he knew this gentleman, but had no doubt of it, when he cried as loud as he could, with his eyes starting out of his head:

"Sir, Mrs. Hominy!

"Lord bless that woman, Mark. She has turned up again!"

"Here she comes, Sir," answered Mr. Tapley. "Pogram knows her. A public character! Always got her eye upon her country, Sir! If that there lady's husband is of my opinion, what a jolly old gentleman he must be!"

A lane was made; and Mrs. Hominy, with the aristocratic stalk, the pocket handkerchief, the clasped hands, and the classical cap, came slowly up it, in a procession of one. Mr. Pogram testified emotions of delight on seeing her, and a general hush prevailed. For it was known that when a woman like Mrs. Hominy encountered a man like Pogram, something interesting must be said.

Their first salutations were exchanged in a voice too low to reach the impatient ears of the throng; but they soon became audible, for Mrs. Hominy felt her position, and knew what was expected of her.

Mrs. H. was hard upon him at first; and put him through a rigid catechism, in reference to a certain vote he had given, which she had found it necessary, as the mother of the modern Gracchi, to deprecate in a line by itself, set up expressly for the purpose in German text. But Mr. Pogram evading it by a well-timed allusion to the star-spangled banner, which, it appeared, had the remarkable peculiarity of flouting the breeze whenever it was hoisted where the wind blew, she forgave him. They now enlarged on certain questions of tariff, commercial treaty, boundary, importation, and exportation, with great effect. And Mrs. Hominy not only talked, as the saying is, like a book, but actually did talk her own books, word for word.

"My! what is this?" cried Mrs. Hominy, opening a little note which was handed her by her excited gentleman-usher. "Do tell! oh, well, now! on'y think!"

And then she read aloud, as follows:

"Two literary ladies present their compliments to the mother of the modern Gracchi, and claim her kind introduction, as their talented countrywoman, to the honourable (and distinguished) Elijah Pogram, whom the two L.L.'s have often contemplated in the speaking marble of the soul-subduing Chiggle. On a verbal intimation from the mother of the M.G., that she will comply with the request of the two L.L.'s, they will have the immediate pleasure of joining the galaxy assembled to do honour to the patriotic conduct of a Pogram. It may be another bond of union between the two L.L.'s and the mother of the M.G. to observe, that the two L.L.'s are Transcendental."

Mrs. Hominy promptly rose, and proceeded to the door, whence she returned, after a minute's interval, with the two L.L.'s, whom she led, through the lane in the crowd, with all that stateliness of deportment which was so remarkably her own, up to the great Elijah Pogram. It was (as the shrill boy cried out in an ecstacy) quite the Last Scene from Coriolanus.

One of the L.L.'s wore a brown wig of uncommon size. Sticking on the forehead of the other, by invisible means, was a massive cameo, in size and shape like the raspberry tart which is ordinarily sold for a penny, representing on its front the Capitol at Washington.

"Miss Toppit, and Miss Codger!" said Mrs. Hominy.

"Codger's the lady so often mentioned in the English newspapers, I should think, Sir," whispered Mark. "The oldest inhabitant, as never remembers anything."

"To be presented to a Pogram," said Miss Codger, "by a Hominy, indeed, a thrilling moment is it in its impressiveness on what we call our feelings. But why we call them so, or why impressed they are, or if impressed they are at all, or if at all we are, or if there really is, oh gasping one! a Pogram or a Hominy, or any active principle to which we give those titles, is a topic, Spirit searching, light abandoned, much too vast to enter on, at this unlooked for crisis."

"Mind and matter," said the lady in the wig, "glide swift into the vortex of immensity. Howls the sublime, and softly sleeps the calm Ideal, in the whispering chambers of Imagination. To hear it, sweet it is. But then, outlaughs the stern philosopher, and saith to the Grotesque, 'What ho! arrest for me that Agency. Go, bring it here!' And so the vision fadeth."

After this, they both took Mr. Pogram by the hand, and pressed it to their lips, as a patriotic palm. That homage paid, the mother of the modern Gracchi called for chairs, and the three literary ladies went to work in earnest, to bring poor Pogram out, and make him show himself in all his brilliant colours.

How Pogram got out of his depth instantly, and how the three L.L.'s were never in theirs, is a piece of history not worth recording. Suffice it, that being all four out of their depths, and all unable to swim, they splashed up words in all directions, and floundered about famously. On the whole, it was considered to have been the severest mental exercise ever heard in the National Hotel. Tears stood in the shrill boy's eyes several times; and the whole company observed that their heads ached with the effort — as well they might.

When it at last became necessary to release Elijah Pogram from the corner, and the Committee saw him safely back again to the next room, they were fervent in their admiration.

"Which," said Mr. Buffum, "must have vent, or it will bust. Toe you, Mr. Pogram, I am grateful. Toe-wards you, Sir, I am inspired with lofty veneration, and with deep e-mo-tion. The sentiment Toe which I would propose to give ex-pression, Sir, is this: 'May you ever be as firm, Sir, as your marble statter! May it ever be as great a terror Toe its ene-mies as you.' "

There is some reason to suppose that it was rather terrible to its friends; being a statue of the Elevated or Goblin School, in which the Honourable Elijah Pogram was represented as in a very high wind, with his hair all standing on end, and his nostrils blown wide open. But Mr. Pogram thanked his friend and countryman for the aspiration to which he had given utterance, and the Committee, after another solemn shaking of hands, retired to bed, except the Doctor; who immediately repaired to the newspaper-office, and there wrote a short poem suggested by the events of the evening, beginning with fourteen stars, and headed, "A Fragment. Suggested by witnessing the Honourable Elijah Pogram engaged in a philosophical disputation with three of Columbia's fairest daughters. By Doctor Ginery Dunkle. Of Troy."

The Patrician's Daughter

[The Patrician's Daughter *was a play by a twenty-three-year-old author named Westland Marston. Though in verse, instead of being a costume drama it was a poetic tragedy of modern life. Macready produced it at Drury Lane in December 1842.*]

To W. C. Macready

Twelfth November, 1842

You pass this house every day on your way to or from the theatre. I wish you would call once as you go by — and soon, that you may have plenty of time to deliberate on what I wish to suggest to you. The more I think of Marston's play, the more sure I feel that a prologue, to the purpose, would help it materially, and almost decide the fate of any ticklish point on the first night. Now I have an idea (not easily explainable in writing, but told in five words), that would take the prologue out of the conventional dress of prologues — quite — get the curtain up with a dash — and begin the play with a sledge-hammer blow. If, on consideration, you should think with me, I will write the prologue, heartily.

[1842]

One suggestion, though it be a late one. Do have upon the table, in the opening scene of the second act, something in a velvet case, or frame, that may look like a large miniature of Mabel, such as one of Ross's, and eschew that picture. It haunted me with a sense of danger. Even a titter at that critical time, with the whole of that act before you, would be a fatal thing. The picture is bad in itself, bad in its effect upon the beautiful room, bad in all its associations with the house. In case of your having nothing at hand, I send you by bearer what would be a million times better.

FROM DICKENS'S PROLOGUE:

No tale of streaming plume and harness bright
Dwells on the poet's maiden harp tonight,
No trumpet's clamour and no battle's fire
Breathes in the trembling accents of his lyre . . .

Awake the Present! Though the steel-clad age
Find life alone within its storied page,
Iron is worn, at heart, by many still —
The tyrant Custom binds the serf-like will;
If sharp rack, and screw, and chain be gone
These latter days have tortures of their own;
The guiltless writhe, while Guilt is stretched in sleep,
And Virtue lies, too often, dungeon deep.

A Blot on the 'Scutcheon

[*The manuscript of Browning's poetic drama had been confided to John Forster, who lent it to Dickens. The play was produced by Macready at Drury Lane on February 11, 1843.*]

To John Forster

25th November 1842

. . . Browning's play, has thrown me into a perfect passion of sorrow. To say that there is anything in its subject save what is lovely, true, deeply affecting, full of the best emotion, the most earnest feeling, and the most true and tender source of interest, is to say that there is no light in the sun, and no heat in blood. It is full of genius, natural and great thoughts, profound and yet simple and beautiful in its vigour. I know nothing that is so affecting, nothing in any book I have ever read, as Mildred's recurrence to that "I was so young — I had no mother." I know no love like it, no passion like it, no moulding of a splendid thing after its conception, like it. And I swear it is a tragedy that MUST be played; and must be played, moreover, by Macready. There are some things I would have changed if I could (they are very slight, mostly broken lines); and I assuredly would have the old servant *begin his tale upon the scene*; and be taken by the throat, or drawn upon, by its master, in its commencement. But the tragedy I never shall forget, or less vividly remember than I do now. And if you tell Browning that I have seen it, tell him that I believe from my soul there is no man living (and not many dead) who could produce such a work. — Macready likes the altered prologue very much.

An Imaginary Play

[*Benjamin Webster, the manager of the Haymarket Theatre, had offered £500 for the best English comedy submitted to him. Dickens was at the time deep in the publication of* Martin Chuzzlewit; *dropping the novel to write a play is, of course, simply a high-spirited joke.*]

To Douglas Jerrold

Thirteenth June 1843

Yes. You have anticipated my occupation. Chuzzlewit be damned, — High Comedy and five hundred pounds are the only matters I can think of. I call it "The One Thing Needful, or a Part is better than the Whole." Here are the characters:

Old Febrile	Mr. Farren.
Young Febrile (his son)	Mr. Howe.
Jack Hessians (his friend)	Mr. W. Lacey.
Chalks (a landlord)	Mr. Gough.
Hon. Harry Staggers	Mr. Mellon.
Sir Thomas Tip	Mr. Buckstone.
Swig	Mr. Webster.
The Duke of Leeds	Mr. Coutts.
Sir Smivin Growler	Mr. Macready.

Servants, gamblers, visitors, etc.

Mrs. Febrile	Mrs. Gallot.
Lady Tip	Mrs. Humby.

Mrs. Sour   Miss W. Clifford.
Fanny   Miss F. A. Smith.

One scene, where old Febrile tickles Lady Tip in the ribs, and afterwards dances out with his hat behind him, his stick before, and his eye on the pit, I expect will bring the house down. There is also another point — where old Febrile, at the conclusion of his disclosures to Swig, rises and says "And now, Swig, tell me, have I acted well?" and Swig says "Well, Mr. Febrile, have you ever acted Ill?" — which will carry off the piece. . . .

. . . I walk up and down the street at the back of the Theatre every night and peep in at the Green Room window — thinking of the time when "Dick — INS" will be called for by excited hundreds, and won't come — 'till Mr. Webster (half Swig and half himself) shall enter from his dressing room, and quelling the tempest with a smile, beseech that wizard if he be in the house (here he looks up at my box) to accept the congratulations of the audience, and indulge them with a sight of the man who has got five hundred pounds in money and it is impossible to say how much in laurels. Then I shall come forward and bow once — twice — thrice — roars of approbation — Brayvo — Brarvo — Hooray — Hoorar — Hooroar — one cheer more — and asking Webster home to supper shall declare eternal friendship for that public-spirited individual — which Talfourd (the Vice) will echo with all his heard and soul and with tears in his eyes; adding in a perfectly audible voice, and in the same breath, that "he's a vewy wetched cweature, but better than Macweady, anyway, for *he* wouldn't play Ion when it was given to him" — after which he will propose said Macweady's health in terms of red hot eloquence. . . .

. . . Faithfully your friend, — The Congreve of the 19th century, — (which I mean to be called in the Sunday papers).

P.S. — I shall dedicate it to Webster, beginning "My dear Sir, when you first proposed to stimulate the slumbering dramatic talent of England, I assure you I had not the least idea" . . .

Birthday Conjuring

[*Throughout the latter part of 1843 and into 1844 Macready was on theatrical tour in America. The birthday party Dickens describes was for Macready's daughter Nina.*]

To W. C. MACREADY

Third January, 1844

You know all the news, and you know I love you; so I no more know why I write than I do why I "come round" after the play to shake hands with you in your dressing-room. I say *come*, as if you were at this present moment the lessee of Drury Lane, and had Jones with a long face on one hand, Smith elaborately explaining that everything in creation is a joint-stock company on the other, the Inimitable B. by the fire, in conversation with Serle, and Forster confidential with everybody about nothing in particular. Well-a-day! I see it all, and smell that extraordinary compound of odd scents peculiar to a theatre, which bursts me when I swing open the little door in the hall; accompanies me as I meet perspiring supers in the narrow passage; goes with me up the two steps; crosses the stage; winds round the third entrance P.S. as I wind; and escorts me safely into your presence, where I find you unwinding something slowly round and round your chest, which is so long that no man can see the end of it.

Oh that you had been at Clarence Terrace on Nina's birthday! Good God, how we missed you, talked of you, drank your health, and wondered what you were doing! Perhaps you are Falkland enough (I swear I suspect you of it) to feel rather sore — just a little bit, you know, the merest trifle in the world — on hearing that Mrs. Macready looked brilliant, blooming, young, and handsome, and that she danced a country dance with the writer hereof (Acres to your Falkland) in a thorough spirit of becoming good humour and enjoyment. Now you don't like to be told that? Nor do you quite like to hear that Forster and I conjured bravely; that a plum-pudding was produced from an empty saucepan, held over a blazing fire kindled in Stanfield's hat without damage to the lining; that a box of bran was changed into a live Guinea-Pig, which ran between my godchild's feet, and was the cause of such a shrill uproar and clapping of hands that you might have heard it (and I daresay did) in America; that three half-crowns being taken from Major Burns and put into a tumbler-glass before his eyes, did then and there give jingling answers to the questions asked of them by me, and knew where you were and what you were doing; to the unspeakable admiration of the whole assembly. Neither do you quite like to be told that we are going to do it again next Saturday, with the addition of Demoniacal dresses from a Masquerade Shop; nor that Mrs. Macready, for her gallant bearing always, and her best sort of best affection, is the best creature I know. Never mind. No man shall gag me; and those are my opinions. . . .

Italian Marionettes

[*Dickens lived in Italy from July 1844 to June 1845, renting first the Villa di Bella Vista (which he called "the Pink Jail") at Albaro, and later the Palazzo Peschiere above Genoa. His Italian theatrical experiences are from the chapter "Genoa and Its Neighborhood" in* Pictures from Italy.]

There are three theatres in the city, besides an old one now rarely opened. The most important — the Carlo Felice: the operahouse of Genoa — is a very splendid, commodious, and beautiful theatre. A company of comedians were acting there, when we arrived: and after their departure, a second-rate opera company came. The great season is not until the carnival time — in the spring. Nothing impressed me, so much, in my visits here (which were pretty numerous) as the uncommonly hard and cruel character of the audience, who resent the slightest defect, take nothing good-humouredly, seem to be always lying in wait for an opportunity to hiss, and spare the actresses as little as the actors. But, as there is nothing else of a public nature at which they are allowed to express the least disapprobation, perhaps they are resolved to make the most of this opportunity.

There are a great number of Piedmontese officers too, who are allowed the privilege of kicking their heels in the pit, for next to nothing: gratuitous, or cheap accommodation for these gentlemen being insisted on, by the Governor, in all public or semi-public entertainments. They are lofty critics in consequence, and infinitely more exacting than if they made the unhappy manager's fortune.

The TEATRO DIURNO, or Day Theatre, is a covered stage in the open air, where the performances take place by daylight, in the cool of the afternoon; commencing at four or five o'clock, and lasting some three hours. It is curious, sitting among the audience, to have a fine view of the neighbouring hills and houses, and to see the neighbours at their windows looking on, and to hear the bells of the churches and convents ringing at most complete cross-purposes with the scene. Beyond this, and the novelty of seeing a play in the fresh pleasant air, with the darkening evening closing in, there is nothing very exciting or characteristic in the performances. The actors are indifferent; and though they sometimes represent one of Goldoni's comedies, the staple of the Drama is French. Anything like nationality is dangerous to despotic governments, and Jesuit-beleaguered kings.

The Theatre of Puppets, or Marionetti — a famous company from Milan — is, without any exception, the drollest exhibition I ever beheld in my life. I never saw anything so exquisitely ridiculous. They *look* between four and five feet high, but are really much smaller; for when a musician in the orchestra happens to put his hat on the stage, it becomes alarmingly gigantic, and almost blots out an actor. They usually play a comedy, and a ballet. The comic man in the comedy I saw one summer night, is a waiter at an hotel. There never was such a locomotive actor, since the world began. Great pains are taken with him. He has extra joints in his legs: and a practical eye, with which he winks at the pit, in a manner that is absolutely insupportable to a stranger, but which the initiated audience, mainly composed of the common people, receive (so they do everything else) quite as a matter of course, and as if he were a man. His spirits are prodigious. He continually shakes his legs, and winks his eye. And there is a heavy father with grey hair, who sits down on the regular conventional stage-bank, and blesses his daughter in the regular conventional way, who is tremendous. No one would suppose it possible that anything short of a real man could be so tedious. It is the triumph of art.

In the ballet, an Enchanter runs away with the Bride, in the very hour of her nuptials. He brings her to his cave, and tries to soothe her. They sit down on a sofa (the regular sofa! in the regular place, O. P. Second Entrance!) and a procession of musicians enters; one creature playing a drum, and knocking himself off his legs at every blow. These failing to delight her, dancers appear. Four first; then two; *the* two; the flesh-coloured two. The way in which they dance;

the height to which they spring; the impossible and inhuman extent
to which they pirouette; the revelation of their preposterous legs; the
coming down with a pause, on the very tips of their toes, when the
music requires it; the gentleman's retiring up, when it is the lady's
turn; and the lady's retiring up, when it is the gentleman's turn; the
final passion of a pas-de-deux; and the going off with a bound! — I
shall never see a real ballet, with a composed countenance, again.

I went, another night, to see these Puppets act a play called "St.
Helena, or the Death of Napoleon." It began by the disclosure of
Napoleon, with an immense head, seated on a sofa in his chamber
at St. Helena; to whom his valet entered, with this obscure announcement:

"Sir Yew ud se on Low!" (the *ow*, as in cow).

Sir Hudson (that you could have seen his regimentals!) was a perfect mammoth of a man, to Napoleon; hideously ugly; with a mon-
strously disproportionate face, and a great clump for the lower-jaw,
to express his tyrannical and obdurate nature. He began his system
of persecution, by calling his prisoner "General Buonaparte"; to
which the latter replied, with the deepest tragedy, "Sir Yew ud se
on Low, call me not thus. Repeat that phrase and leave me! I am
Napoleon, Emperor of France!" Sir Yew ud se on, nothing daunted,
proceeded to entertain him with an ordinance of the British Government, regulating the state he should preserve, and the furniture
of his rooms: and limiting his attendants to four or five persons.
"Four or five for *me!*" said Napoleon. "Me! One hundred thousand
men were lately at my sole command; and this English officer talks
of four or five for *me!*" Throughout the piece, Napoleon (who talked
very like the real Napoleon, and was, for ever, having small soliloquies by himself) was very bitter on "these English officers," and
"these English soldiers:" to the great satisfaction of the audience,
who were perfectly delighted to have Low bullied; and who, whenever Low said "General Buonaparte" (which he always did: always
receiving the same correction) quite execrated him. It would be hard
to say why; for Italians have little cause to sympathise with Napoleon, Heaven knows.

There was no plot at all, except that a French officer, disguised as
an Englishman, came to propound a plan of escape; and being discovered, but not before Napoleon had magnanimously refused to

steal his freedom, was immediately ordered off by Low to be hanged. In two very long speeches, which Low made memorable, by winding up with "Yas!" — to show that he was English — which brought down thunders of applause. Napoleon was so affected by this catastrophe, that he fainted away on the spot, and was carried out by two other puppets. Judging from what followed, it would appear that he never recovered the shock; for the next act showed him, in a clean shirt, in his bed (curtains crimson and white), where a lady, prematurely dressed in mourning, brought two little children, who kneeled down by the bed-side, while he made a decent end; the last word on his lips being "Vatterlo."

It was unspeakably ludicrous. Buonaparte's boots were so wonderfully beyond control, and did such marvellous things of their own accord: doubling themselves up, and getting under tables, and dangling in the air, and sometimes skating away with him, out of all human knowledge, when he was in full speech — mischances which were not rendered the less absurd, by a settled melancholy depicted in his face. To put an end to one conference with Low, he had to go to a table, and read a book: when it was the finest spectacle I ever beheld, to see his body bending over the volume, like a boot-jack, and his sentimental eyes glaring obstinately into the pit. He was prodigiously good, in bed, with an immense collar to his shirt, and his little hands outside the coverlet. So was Dr. Antonomarchi, represented by a puppet with long lank hair, like Mawworm's, who, in consequence of some derangement of his wires, hovered about the couch like a vulture, and gave medical opinions in the air. He was almost as good as Low, though the latter was great at all times — a decided brute and villain, beyond all possibility of mistake. Low was especially fine at the last, when, hearing the doctor and the valet say, "The Emperor is dead!" he pulled out his watch, and wound up the piece (not the watch) by exclaiming, with characteristic brutality, "Ha! ha! Eleven minutes to six! The General dead! and the spy hanged!" This brought the curtain down, triumphantly.

[*During another trip to Italy, nine years later, Dickens went to a marionette theater in the stable of a decayed Roman palace.*]

To John Forster

[*November*] 1853

. . . It was a wet night, and there was no audience but a party of French officers and ourselves. We all sat together. I never saw anything more amazing than the performance — altogether only an hour long, but managed by as many as ten people, for we saw them all go behind at the ringing of a bell. The saving of a young lady by a good fairy from the machinations of an enchanter, coupled with the comic business of her servant Pulcinella (the Roman Punch) formed the plot of the first piece. A scolding old peasant woman, who always leaned forward to scold and put her hands in the pockets of her apron, was incredibly natural. Pulcinella, so airy, so life-like, so graceful, he was irresistible. To see him carrying an umbrella over his mistress's head in a storm, talking to a prodigious giant whom he met in the forest, and going to bed with a pony, were things never to be forgotten. And so delicate are the hands of the people who move them, that every puppet was an Italian, and did exactly what an Italian does. If he pointed at any object, if he saluted anybody, if he laughed, if he cried, he did it as never Englishman did it since Britain first at Heaven's command arose — arose — arose, &c. There was a ballet afterwards, on the same scale, and we came away really quite enchanted with the delicate drollery of the thing. French officers more than ditto. . . .

Parisian Theaters

[*During a brief visit to Paris in December 1844 Dickens saw the performances of Madame St. George in* Christine *and of Giulia Grisi in* Il Pirato *described in the following letter.*]

To JOHN FORSTER

[*December 1844*]

. . . I went with Macready to the Odéon to see Alexander Dumas' Christine played by Madame St. George, once Napoleon's mistress; now of an immense size, from dropsy I suppose; and with little weak legs which she can't stand upon. Her age, withal, somewhere about 80 or 90. I never in my life beheld such a sight. Every stage conventionality she ever picked up (and she has them all) has got the dropsy too, and is swollen and bloated hideously. The other actors never looked at one another, but delivered all their dialogues to the pit, in a manner so egregiously unnatural and preposterous that I couldn't make up my mind whether to take it as a joke or an outrage. . . . You and I, sir, will reform this altogether . . . .

. . . The passion and fire of a scene between her [Grisi], Mario, and Fornasari, was as good and great as it is possible for anything operatic to be. They drew on one another, the two men — not like stageplayers, but like Macready himself: and she, rushing in between them; now clinging to this one, now to that, now making a sheath for their naked swords with her arms, now tearing her hair in distraction as they broke away from her and plunged again at each other; was prodigious. . . .

Orrors and Ogres

[The summer of 1845 Dickens spent at the little seaside village of Broadstairs, sallying forth to such entertainments as the two noted below.]

To John Forster

19th August, 1845

. . . I went to a circus at Ramsgate on Saturday night, where Mazeppa was played in three long acts without an H in it: as if for a wager. Evven, and edds, and orrors, and ands, were as plentiful as blackberries; but the letter H was neither whispered in Evven, nor muttered in Ell, nor permitted to dwell in any form on the confines of the sawdust. With this I will couple another theatrical experience of this holiday, when we saw a Giant played by a village comedian with a quite Gargantuesque felicity, and singled out for admiration his fine manner of sitting down to a hot supper (of children), with the self-lauding exalting remark, by way of grace, "How pleasant is a quiet conscience and an approving mind!"

Enter Bobadil

[*On September 20, 1845, at the private theater of the retired actress Frances Kelly, in Dean Street, Dickens and his friends staged a performance of* Every Man in His Humour *for an invited audience glittering with celebrities. Its success was so phenomenal that two months later, to accommodate the crowds who wanted to see it, the players gave a benefit performance at the St. James's Theatre. The letters that follow vividly reflect Dickens's exertions and enthusiasm, both in his function as director and in his leading role as the braggart Bobadil.*]

To Clarkson Stanfield

Fifteenth July, 1845

. . . As I write to you now, not as a Private Friend, but as a Stage Manager, I have half a mind to damn your eyes by way of beginning.

Our play, Sir. Our play.

Every Man in his Humour, and the Mayor of Garratt. The prompt book is Cumberland's Edition in both cases. They are both cast, and really very well. I should say, the St. James's Theatre when we are quite ready. . . . In the meantime merry rehearsals innumerable.

You will find Downright (your part in Every Man in his Humour) very much in the Sir Anthony Absolute line, and as your best business is with me (I am Bobadil) we will make it out brilliantly. Take also, Sir Jacob Jollop in the Farce. . . . Stick to us nobly — My steam is up! . . .

To John Forster

July 22nd 1845

. . . Heavens! such a scene as I have had with Miss Kelly here, this morning! She wanted us put off until the theatre should be cleaned and brushed up a bit, and she would and she would not, for she is eager to have us and alarmed when she thinks of us. By the foot of the Pharaoh, it was a great scene! Especially when she choked, and had the glass of water brought. She exaggerates the importance of our occupation, dreads the least prejudice against her establishment in the minds of any of our company, says the place already has quite ruined her, and with tears in her eyes protests that any jokes at her additional expense in print would drive her mad. By the body of Caesar, the scene was incredible! It's like a preposterous dream. . . .

To T. J. Thompson

Twenty-Eighth July 1845

I hope, if you have no decided objection, you will do Wellbred in the comedy — if for no other reason, to oblige *me*, as I should very much like you to be in it. You will find the "company" perfectly good-natured and most agreeable. I never saw men go to anything in such a hearty spirit. . . .

[Forster had suggested that Dickens accompany him to a special performance of James Shirley's comedy The Gamester. *The mock indignation and inflated rhetoric of Dickens's reply parody the characteristic manner of Bobadil in Jonson's play. "The player Mac" is, of course, William Charles Macready, and "short-necked Fox" is the journalist William Johnson Fox.]*

To John Forster

[August 1845]

. . . Man of the House. *Gamester!* By the foot of Pharaoh, I will not see the *Gamester.* Man shall not force, nor horses drag, this poor gentleman-like carcass into the presence of the *Gamester*. I have stid it. . . . The player Mac hath bidden me to eat and likewise drink with him, thyself, and short-necked Fox to-night. An' I go not, I am a hog, and not a soldier. But an' thou goest not — Beware citizen! Look to it. . . . Thine as thou meritest. BOBADIL (Captain). Unto Master Kitely. These.

To George Cruikshank

[August 22nd] 1845

You have heard of our intended Play. I want you to take a part in it — a good part, which would not cost you much trouble, and which you would do, admirably.

First let me tell you how it comes to be vacant.

We arranged this Play one day at a country-dinner — quite off-hand — and have taken nobody in, since, but two walking gentlemen. We have often wanted, among ourselves, to get you in, but have never had a reasonably good part to offer you.

The one I propose now, is *Downright* in the inclosed comedy. It begins in the first scene of the second act. Until within an hour ago, it was Stanfield's but he is so much bothered, and has so much to do with his other duties of Stage Director and manager of the Scenery and Carpenters that he has come to me and said he will be glad to resign it, if *you* will take it. Now, do take it; and make one in as pleasant a party as was ever got together for such a purpose.

We have Miss Kelly's little Theatre — which is strictly and perfectly private. We play on Saturday the 20th of next month — a month hence. We rehearse, on the stage, generally once a week; and the next Rehearsal is on Tuesday Evening at a quarter before Seven. If you join us, and would come up to it, I can give you a Bed. No names will be printed in our Bills, but the names of the characters. It will be done with every possible appliance in the way of arrangement, correct costume, and so forth. The admissions will be by a printed card of Invitation, addressed to the person invited by all concerned, as if it were a party. And no man can have any visitor (being obliged to make the names of his list known to the rest beforehand) to whom any one else objects. I think it will be as brilliant an audience, and as good an amateur Play, as was ever seen. The

expense to *each, exclusive of the dress* (which every man finds for
himself) will not exceed Two Guineas.

I almost rely upon you from this moment, as one of the party.
Write me by Sunday night's post, *or at the latest by Monday's,* a
definite answer. Every actor will have the privilege of inviting about
five and thirty friends. The names of the actors, I have written below.
Don't mind any pen and ink marks you find in the book, as they
were made for my private edification. . . .

Kitely	Forster	Captain Bobadil	Myself
Old Knowell	Mayhew	Cash	Augustus Dickens
Young Knowell	F. Dickens	Formal	Evans
Wellbred	Thompson	Cob	Leigh
Master Stephen	Jerrold	Brainworm	Lemon
Master Mathew	Leech	Mrs. Kitely	Fortescue
Justice Clement	Stone	Bridget	Miss Jackson
Downright (I hope)	You	Tib	Miss M. Jackson

To W. C. MACREADY

Eighteenth September, 1845

We have a little supper, sir, after the farce, at No. 9, Powis Place,
Great Ormond Street, in an empty house, belonging to one of the
company. There I am requested by my fellows to beg the favour of
thy company and that of Mrs. Macready. The guests are limited to
the actors and their ladies — with the exception of yourselves, and
D'Orsay, and George Cattermole, "or so" — that sounds like Bobadil
a little.

I am going to adopt your reading of the fifth act with the worst
grace in the world. It seems to me that you don't allow enough for
Bobadil having been frequently beaten before, as I have no doubt
he had been. The part goes down hideously on this construction,
and the end is mere lees. But never mind, sir, I intend bringing you
up with the farce in the most brilliant manner. . . .

N. B. — Observe. I think of changing my present mode of life,
and am open to an engagement.

N. B. No. 2. — I will undertake not to play Tragedy, though Passion is my strength.

N. B. No. 3. — I consider myself a chained lion.

To Mme. de la Rue

Twenty-Seventh Sept., 1845

I received your letter last Monday morning, when I was still in a whirl from the uproar of Saturday night. . . .

Good Heaven, how I wish you could have been there! It really was a brilliant sight. The audience so distinguished for one thing or another, everyone so elegantly dressed, all in such a state of excitement and expectation. As to the acting, modesty forbids me to say more than that it has been the town talk ever since. I have known nothing short of a murder to make such a noise before. We are overwhelmed with invitations, applications, petitions, and memorials, for a repetition of the Performance; and on the night it was as much as we could do with a strong body of Police to keep the doors from being carried by force. It got into the papers, notwithstanding all our precautions; and I sent you a *Times* the other day with some account of the proceedings. I hope it reached you safely.

We numbered every seat in the House; and assigned each by lot. . . . The Duke of Devonshire travelled a couple of hundred miles in one direction to be present; and Alfred Tennyson (our friend) travelled a couple of hundred miles in another. So the attraction spread itself to all sorts and conditions of men. We newly-painted all the scenery; newly-carpentered all the machinery; had the dresses (they were bright colours, you may be sure, to please my managerial eye) made expressly from old pictures; and worked away at it, rehearsing and re-rehearsing, night after night, and day after day, as if it were the whole business of our lives. But I have always had a misgiving, in my inmost heart, that I was born to be the manager of a Theatre, and now I am quite sure of it. I send you a bill, as a little curiosity. There are whispers of gold snuff-boxes for the indefatigable manager from the performers — Hem!

. . . Forster . . . is quite well and played admirably the other night, though he imitated Macready too much. I suspect Macready thought so; and would have been better pleased if the resemblance had been less near. Talking of him, reminds me of Maclise, who is exactly in his old state; from which he has in nothing made any departure, except in being so nervous when the overture to the comedy was playing the other night, that he turned a deadly white, and had nearly fainted away. . . .

The affair at Manchester is on the Twenty-Third of October. I suppose there will be an audience of some two thousand people. I will look into the local papers, and send you the best report I see. I have been much solicited to go to Sheffield at the same time, and to Birmingham; and have had other public receptions tendered to me, both in the country and in London. . . .

I have forgotten to say in its right place that I took the glass you gave me to the Theatre, in my Portmanteau of Costumes; and drank a bottle of old Sherry from it in my dressing-room at divers fatiguing periods of the evening; and I drank to you in a great black wig, and with a peaked beard and black moustache, all stuck on singly, by the individual hair! I had a dresser from one of the large Theatres to do it; and I never was so much astonished in my life as at the time it took. After I was beaten, I had all this taken off (an idea of my own) and put on lank and straight — the moustache, which had curled up towards the eyes, twined drooping down — and every hair dishevelled. You never saw such a Devil. But I wore real armour on my throat and heart; and most enormous boots and spurs — and looked like an old Spanish Portrait, I assure you. Maclise is going to paint the figure as an ideal one; and I have sat to him already in the Dress. I am constantly reverting to this Play, I find; but only because I know you will like to hear whatever I happen to remember about it. It is not unlikely we may act again — some other play — at Christmas. Mr. Lemon, the Editor of *Punch*, who played Brainworm in the comedy, and acted with me in the Farce, is an excellent actor. But everybody's understanding of what he was about, and what the author meant, was truly interesting in a very high degree.

General Theatrical Fund Speech

[The Fund had been established to provide for aged, sick, and indigent actors. Dickens presided as chairman at its first anniversary dinner at the London Tavern, April 6, 1846.]

. . . The association whose anniversary we celebrate tonight, was founded seven years ago, for the purpose of granting permanent pensions to such members of the *corps dramatique* as had retired from the stage, either from a decline in their years or a decay in their powers. Collected within the scope of its benevolence are all actors and actresses, singers or dancers, of five years' standing in the profession. To relieve their necessities and to protect them from want is the great aim of the society; and it is good to know that for seven years the members of it have steadily, patiently, quietly, and perseveringly pursued this end, advancing by regular contribution moneys which many of them could ill afford, and cheered by no external help or assistance whatsoever. It has thus served a regular apprenticeship; but I trust that we shall establish tonight that its time is out, and that henceforth the Fund will enter upon a flourishing and brilliant career.

I have no doubt that you are all aware that there are, and were when this institution was founded, two other institutions existing, of a similar nature — Covent Garden and Drury Lane — both of long standing, both richly endowed. It cannot, however, be too distinctly understood that the present institution is not in any way adverse to those. How can it be, when it is only a wide and broad extension of all that is most excellent in the principles on which they are founded? That such an extension was absolutely necessary was sufficiently proved by the fact that the great body of the dramatic corps were excluded from the benefits conferred by a membership of either of these institutions; for it was essential in order to become a member of the Drury Lane society that the applicant, either he or she, should have been engaged for three consecutive seasons as a performer. This was afterwards reduced, in the case of Covent Garden, to a period of two years; but it really is as exclusive one way as another, for I need not tell you that Covent Garden is now but a vision of the past. You might play the bottle-conjuror with its dramatic company, and put them all into a pint bottle. . . . The only run there, is the run of rats and mice. In like manner Drury Lane is so devoted to foreign ballets and foreign operas that it is more deserving of the name of the Opéra Comique, than of a national theatre; while the statue of Shakespeare is well placed over its portal, since it serves as emphatically to point out his grave as does his bust at Stratford-upon-Avon. How can the profession generally hope to qualify for the Drury Lane or Covent Garden institutions, when the oldest and most distinguished members have been driven from the boards on which they earned their reputations, to delight the town in theatres to which the General Theatrical Fund alone extends?

I will again repeat that I attach no reproach to those other Funds, with which I have had the honour of being connected at different periods of my life. At the time those associations were established, an engagement at one of those theatres was almost a matter of course, and a successful engagement would last a whole life; but an engagement of two months' duration at Covent Garden would be a perfect Old Parr of an engagement just now. It should never be forgotten that when those two funds were established the two great theatres were protected by patent, and that at that time the minor theatres were condemned by law to the representation of the most preposterous nonsense, and some gentlemen whom I see around me could have no more belonged to the minor theatres of that day than they could now belong to St. Bartholomew's Fair.

As I honour the two old Funds for the great good which they have done, so I honour this for the much greater good it is resolved to do. It is not because I love them less, but because I love this more — because it includes more in its operation.

Let us ever remember that there is no class of actors who stand so much in need of a retiring fund as those who do not win the great prizes, but who are nevertheless an essential part of the theatrical system, and by consequence bear a part in contributing to our pleasure. We owe them a debt which we ought to pay. The beds of such men are not of roses, but of very artificial flowers indeed. Their lives are full of care and privation, and hard struggles with very stern realities. It is from among the poor actors who drink wine from goblets, in colour marvellously like toast and water, and who preside at Barmecide feasts with wonderful appetites for steaks, — it is from their ranks that the most triumphant favourites have sprung. And surely, besides this, the greater the instruction and delight we derive from the rich English drama, the more we are bound to succour and protect the humblest of those votaries of the art, who add to our instruction and amusement.

Hazlitt has well said that "There is no class of society whom so many people regard with affection as actors. We greet them on the stage, we like to meet them in the streets; they almost always recall to us pleasant associations." When they have strutted and fretted their hour upon the stage, let them not be heard no more, — but let them be heard sometimes to say that they are happy in their old age. When they have passed for the last time behind that glittering row of lights with which we are all familiar, let them not pass away into the gloom and darkness; but let them pass into cheerfulness and light, into a contented and happy home.

This is the object for which we have met; and I am too familiar with the English character not to know that it will be effected. When we come suddenly in a crowded street upon the careworn features of a familiar face, crossing us like the ghost of pleasant hours forgotten, let us not recall those features in pain, in sad remembrance of what they once were; but let us in joy recognize, and go back a pace or two to meet it once again, as that of a friend who has beguiled us of a moment of care, who has taught us to sympathize with virtuous grief cheating us to tears for sorrows not our own — and we all know how pleasant are such tears. Let such a face be ever remembered as that of our benefactor and our friend.

I tried to recollect, in coming here, whether I had ever been in any theatre in my life from which I had not brought away some pleasant association, however poor the theatre; and I protest, out of my varied experience, I could not remember even one from which I had not brought some favourable impression — and that, commencing with the period when I believed that the Clown was a being born into the world with infinite pockets, and ending with that in which I saw the other night, outside one of the "Royal Saloons," a playbill which showed me ships completely rigged, carrying men and careering over boundless and tempestuous oceans. And now, bespeaking your kindest remembrance of our theatres and actors, I beg to propose that you drink as heartily and freely as ever a toast was drunk in this toast-drinking city, "Prosperity to the General Theatrical Fund."

More Parisian Drama

[Again in Paris, in the winter of 1847-1848, Dickens was joined in mid-January by his friend John Forster, who had come over for a fortnight's holiday. With "dreadful insatiability," the two men plunged into a round of entertainment.]

To the Countess of Blessington

[*Paris*], *Twenty-fourth January,* 1847

Among the multitude of sights, we saw our pleasant little bud of a friend, Rose Chéri, play Clarissa Harlowe the other night. I believe she does it in London just now, and perhaps you may have seen it. A most charming, intelligent, modest, affecting piece of acting it is, with a death superior to anything I ever saw on the stage, except Macready's Lear. The theatres are admirable just now. We saw Gentil Bernard at the Variétés last night, acted in a manner that was absolutely perfect. It was a little picture of Watteau, animated and talking from beginning to end. At the Cirque there is a new showpiece called The French Revolution, in which there is a representation of the National Convention, and a series of battles (fought by some five hundred people, who look like five thousand) that are wonderful in their extraordinary vigour and truth. Gun-cotton gives its name to the general annual jocose review at the Palais Royal, which is dull enough, saving for the introduction of Alexandre Dumas, sitting in his study beside a pile of quarto volumes about five feet high, which he says is the first tableau of the first act of the first piece to be played on the first night of his new theatre. The revival of Molière's Don Juan, at the Français, has drawn money. It is excellently played, and it is curious to observe how different *their* Don Juan and valet are from our English ideas of master and man. They are playing Lucretia Borgia again at the Porte St. Martin, but it is poorly performed and hangs fire drearily, though a very remarkable and striking play. We were at Victor Hugo's house last Sunday week, a most extraordinary place, looking like an old curiosity shop, or the property-room of some gloomy, vast, old theatre. I was much struck by Hugo himself, who looks like a genius as he is, every inch of him, and is very interesting and satisfactory from head to foot. His wife is a handsome woman, with flashing black eyes. There is also a charming ditto daughter of fifteen or sixteen, with ditto eyes. Sitting among old armour and old tapestry, and old coffers, and grim old chairs and tables, and old canopies of state from old palaces, and old golden lions going to play at skittles with ponderous old golden balls, they made a most romantic show, and looked like a chapter out of one of his own books. . . .

To Rev. Edward Tagart

Twenty-Eighth January, 1847

. . . There is a melodrama, called The French Revolution, now playing at the Cirque, in the first act of which there is the most tremendous representation of a *people* that can well be imagined. There are wonderful battles and so forth in the piece, but there is a power and massiveness in the mob which is positively awful. At another theatre Clarissa Harlowe is still the rage. There are some things in it rather calculated to astonish the ghost of Richardson, but Clarissa is very admirably played, and dies better than the original to my thinking; but Richardson is no great favourite of mine, and never seems to me to take his top-boots off, whatever he does. Several pieces are in course of representation, involving rare portraits of the English. In one, a servant, called "Tom Bob," who wears a particularly English waistcoat trimed with gold lace and concealing his ankles, does very good things indeed. In another, a Prime Minister of England, who has ruined himself by railway speculations, hits off some of our national characteristics very happily, frequently making incidental mention of "Vishmingster," "Regeenstreet," and other places with which you are well acquainted. "Sir Fakson" is one of the characters in another play — English to the Core; and I saw a Lord Mayor of London at one of the small theatres the other night, looking uncommonly well in a stage-coachman's waistcoat, the order of the Garter, and a very low-crowned broad-brimmed hat, not unlike a dustman.

Barnstorming North from London

[In July 1847 Dickens revived Every Man in His Humour *for the benefit of Leigh Hunt and the aging dramatist John Poole, and gave performances at Manchester and Liverpool. The excitement of these activities had barely subsided when he learned that James Sheridan Knowles, the author of* Virginius *and* The Hunchback, *had gone bankrupt. Fired with a new project, Dickens determined on an entire series of further performances, adding* The Merry Wives of Windsor, *producing both plays at the Haymarket in London and then taking them to Liverpool, Birmingham, and Manchester, even to Glasgow and Edinburgh. This second series of performances went on through May 1848 to almost the end of July, and earned over £2500.]*

To T. J. Thompson

Ninth June 1847

Out of the Merry Wives, I fear; the "shares" not yet "allotted" being poor. But certainly *not* out of the provincial trip, as we should not dream of acting the same play at Manchester and Liverpool, and shall undoubtedly act Every man in his Humour, at one of the two places.

— To say nothing of the chances of our playing a new Farce, in which I should hope to provide better for you. In Comfortable Lodgings, which we acted for Miss Kelly, and shall now repeat, there is a mysterious Préfet of Police — very well acted by Forster, last time — who has one uncommonly good scene, in the acting, with me. If you would like to take it, Forster will be happy to relinquish it. The dress and making-up are good; and the one scene is very funny. Understand, that Forster is cast for it again, and ready to play it again — but I suggested that you might not dislike it.

The only unappropriated parts in the Merry Wives are, Bardolph, Simple, and John Rugby. The fact is, that Stone, as an artist (we are trying hard, to get some more artists, as we think it very important to the scheme) was too valuable to let go; and in his damnable impracticability, and Bardolphian inquiry, had settled within himself that Shakespeare, by unconscious predestination, wrote Page expressly for him (Stone) to act, in the year eighteen hundred and forty seven. For which, may jackasses browse upon his father's grave! — . . .

We can't get the Italian Opera until after their season — though then we could have the whole establishment for nothing. I am now stirring up the sub-committee of Drury Lane Theatre.

To Mark Lemon

Third May 1848

Do you think you could manage before we meet tomorrow to get from the Musical Director of the Haymarket (whom I don't know) a note of the overtures he proposes playing on our two nights. I am obliged to correct and send back the Bill-proofs to-morrow (they are to be brought to Miss Kelly's), and should like, for completeness' sake, to put the Music in. — Before the Merry Wives, it must be something Shakespearian. Before Animal Magnetism, something very telling and light — like Fra Diavolo. Wednesday night's music "in a concatenation accordingly," and jolly little Polkas and Quadrilles between the pieces: always beginning the moment the Act Drop is down. If any little additional strength should be really required in the orchestra, so be it.

Can you come to Miss Kelly's by *three?* I should like to show you bills, tickets, and so forth, before they are worked. In order that they may not interfere with or confuse the Rehearsal, I have appointed Peter Cunningham to meet me there at 3, instead of half-past. —

To John Leech

May Seventh 1848

I am so uneasy about Animal Magnetism that I cannot help writing you a note on the subject of your part.

It is of the greatest importance to the Piece. That the words should be correctly spoken, is essential, — because so much of the business depends upon them and takes its cue from them, that the farce and everybody in it go staggering and wandering about, at a dead stoppage and loss, unless they are spoken at the right time. Thus, last night, although all the rest are nearly if not quite perfect, all were perplexed and put out by the gallant Marquis. And this at the two most critical points of the piece, especially.

If you could get the words you would play it capitally, and look it too infinitely better than any other among us. But I am quite sure that if you cannot get the words by the next Rehearsal, you will be placed in a most uncomfortable and awkward position on the night, in a first piece of that kind, and will maim the piece dreadfully, besides. What I would urge upon you is, — if you feel you can safely and certainly get them, *do get them at once,* (and this I should like much better than anything else) but if you have a doubt about it, or feel that you cannot get them, will it not be better to try and get some one else into the part, before it is too late? At a week's notice there would be little difficulty in filling it, but to let the time run out, without being perfect yourself or enabling us to become so either, would not only be injurious to the play but most mortifying to you, I am certain. Believe me, if you are not in a condition to rehearse such a character *perfectly*, at least three times, it is sure to be distressing on the night of performance. The rapidity of the farce, the interruptions of the audience, and the exaggeration of the whole thing are enough to drive words out of any head that does not hold entire command of them; and such a situation is very ridiculous.

To Angus Fletcher

Twenty-Second June 1848

I am greatly obliged to you for your letter, received last night. The cordial response we have received both from Edinburgh and Glasgow (where they are making great preparation) assures me of a glorious conclusion to our exertions for Knowles. He needs them sorely, poor fellow!

To make my letter the clearer and easier for reference, I will write what I have to write under separate heads; premising that we are *obliged* to make the night Monday the 17th.

PLAYBILLS

I send you the draught of the bills. You will observe that one part (Nym) is left blank. It must remain so, in the first impression, as I am not quite certain who will play it, in the Northern Expedition. As soon as I hear, you shall know. Anything the Committee may wish to add about the distribution of tickets, had best be added where I have left the blank for the prices. You will order such posting bills to be printed for the walls and so forth as your local knowledge suggests the necessity of. I would merely ask that no greater prominence is given to my name, than to those of the other gentlemen concerned — unless it should be deemed indispensably necessary. We usually put at the bottom of the bills and tickets, Evening Dress, but that you will insert or omit as you think right.

TICKETS

I send you the form of ticket I have always hitherto adopted. It is printed on a card which is cut as the rough draught is. The ticket-taker tears off the smaller portion, and returns it (the bit torn off) to the person entering; it then becomes the authority and reference to the place-keeper to give him or her that particular seat. The same form with the substitution of "pit" for "Box," or whatever it may be answers for all parts of the house. You will observe that there is some printing on the back of the card.

It is a great convenience and avoidance of confusion to use a different coloured card for each description of places, a red for the pit, green for the lower boxes, yellow for the upper boxes etc. Every seat, except in the galleries, should be numbered.

BAND

It will require to be a larger and a better one, I imagine, than the usual orchestra of the Theatre. But the Leader will undertake to augment and make it an efficient one, if he be spoken to and authorised to do so. That will not be very expensive. I have selected the overtures (subject to his assent) and put them in the bill.

STAGE

Mr. Willmott (Mr. Macready's Stage Director at Drury Lane and Covent Garden) will make an appointment to meet the master carpenter, property man, etc. a day or two beforehand and will bring his scene and property plots with him. Also a list of the required supers etc. This is a babylonic kind of jargon to read, but Murray will understand it, and it will set his mind at rest as to that part of the proceedings. I should ask him, through you, as an especial favor to take care for us that the stage is kept perfectly clear and that nobody (himself excepted, of course) comes behind, who is not engaged on the night.

Looking over your kind letter, and thanking you very earnestly for the trouble you are taking with so much cordiality, I see nothing else that I need mention, except the Committee. I will tell you candidly how this point stands on our side. Wherever we have been, on a similar occasion, the first men in the place have always connected themselves with the occasion, and this, my band, I know, feel a kind of attention and recognition, which is of a different sort of importance from any amount of attraction that the names of such a committee would present to the local satellites. Therefore I do not hesitate to say, that they would greatly esteem an Edinburgh Committeeship, and missing a general public knowledge that there *was* an influential committee, would beset me with enquiries why Edinburgh was different in this regard, from all other places. If it be practicable therefore to make it notorious in the place that the influential and worthy take an interest in the arrangements, and are not aloof from their general direction, I would ask that much of my friends, as urgently as I may.

To George Cruikshank

First July 1848

Whichever of these two enclosed parts in Used Up, you *don't* undertake, Lemon *will,* choose for yourself. The blacksmith John Ironhall, is a rough bare-armed strong fellow, always in a passion. Sir Adonis Leech is a middle-aged dandy with no heart and a mighty appetite. You will observe that there are a good many words in Iron-hall, and that there is not a very long time to study them in.

Will you come here, on *Monday evening at 7,* to read the play and compare the parts . . .

To G. H. Lewes

Ninth July 1848

Mrs. Cruikshank (whom the Saints confound!) is suddenly well again, and George wants his blacksmith back. Will you give me the Adonis Leech for Lemon, and take back Tom Saville?

O questa femina maladetta! O Impressario sfortunato! — ma, sempre dolce, tranquillissimo, cristianissimo, exempio di pazienza! Impressario admirabile! Uomo di buona pasta! In una parola — CARLO.

To Mark Lemon

Eleventh July 1848

I am tired out, with last night and many less agreeable matters, but I can't go to bed without sending you the enclosed, and entreating you not to think of James. The parts are distributed — I went to Lewes's myself today — and I am fully convinced that your not playing Leech *or* the Blacksmith would sacrifice the piece. Pray remember that Leech was your own idea originally, and don't make a Jackass of yourself by coming out with such preposterous suggestions. I think of playing James myself, and giving Sir Charles to Stone — or I soon shall, if you go on with such monstrous imaginings.

Rehearsals on Thursday and Friday evenings, at 7. — Ever yours amiably — (though indignantly) — *In*-Flexible.

[*After these theatrical intoxications, Dickens often fell into moods of depression, like that which he caricatures in the first paragraph below.*]

To Mrs. Cowden Clarke

Twenty-Second July, 1848

I have no energy whatever, I am very miserable. I loathe domestic hearths. I yearn to be a vagabond. Why can't I marry Mary! Why have I seven children — not engaged at sixpence a-night apiece, and dismissable for ever, if they tumble down, not taken on for an indefinite time at a vast expense, and never, — no never, never, — wearing lighted candles round their heads. I am deeply miserable. A real house like this is insupportable, after that canvas farm wherein I was so happy. What is a humdrum dinner at half-past five, with nobody (but John) to see me eat it, compared with *that* soup, and the hundreds of pairs of eyes that watched its disappearance? Forgive this tear. It is weak and foolish, I know.

Pray let me divide the little excursional excesses of the journey among the gentlemen, as I have always done before, and pray believe that I have had the sincerest pleasure and gratification in your cooperation and society, valuable and interesting on all public accounts, and personally of no mean worth, nor held in slight regard.

Mrs. Gamp with the Strollers

[This joking account of the amateur players and their expedition to Manchester and Liverpool Dickens puts into the mouth of Sairey Gamp, the outrageous sick-nurse from Martin Chuzzlewit, *as what she calls a new "Piljian's Projiss." The persons she describes were all members of the troupe: Mr. Wilson, the hairdresser; the caricaturists George Cruikshank and John Leech; the writers Mark Lemon, Douglas Jerrold, and Dudley Costello; the artists Frank Stone and Augustus Egg; and John Forster, Dickens's friend and, later, his biographer. The piece was first published in Forster's* Life of Charles Dickens.]*

I. MRS. GAMP'S ACCOUNT OF HER CONNEXION
WITH THIS AFFAIR

Which Mrs. Harris's own words to me, was these: "Sairey Gamp," she says, "why not go to Margate? Srimps," says that dear creetur, "is to your liking, Sairey; why not go to Margate for a week, bring your constitootion up with srimps, and come back to them loving arts as knows and wallies of you, blooming? Sairey," Mrs. Harris says, "you are but poorly. Don't denige it, Mrs. Gamp, for books is in your looks. You must have rest. Your mind," she says, "is too strong for you; it gets you down and treads upon you, Sairey. It is useless to disguige the fact — the blade is a wearing out the sheets." "Mrs. Harris," I says to her, "I could not undertake to say, and I will not deceive you ma'am, that I am the woman I could wish to be. The time of worrit as I had with Mrs. Colliber, the baker's lady, which was so bad in her mind with her first, that she would not so much as look at bottled stout, and kept to gruel through the month, has agued me, Mrs. Harris. But ma'am," I says to her, "talk not of Margate, for if I do go anywheres, it is elsewheres and not there." "Sairey," says Mrs. Harris, solemn, "whence this mystery? If I have ever deceived the hardest-working, soberest, and best of women, which her name is well beknown is S. Gamp Midwife Kingsgate Street High Holborn, mention it. If not," says Mrs. Harris, with the tears a standing in her eyes, "reweal your intentions." "Yes, Mrs. Harris," I says, "I will. Well I knows you Mrs. Harris; well you knows me; well we both knows wot the characters of one another is. Mrs. Harris then," I says, "I *have* heerd as there *is* a expedition going down to Manjestir and Liverspool, a play-acting. If I goes anywheres for change, it is along with that." Mrs. Harris clasps her hands, and drops into a chair, as if her time was come — which I know'd it couldn't be, by rights, for six weeks odd. "And have I lived to hear," she says, "of Sairey Gamp, as always kept hersef respectable, in company with play-actors!" "Mrs. Harris," I says to her, "be not alarmed — not reg'lar play-actors — hammertoors." "Thank Evans!" says Mrs. Harris, and bustiges into a flood of tears.

When the sweet creetur had compoged hersef (which a sip of brandy and water warm, and sugared pleasant, with a little nutmeg did it), I proceeds in these words. "Mrs. Harris, I am told as these hammertoors are litter'ry and artistickle." "Sairey," says that best of wimmin, with a shiver and a slight relasp, "go on, it might be worse." "I likewise hears," I says to her, "that they're agoin play-acting, for the benefit of two litter'ry men; one as has had his wrongs a long time ago, and has got his rights at last, and one as has made a many people merry in his time, but is very dull and sick and lonely his own sef, indeed." "Sairey," says Mrs. Harris, "you're an Inglish woman, and that's no business of you'rn."

"No, Mrs. Harris," I says, "that's very true; I hope I knows my dooty and my country. But," I says, "I am informed as there is Ladies in this party, and that half a dozen of 'em, if not more, is in various stages of a interesting state. Mrs. Harris, you and me well knows what Ingeins often does. If I accompanies this expedition, unbeknown and second cladge, may I not combine my calling with change of air, and prove a service to my feller creeturs?" "Sairey," was Mrs. Harris's reply, "you was born to be a blessing to your sex, and bring 'em through it. Good go with you! But keep your distance till called in, Lord bless you Mrs. Gamp; for people is known by the company they keeps, and litterary and artistickle society might be the ruin of you before you was aware, with your best customers, both sick and monthly, if they took a pride in themselves."

II. MRS. GAMP IS DESCRIPTIVE

The number of the cab had a seven in it I think, and a ought I know — and if this should meet his eye (which it was a black 'un, new done, that he saw with; the other was tied up), I give him warning that he'd better take that umbereller and patten to the Hackney-coach Office before he repents it. He was a young man in a weskit with sleeves to it and strings behind, and needn't flatter himsef with a suppogition of escape, as I gave this description of him to the Police the moment I found he had drove off with my property; and if he thinks there an't laws enough he's much mistook — I tell him that.

I do assure you, Mrs. Harris, when I stood in the railways office that morning with my bundle on my arm and one patten in my hand, you might have knocked me down with a feather, far less porkmangers which was a lumping against me, continual and sewere all round. I was drove about like a brute animal and almost worritted into fits, when a gentleman with a large shirt-collar and a hook nose, and a eye like one of Mr. Sweedlepipes's hawks, and long locks of hair, and wiskers that I wouldn't have no lady as I was engaged to meet suddenly a turning round a corner, for any sum of money you could offer me, says, laughing, "Halloa, Mrs. Gamp, what are *you* up to!" I didn't know him from a man (except by his clothes); but I says faintly, "If you're a Christian man, show me where to get a second-cladge ticket for Manjester, and have me put in a carriage, or I shall drop!" Which he kindly did, in a cheerful kind of a way, skipping about in the strangest manner as ever I see, making all kinds of actions, and looking and vinking at me from under the brim of his hat (which was a good deal turned up), to that extent, that I should have thought he meant something but for being so flurried as not to have no thoughts at all until I was put in a carriage along with a individgle — the politest as ever I see — in a shepherd's plaid suit with a long gold watch-guard hanging round his neck, and his hand a trembling through nervousness worse than a aspian leaf.

"I'm wery appy, ma'am," he says — the politest vice as ever I heerd! — "to go down with a lady belonging to our party."

"Our party, sir!" I says.

"Yes, ma'am," he says, "I'm Mr. Wilson. I'm going down with the wigs."

Mrs. Harris, wen he said he was agoing down with the wigs, such was my state of confugion and worrit that I thought he must be connected with the Government in some ways or another, but directly moment he explains himsef, for he says:

"There's not a theatre in London worth mentioning that I don't attend punctually. There's five-and-twenty wigs in these boxes, ma'am," he says, a pinting towards a heap of luggage, "as was worn at the Queen's Fancy Ball. There's a black wig, ma'am," he says, "as was worn by Garrick; there's a red one, ma'am," he says, "as was worn by Kean; there's a brown one, ma'am," he says, "as was worn by Kemble; there's a yellow one, ma'am," he says, "as was made for Cooke; there's a grey one, ma'am," he says, "as I measured Mr. Young for, mysef; and there's a white one, ma'am, that Mr. Macready went mad in. There's a flaxen one as was got up express for Jenny Lind the night she came out at the Italian Opera. It was very much applauded was that wig, ma'am, through the evening. It had a great reception. The audience broke out, the moment they see it."

"Are you in Mr. Sweedlepipes's line, sir?" I says.

"Which is that, ma'am?" he says — the softest and genteelest vice I ever heerd, I do declare, Mrs. Harris!

"Hair-dressing," I says.

"Yes, ma'am," he replies, "I have that honour. Do you see this, ma'am?" he says, holding up his right hand.

"I never see such a trembling," I says to him. And I never did!

"All along of Her Majesty's Costume Ball, ma'am," he says. "The excitement did it. Two hundred and fifty-seven ladies of the first rank and fashion had their heads got up on that occasion by this hand, and my t'other one. I was at it eight-and-forty hours on my feet, ma'am, without rest. It was a Powder ball, ma'am. We have a Powder piece at Liverpool. Have I got the pleasure," he says, looking at me curious, "of addressing Mrs. Gamp?"

"Gamp I am, sir," I replies. "Both by name and natur."

"Would you like to see your beeograffer's moustache and wiskers, ma'am?" he says, "I've got 'em in this box."

"Drat my beeograffer, sir," I says, "he has given me no region to wish to know anythink about him."

"Oh, Missus Gamp, I ask your parden" — I never see such a polite man, Mrs. Harris! "P'raps," he says, "if you're not of the party, you don't know who it was that assisted you into this carriage!"

"No, sir," I says, "I don't, indeed."

"Why, ma'am," he says, a wisperin', "that was George, ma'am."

"What George, sir? I don't know no George," says I.

"The great George, ma'am," says he. "The Crookshanks."

If you'll believe me, Mrs. Harris, I turns my head, and see the wery man a making picturs of me on his thumb nail, at the winder! while another of 'em — a tall, slim, melancholy gent, with dark hair and a bage vice — looks over his shoulder, with his head o' one side as if he understood the subject, and cooly says, *"I've* draw'd her several times — in Punch," he says too! The owdacious wretch!

"Which I never touches, Mr. Wilson," I remarks out loud — I couldn't have helped it, Mrs. Harris, if you had took my life for it! — "which I never touches, Mr. Wilson, on account of the lemon!"

"Hush!" says Mr. Wilson. "There he is!"

I only see a fat gentleman with curly black hair and a merry face, a standing on the platform rubbing his two hands over one another, as if he was washing of 'em, and shaking his head and shoulders wery much; and I was a wondering wot Mr. Wilson meant, wen he says, "There's Dougladge, Mrs. Gamp!" he says. "There's him as wrote the life of Mrs. Caudle!"

Mrs. Harris, wen I see that little willian bodily before me, it give me such a turn that I was all in a tremble. If I hand't lost my umbereller in the cab, I must have done him a injury with it! Oh the bragian little traitor! right among the ladies, Mrs. Harris; looking his wickedest and deceitfullest of eyes while he was a talking to 'em; laughing at his own jokes as loud as you please; holding his hat in one hand to cool his-sef, and tossing back his iron-grey mop of a head of hair with the other, as if it was so much shavings — there, Mrs. Harris, I see him, getting encouragement from the pretty delooded creeturs, which never know'd that sweet saint, Mrs. C, as I did, and being treated with as much confidence as if he'd never wiolated none of the domestic ties, and never showed up nothing! Oh the aggrawation of that Dougladge! Mrs. Harris, if I hadn't apologiged to Mr. Wilson, and put a little bottle to my lips which was in my pocket for the journey, and which it is very rare indeed I have about me, I could not have abared the sight of him — there, Mrs. Harris! I could not! — I must have tore him, or have give way and fainted.

While the bell was a ringing, and the luggage of the hammertoors in great confugion — all a litter'ry indeed — was handled up, Mr. Wilson demeens his-sef politer than ever. "That," he says, "Mrs. Gamp," a pinting to a officer-looking gentleman, that a lady with a little basket was a taking care on, "is another of our party. He's a author too — continivally going up the walley of the Muses, Mrs. Gamp. There," he says, alluding to a fine looking, portly gentleman, with a face like a amiable full moon, and a short mild gent, with a pleasant smile, "is two more of our artists, Mrs. G, well beknowed at the Royal Academy, as sure as stones is stones, and eggs is eggs. This resolute gent," he says, "a coming along here as is aperrently going to take the railways by storm — him with the tight legs, and his weskit very much buttoned, and his mouth very much shut, and his coat a flying open, and his heels a giving it to the platform, is a cricket and beeograffer, and our principal tragegian." "But who," says I, when the bell had left off, and the train had begun to move, "who, Mr. Wilson, is the wild gent in the prespiration, that's been a tearing up and down all this time with a great box of papers under his arm, a talking to everybody wery indistinct, and exciting of himself dreadful?" "Why?" says Mr. Wilson, with a smile. "Because, sir," I says, "he's being left behind." "Good God!" cries Mr. Wilson, turning pale and putting out his head, "It's *your* beeograffer — the Manager — and he has got the money, Mrs. Gamp!" Hous'ever, some one chucked him into the train and we went off. At the first shreek of the whistle, Mrs. Harris, I turned white, for I had took notice of some of them dear creeturs as was the cause of my being in company, and I know'd the danger that — but Mr. Wilson, which is a married man, puts his hand on mine, and says, "Mrs. Gamp, calm yourself; it's only the Ingein."

Magic at Bonchurch

[*From Bonchurch, on the Isle of Wight, where Dickens and his family spent the summer of* 1849, *comes the following burlesque play-bill for an evening of conjuring.*]

[September 1849]

The Unparalleled Necromancer
RHIA RHAMA RHOOS
educated cabalistically in the Orange Groves of Salamanca and the Ocean Caves of Alum Bay

THE LEAPING CARD WONDER.

Two Cards being drawn from the Pack by two of the company, and placed, with the Pack, in the Necromancer's box, will leap forth at the command of any lady of not less than eight, or more than eighty, years of age.

∴ *This wonder is the result of nine years' seclusion in the mines of Russia.*

THE PYRAMID WONDER.

A shilling being lent to the Necromancer by any gentleman of not less than twelve months, or more than one hundred years, of age, and carefully marked by the said gentleman, will disappear from within a brazen box at the word of command, and pass through the hearts of an infinity of boxes, which will afterwards build themselves into pyramids and sink into a small mahogany box, at the Necromancer's bidding.

∴ *Five thousand guineas were paid for the acquisition of this wonder, to a Chinese Mandarin, who died of grief immediately after parting with the secret.*

THE CONFLAGRATION WONDER.

A Card being drawn from the Pack by any lady, not under a direct and positive promise of marriage, will be immediately named by the Necromancer, destroyed by fire, and reproduced from its own ashes.

∴ *An annuity of one thousand pounds has been offered to the Necromancer by the Directors of the Sun Fire Office for the secret of this wonder — and refused! ! !*

THE LOAF OF BREAD WONDER.

The watch of any truly prepossessing lady, of any age, single or married, being locked by the Necromancer in a strong box, will fly at the word of command from within that box into the heart of an ordinary half-quartern loaf, whence it shall but cut out in the presence of the whole company, whose cries of astonishment will be audible at a distance of some miles.

∴ *Ten years in the Plains of Tartary were devoted to the study of this wonder.*

THE TRAVELLING DOLL WONDER.

The travelling doll is composed of solid wood throughout, but, by putting on a travelling dress of the simplest construction, becomes invisible, performs enormous journeys in half a minute, and passes from visibility to invisibility with an expedition so astonishing that no eye can follow its transformations.

∴ *The Necromancer's attendant usually faints on beholding this wonder, and is only to be revived by the administration of brandy and water.*

THE PUDDING WONDER.

The company having agreed among themselves to offer to the Necromancer, by way of loan, the hat of any gentleman whose head has arrived at maturity of size, the Necromancer, without removing that hat for an instant from before the eyes of the delighted company, will light a fire in it, make a plum-pudding in his magic saucepan, boil it over the said fire, produce it in two minutes, thoroughly done, cut it, and dispense it in portions to the whole company, for their consumption then and there; returning the hat at last, wholly uninjured by fire, to its lawful owner.

∴. *The extreme liberality of this wonder awakening the jealousy of the beneficent Austrian Government, when exhibited in Milan, the Necromancer had the honour to be seized, and confined for five years in the fortress of that city.*

Comedy at Broadstairs

[Dickens puts a conversation with the proprietor of his hotel, Mr. Ballard, into play-form:]

To John Leech

Hotel Ballard,   Broadstairs Sur Mer
Ninth October 1849

. . . I don't think there is anyone in the hotel but ourselves . . . I hope you really will come, and give Ballard a turn.

As to him, he is a more decided and hopeless maniac in point of contradiction, than he ever was. The last summer seems to have ripened him thoroughly. He won't let me have an opinion of my own, and bruises me (as Maclise would say) and dances on my body every day at dinner. Here is a specimen.

SCENE. — *Our room.* TIME. — *Half past 5 P.M.* KATE, GEORGINA *and* INIMITABLE, *seated at dinner. In attendance,* BALLARD, *and the amiable waiter* (*the latter, decidedly the most affectionate and soft-hearted man in the world*).

INIMITABLE (*taking punch*). And how's Miss Collin going on, Ballard?

BALLARD. Oh, well, Sir, she ain't going on at all — not what can be called going on, Sir, you know.

INIMITABLE (*after being a little put down, and slightly recovering*). Is she going off at all? Is she going to be married?

BALLARD. No, Sir, not much of that.

INIMITABLE. No, I suppose not! (*Smiles*).

BALLARD (*quickly*). Not but what she's been very near it, Sir, once or twice — and is now, indeed. But I never believe a thing you know, Sir, till it's done, Sir. (*The ladies laugh.*)

GEORGINA (*here you must suppose the imitation*). But she drinks, don't she, Mr. Ballard?

BALLARD. Oh dear no, Miss!

INIMITABLE (*to* GEORGINA *fiercely*). What the devil are you so fond of disparaging people for? Drinks! who ever heard of her drinking! What a damned extraordinary thing it is, that you can't hold your tongue! *I* never heard of her drinking (*to* BALLARD) nor anybody else.

BALLARD (*with a smile of pity*). Oh everybody *here*, has heard of it Sir — and knows it well, but we don't see these things in Broadstairs, Sir, and make it a rule among ourselves never to mention 'em, you know Sir. It's best not.

INIMITABLE (*much affected by this Christian axiom*). You're quite right, Ballard. Nobody need know anything about it.

BALLARD. Oh! They can't help knowing all about it, Sir.

INIMITABLE (*disconcerted*). Why?

BALLARD. Why, you see, Sir, when you come to be picked up in the street, four times in one winter, it gets talked about you know. It gets to be the talk of the whole place, and who can wonder at it!

[*Exit* BALLARD *with dish-cover. Waiter takes round punch and scene closes.*]

High-Jinks at Rockingham

[*A November vacation in 1849 Dickens and his wife spent at Rockingham Castle in Northamptonshire, the ancestral home of their friends the Honorable Mr. and Mrs. Richard Watson, where the festivities included both playacting and prestidigitation.*]

To W. F. De Cerjat

Twenty-Ninth December, 1849

We had a most delightful time at Watsons' (for both of them we have preserved and strengthened a real affection), and were the gayest of the gay. There was a Miss Boyle staying in the house, who is an excellent amateur actress, and she and I got up some scenes from The School for Scandal and from Nickleby, with immense success. We played in the old hall, with audience filled up and running over with servants. The entertainments concluded with feats of legerdemain (for the performance of which I have a pretty good apparatus, collected at divers times and in divers places), and we then fell to country dances of a most frantic description, and danced all night.

To John Forster

Rockingham Castle, Thirtieth November, 1849

. . . Picture to yourself, my dear F, a large old castle, approached by an ancient keep, portcullis, &c, &c, filled with company, waited on by six-and-twenty servants; the slops (and wine-glasses) continually being emptied; and my clothes (with myself in them) always being carried off to all sorts of places; and you will have a faint idea of the mansion in which I am at present staying. I should have written to you yesterday, but for having had a very busy day. Among the guests is a Miss B, sister of the honourable Miss B (of Salem, Mass.), whom we once met at the house of our distinguished literary countryman Colonel Landor. This lady is renowned as an amateur actress, so last night we got up in the great hall some scenes from the School for Scandal; the scene with the lunatic on the wall, from the Nicholas Nickleby of Major-General the Hon. C. Dickens (Richmond, Va.); some conjuring; and then finished off with country dances; of which we had two admirably good ones, quite new to me, though really old. Getting the words, and making the preparations, occupied (as you may believe) the whole day; and it was three o'clock before I got to bed. It was an excellent entertainment, and we were all uncommonly merry. . . . I had a very polite letter from our enterprising countryman Major Bentley (of Lexington, Ky.), which I shall show you when I come home. We leave here this afternoon, and I shall expect you according to appointment, at a quarter past ten A.M. tomorrow. Of all the country-houses and estates I have yet seen in England, I think this is by far the best. Everything undertaken eventuates in a most magnificent hospitality; and you will be pleased to hear that our celebrated fellow citizen General Boxall (Pittsburg, Penn.) is engaged in handing down to posterity the face of the owner of the mansion and of his youthful son and daughter. At a future time it will be my duty to report on the turnips, mangel-wurzel, ploughs, and live stock; and for the present I will only say that I regard it as a fortunate circumstance for the neighbouring community that this patrimony should have fallen to my spirited and enlightened host. Every one has profited by it, and the labouring people in especial are thoroughly well cared-for and looked after. To see all the household, headed by an enormously fat housekeeper, occupying the back benches last night, laughing and applauding without any restraint; and to see a blushing sleek-headed footman produce, for the watch-trick, a silver watch of the most portentous dimensions, amidst the rapturous delight of his brethren and sisterhood; was a very pleasant spectacle, even to a conscientious republican like yourself or me, who cannot but contemplate the parent country with feelings of pride in our own land, which (as was well observed by the Honourable Elias Deeze, of Hartford, Conn.) is truly the land of the free. Best remembrances from Columbia's daughters.

David Copperfield at the Play

[David, now in his late teens, has come up to London for a brief vacation, and is staying at the Golden Cross, where he is just ordering his dinner from the waiter. The visit to Covent Garden that follows glows with all Dickens's own early delight in the drama. David Copperfield was published in monthly installments between May 1849 and November 1850; this short episode is from Chapter 19.]

A waiter showed me into the coffee-room; and a chambermaid introduced me to my small bedchamber, which smelt like a hackney-coach, and was shut up like a family vault. I was still painfully conscious of my youth, for nobody stood in any awe of me at all: the chambermaid being utterly indifferent to my opinions on any subject, and the waiter being familiar with me, and offering advice to my inexperience.

"Well now," said the waiter, in a tone of confidence, "what would you like for dinner? Young gentlemen likes poultry in general: have a fowl!"

I told him, as majestically as I could, that I wasn't in the humour for a fowl.

"Ain't you?" said the waiter. "Young gentlemen is generally tired of beef and mutton: have a weal cutlet!"

I assented to this proposal, in default of being able to suggest anything else.

"Do you care for taters?" said the waiter, with an insinuating smile, and his head on one side. "Young gentlemen generally has been overdosed with taters."

I commanded him, in my deepest voice, to order a veal cutlet and potatoes, and all things fitting; and to inquire at the bar if there were any letters for Trotwood Copperfield, Esquire — which I knew there were not, and couldn't be, but thought it manly to appear to expect.

He soon came back to say that there were none (at which I was much surprised), and began to lay the cloth for my dinner in a box by the fire. While he was so engaged, he asked me what I would take with it; and on my replying "Half a pint of sherry," thought it a favourable opportunity, I am afraid, to extract that measure of wine from the stale leavings at the bottoms of several small decanters. I am of this opinion, because, while I was reading the newspaper, I observed him behind a low wooden partition, which was his private apartment, very busy pouring out of a number of those vessels into one, like a chemist and druggist making up a prescription. When the wine came, too, I thought it flat; and it certainly had more English crumbs in it, than were to be expected in a foreign wine in anything like a pure state; but I was bashful enough to drink it, and say nothing.

Being then in a pleasant frame of mind (from which I infer that poisoning is not always disagreeable in some stages of the process), I resolved to go to the play. It was Covent Garden Theatre that I chose; and there, from the back of a centre box, I saw Julius Cæsar and the new Pantomime. To have all those noble Romans alive before me, and walking in and out for my entertainment, instead of being the stern taskmasters they had been at school, was a most novel and delightful effect. But the mingled reality and mystery of the whole show, the influence upon me of the poetry, the lights, the music, the company, the smooth stupendous changes of glittering and brilliant scenery, were so dazzling, and opened up such illimitable regions of delight, that when I came out into the rainy street, at twelve o'clock at night, I felt as if I had come from the clouds, where I had been leading a romantic life for ages, to a bawling, splashing, link-lighted, umbrella-struggling, hackney-coach-jostling, pattern-clinking, muddy, miserable world.

I had emerged by another door, and stood in the street for a little while, as if I really were a stranger upon earth; but the unceremonious pushing and hustling that I received, soon recalled me to myself, and put me in the road back to the hotel; whither I went, revolving the glorious vision all the way; and where, after some porter and oysters, I sat revolving it still, at past one o'clock, with my eyes on the coffee-room fire.

I was so filled with the play, and with the past — for it was, in a manner, like a shining transparency, through which I saw my earlier life moving along — that I don't know when the figure of a handsome well-formed young man, dressed with a tasteful easy negligence which I have reason to remember very well, became a real presence to me. But I recollect being conscious of his company without having noticed his coming in — and my still sitting, musing, over the coffee-room fire.

At last I rose to go to bed, much to the relief of the sleepy waiter, who had got the fidgets in his legs, and was twisting them, and hitting them, and putting them through all sorts of contortions in his small pantry. In going towards the door, I passed the person who had come in, and saw him plainly. I turned directly, came back, and looked again. He did not know me, but I knew him in a moment.

At another time I might have wanted the confidence of the decision to speak to him, and might have put it off until next day, and might have lost him. But, in the then condition of my mind, where the play was still running high, his former protection of me appeared so deserving of my gratitude, and my old love for him overflowed my breast so freshly and spontaneously, that I went up to him at once, with a fast-beating heart, and said:

"Steerforth! won't you speak to me?"

He looked at me — just as he used to look, sometimes — but I saw no recognition in his face.

"You don't remember me, I am afraid," said I.

"My God!" he suddenly exclaimed. "It's little Copperfield!"

I grasped him by both hands, and could not let them go. But for very shame, and the fear that I might displease him, I could have held him round the neck and cried.

"I never, never, never was so glad! My dear Steerforth, I am so overjoyed to see you!"

"And I am rejoiced to see you, too!" he said, shaking my hand heartily. "Why, Copperfield, old boy, don't be overpowered!" And yet he was glad, too, I thought, to see how the delight I had in meeting him affected me.

I brushed away the tears that my utmost resolution had not been able to keep back, and I made a clumsy laugh of it, and we sat down together, side by side.

"Why, how do you come to be here?" said Steerforth, clapping me on the shoulder.

"I came here by the Canterbury coach, to-day. I have been adopted by an aunt down in that part of the country, and have just finished my education there. How do *you* come to be here, Steerforth?"

"Well, I am what they call an Oxford man," he returned; "that is to say, I get bored to death down there, periodically — and I am on my way now to my mother's. You're a devilish amiable-looking fellow, Copperfield. Just what you used to be, now I look at you! Not altered in the least!"

"I knew *you* immediately," I said; "but you are more easily remembered."

He laughed as he ran his hand through the clustering curls of his hair, and said gaily:

"Yes, I am on an expedition of duty. My mother lives a little way out of town; and the roads being in a beastly condition, and our house tedious enough, I remained here to-night instead of going on. I have not been in town half-a-dozen hours, and those I have been dozing and grumbling away at the play."

"I have been at the play, too," said I. "At Covent Garden. What a delightful and magnificent entertainment, Steerforth!"

Steerforth laughed heartily.

"My dear young Davy," he said, clapping me on the shoulder again, "you are a very Daisy. The daisy of the field, at sunrise, is not fresher than you are. I have been at Covent Garden, too, and there never was a more miserable business. Holloa, you sir!"

This was addressed to the waiter, who had been very attentive to our recognition, at a distance, and now came forward deferentially.

"Where have you put my friend, Mr. Copperfield?" said Steerforth.

"Beg your pardon, sir?"

"Where does he sleep? What's his number? You know what I mean," said Steerforth.

"Well, sir," said the waiter, with an apologetic air. "Mr. Copperfield is at present in forty-four, sir."

"And what the devil do you mean," retorted Steerforth, "by putting Mr. Copperfield into a little loft over a stable?"

"Why, you see we wasn't aware, sir," returned the waiter, still apologetically, "as Mr. Copperfield was anyways particular. We can give Mr. Copperfield seventy-two, sir, if it would be preferred. Next you, sir."

"Of course it would be preferred," said Steerforth. "And do it at once."

The waiter immediately withdrew to make the exchange. Steerforth, very much amused at my having been put into forty-four, laughed again, and clapped me on the shoulder again, and invited me to breakfast with him next morning at ten o'clock — an invitation I was only too proud and happy to accept. It being now pretty late, we took our candles and went up-stairs, where we parted with friendly heartiness at his door, and where I found my new room a great improvement on my old one, it not being at all musty, and having an immense four-post bedstead in it, which was quite a little landed estate. Here, among pillows enough for six, I soon fell asleep in a blissful condition, and dreamed of ancient Rome, Steerforth, and friendship, until the early morning coaches, rumbling out of the archway underneath, made me dream of thunder and the gods.

Joe Whelks and the Drama

[*These two papers were published in Dickens's weekly magazine* . Household Words, *the first on March 30, 1850, the second on April 30, 1850. Joe Whelks is an imaginary cockney; the dramas described are typical nineteenth-century melodramas.*]

THE AMUSEMENTS OF THE PEOPLE

I

As one half of the world is said not to know how the other half lives, so it may be affirmed that the upper half of the world neither knows nor greatly cares how the lower half amuses itself. Believing that it does not care, mainly because it does not know, we purpose occasionally recording a few facts on this subject.

The general character of the lower class of dramatic amusements is a very significant sign of a people, and a very good test of their intellectual condition. We design to make our readers acquainted in the first place with a few of our experiences under this head in the metropolis.

It is probable that nothing will ever root out from among the common people an innate love they have for dramatic entertainment in some form or other. It would be a very doubtful benefit to society, we think, if it could be rooted out. The Polytechnic Institution in Regent Street, where an infinite variety of ingenious models are exhibited and explained, and where lectures comprising a quantity of useful information on many practical subjects are delivered, is a great public benefit and a wonderful place, but we think a people formed *entirely* in their hours of leisure by Polytechnic Institutions would be

an uncomfortable community. We would rather not have to appeal
to the generous sympathies of a man of five-and-twenty, in respect
of some affliction of which he had had no personal experience, who
had passed all his holidays, when a boy, among cranks and cog-
wheels. We should be more disposed to trust him if he had been
brought into occasional contact with a Maid and a Magpie; if he had
made one or two diversions into the Forest of Bondy; or had even
gone the length of a Christmas Pantomime. There is a range of imagination in most of us, which no amount of steam-engines will satisfy;
and which The-great-exhibition-of-the-works-of-industry-of-all-nations,
itself, will probably leave unappeased. The lower we go, the more
natural it is that the best-relished provision for this should be found
in dramatic entertainments; as at once the most obvious, the least
troublesome, and the most real, of all escapes out of the literal world.
Joe Whelks, of the New Cut, Lambeth, is not much of a reader, has
no great store of books, no very commodious room to read in, no
very decided inclination to read, and no power at all of presenting
vividly before his mind's eye what he reads about. But put Joe in the
gallery of the Victoria Theatre; show him doors and windows in the
scene that will open and shut, and that people can get in and out of;
tell him a story with these aids, and by the help of live men and
women dressed up, confiding to him their innermost secrets, in voices
audible half a mile off; and Joe will unravel a story through all its
entanglements, and sit there as long after midnight as you have anything left to show him. Accordingly, the Theatres to which Mr.
Whelks resorts, are always full; and whatever changes of fashion the
drama knows elsewhere, it is always fashionable in the New Cut.

The question, then, might not unnaturally arise, one would suppose, whether Mr. Whelks's education is at all susceptible of improvement, through the agency of his theatrical tastes. How far it is improved at present, our readers shall judge for themselves.

In affording them the means of doing so, we wish to disclaim any
grave imputation on those who are concerned in ministering to the
dramatic gratification of Mr. Whelks. Heavily taxed, wholly unassisted
by the State, deserted by the gentry, and quite unrecognised as a
means of public instruction, the higher English Drama has declined.
Those who would live to please Mr. Whelks, must please Mr. Whelks
to live. It is not the Manager's province to hold the Mirror up to

Nature, but to Mr. Whelks — the only person who acknowledges him. If, in like manner, the actor's nature, like the dyer's hand, becomes subdued to what he works in, the actor can hardly be blamed for it. He grinds hard at his vocation, is often steeped in direful poverty, and lives, at the best, in a little world of mockeries. It is bad enough to give away a great estate six nights a-week, and want a shilling; to preside at imaginary banquets, hungry for a mutton chop; to smack the lips over a tankard of toast and water, and declaim about the mellow produce of the sunny vineyard on the banks of the Rhine; to be a rattling young lover, with the measles at home; and to paint sorrow over, with burnt cock and rouge; without being called upon to despise his vocation too. If he can uttter the trash to which he is condemned, with any relish, so much the better for him, Heaven knows; and peace be with him!

A few weeks ago, we went to one of Mr. Whelks's favourite Theatres, to see an attractive Melo-Drama called *May Morning, or The Mystery of 1715, and the Murder!* We had an idea that the former of these titles might refer to the month in which either the mystery or the murder happened, but we found it to be the name of the heroine, the pride of Keswick Vale; who was "called May Morning" (after a common custom among the English Peasantry) "from her bright eyes and merry laugh." Of this young lady, it may be observed, in passing, that she subsequently sustained every possible calamity of human existence, in a white muslin gown with blue tucks; and that she did every conceivable and inconceivable thing with a pistol, that could anyhow be effected by that description of fire-arms.

The Theatre was extremely full. The prices of admission were, to the boxes, a shilling; to the pit, sixpence; to the gallery, threepence. The gallery was of enormous dimensions (among the company, in the front row, we observed Mr. Whelks); and overflowing with occupants. It required no close observation of the attentive faces, rising one above another, to the very door in the roof, and squeezed and jammed in, regardless of all discomforts, even there, to impress a stranger with a sense of its being highly desirable to lose no possible chance of effecting any mental improvement in that great audience.

The company in the pit were not very clean or sweet-savoured, but there were some good-humoured young mechanics among them, with their wives. These were generally accompanied by "the baby," insomuch that the pit was a perfect nursery. No effect made on the stage was so curious, as the looking down on the quiet faces of these babies fast asleep, after looking up at the staring sea of heads in the gallery. There were a good many cold fried soles in the pit, besides; and a variety of flat stone bottles, of all portable sizes.

The audience in the boxes was of much the same character (babies and fish excepted) as the audience in the pit. A private in the Foot Guards sat in the next box; and a personage who wore pins on his coat instead of buttons, and was in such a damp habit of living as to be quite mouldy, was our nearest neighbour. In several parts of the house we noticed some young pickpockets of our acquaintance; but as they were evidently there as private individuals, and not in their public capacity, we were little disturbed by their presence. For we consider the hours of idleness passed by this class of society as so much gain to society at large; and we do not join in a whimsical sort of lamentation that is generally made over them, when they are found to be unoccupied.

As we made these observations the curtain rose, and we were presently in possession of the following particulars.

Sir George Elmore, a melancholy Baronet with every appearance of being in that advanced stage of indigestion in which Mr. Morrison's patients usually are, when they happen to hear through Mr. Moat, of the surprising effects of his Vegetable Pills, was found to be living in a very large castle, in the society of one round table, two chairs, and Captain George Elmore, "his supposed son, the Child of Mystery, and the Man of Crime." The Captain, in addition to an undutiful habit of bullying his father on all occasions, was a prey to many vices: foremost among which may be mentioned his desertion of his wife, "Estella de Neva, a Spanish lady," and his determination unlawfully to possses himself of May Morning; M. M. being then on the eve of marriage to Will Stanmore, a cheerful sailor, with very loose legs.

The strongest evidence, at first, of the Captain's being the Child of Mystery and the Man of Crime was deducible from his boots, which, being very high and wide, and apparently made of sticking-plaister, justified the worst theatrical suspicions to his disadvantage. And indeed he presently turned out as ill as could be desired: getting into May Morning's Cottage by the window after dark; refusing

to "unhand" May Morning when required to do so by that lady;
waking May Morning's only surviving parent, a blind old gentleman
with a black ribbon over his eyes, whom we shall call Mr. Stars, as his
name was stated in the bill thus * * * and showing himself desperately bent on carrying off May Morning by force of arms. Even
this was not the worst of the Captain; for, being foiled in his diabolical purpose — temporarily by means of knives and pistols, providentially caught up and directed at him by May Morning, and finally,
for the time being, by the advent of Will Stanmore — he caused
one Slink, his adherent, to denounce Will Stanmore as a rebel,
and got that cheerful mariner carried off, and shut up in prison. At
about the same period of the Captain's career, there suddenly appeared in his father's castle, a dark complexioned lady of the name
of Manuella, "a Zingara Woman from the Pyrenean Mountains; the
Wild Wanderer of the Heath, and the Pronouncer of the Prophecy,"
who threw the melancholy baronet, his supposed father, into the
greatest confusion by asking him what he had upon his conscience,
and by pronouncing mysterious rhymes concerning the Child of Mystery and the Man of Crime, to a low trembling of fiddles. Matters
were in this state when the Theatre resounded with applause, and
Mr. Whelks fell into a fit of unbounded enthusiasm, consequent on
the entrance of "Michael the Mendicant."

At first we referred something of the cordiality with which Michael
the Mendicant was greeted, to the fact of his being "made up" with
an excessively dirty face, which might create a bond of union between
himself and a large majority of the audience. But it soon came out
that Michael the Mendicant had been hired in old time by Sir George
Elmore, to murder his (Sir George Elmore's) elder brother — which
he had done; notwithstanding which little affair of honour, Michael
was in reality a very good fellow; quite a tender-hearted man; who,
on hearing of the Captain's determination to settle Will Stanmore,
cried out, "What! more bel-ood!" and fell flat — overpowered by his
nice sense of humanity. In like manner, in describing that small error
of judgment into which he had allowed himself to be tempted by
money, this gentleman exclaimed, "I ster-ruck him down, and fel-ed
in er-orror!" and further he remarked, with honest pride, "I have
liveder as a beggar — a roadersider vaigerant, but no ker-rime since
then has stained these hands!" All these sentiments of the worthy man

were hailed with showers of applause; and when, in the excitement of his feelings on one occasion, after a soliloquy, he "went off" *on his back*, kicking and shuffling along the ground, after the manner of bold spirits in trouble, who object to be taken to the station-house, the cheering was tremendous.

And to see how little harm he had done, after all! Sir George Elmore's elder brother was NOT dead. Not he! He recovered, after this sensitive creature had "fel-ed in er-orror," and, putting a black ribbon over his eyes to disguise himself, went and lived in a modest retirement with his only child. In short, Mr. Stars was the identical individual! When Will Stanmore turned out to be the wrongful Sir George Elmore's son, instead of the Child of Mystery and the Man of Crime, who turned out to be Michael's son (a change having been effected, in revenge, by the lady from the Pyrenean Mountains, who became the Wild Wanderer of the Heath, in consequence of the wrongful Sir George Elmore's perfidy to her and desertion of her), Mr. Stars went up to the Castle, and mentioned to his murdering brother how it was. Mr. Stars said it was all right; he bore no malice; he had kept out of the way, in order that his murdering brother (to whose numerous virtues he was no stranger) might enjoy the property; and now he would propose that they should make it up and dine together. The murdering brother immediately consented, embraced the Wild Wanderer, and it is supposed sent instructions to Doctors' Commons for a license to marry her. After which, they were all very comfortable indeed. For it is not much to try to murder your brother for the sake of his property, if you only suborn such a delicate assassin as Michael the Mendicant!

All this did not tend to the satisfaction of the Child of Mystery and Man of Crime, who was so little pleased by the general happiness, that he shot Will Stanmore, now joyfully out of prison and going to be married directly to May Morning, and carried off the body, and May Morning to boot, to a lone hut. Here, Will Stanmore, laid out for dead at fifteen minutes past twelve, P.M., arose at seventeen minutes past, infinitely fresher than most daisies, and fought two strong men single-handed. However, the Wild Wanderer, arriving with a party of male wild wanderers, who were always at her disposal — and the murdering brother arriving arm-in-arm with Mr. Stars —

stopped the combat, confounded the Child of Mystery and Man of Crime, and blessed the lovers.

The adventures of *Red Riven the Bandit* concluded the moral lesson of the evening. But, feeling by this time a little fatigued, and believing that we already discerned in the countenance of Mr. Whelks a sufficient confusion between right and wrong to last him for one night, we retired: the rather as we intended to meet him, shortly, at another place of dramatic entertainment for the people.

II

Mr. Whelks being much in the habit of recreating himself at a class of theatres called "Saloons," we repaired to one of these, not long ago, on a Monday evening; Monday being a great holiday-night with Mr. Whelks and his friends.

The Saloon in question is the largest in London (that which is known as the Eagle, in the City Road, should be excepted from the generic term, as not presenting by any means the same class of entertainment), and is situate not far from Shoreditch Church. It announces "The People's Theatre," as its second name. The prices of admission are, to the boxes, a shilling; to the pit, sixpence; to the lower gallery, fourpence; to the upper gallery and back seats, threepence. There is no half-price. The opening piece on this occasion was described in the bills as "The greatest hit of the season, the grand new legendary and traditionary drama, combining supernatural agencies with historical facts, and identifying extraordinary superhuman causes with material, terrific, and powerful effects." All the queen's horses and all the queen's men could not have drawn Mr. Whelks into the place like this description. Strengthened by lithographic representations of the principal superhuman causes, combined with the most popular of the material, terrific, and powerful effects, it became irresistible. Consequently, we had already failed, once, in finding six square inches of room within the walls, to stand upon; and when we now paid our money for a little stage box, like a dry shower-bath, we did so in the midst of a stream of people who persisted on paying theirs for other parts of the house in despite of the representations of the Money-taker that it was "very full, everywhere."

The outer avenues and passages of the People's Theatre bore

abundant testimony to the fact of its being frequented by very dirty people. Within, the atmosphere was far from odoriferous. The place was crammed to excess, in all parts. Among the audience were a large number of boys and youths, and a great many very young girls grown into bold women before they had well ceased to be children. These last were the worst features of the whole crowd and were more prominent there than at any other sort of public assembly that we know of, except at a public execution. There was no drink supplied, beyond the contents of the porter-can (magnified in its dimensions, perhaps), which may be usually seen traversing the galleries of the largest Theatres as well as the least, and which was here seen everywhere. Huge ham sandwiches, piled on trays like deals in a timber-yard, were handed about for sale to the hungry; and there was no stint of oranges, cakes, brandy-balls, or other similar refreshments. The Theatre was capacious, with a very large, capable stage, well lighted, well appointed, and managed in a business-like, orderly manner in all respects; the performances had begun so early as a quarter past six, and had been then in progress for three-quarters of an hour.

It was apparent here, as in the theatre we had previously visited, that one of the reasons of its great attraction was its being directly addressed to the common people, in the provision made for their seeing and hearing. Instead of being put away in a dark gap in the roof of an immense building, as in our once National Theatres, they were here in possession of eligible points of view, and thoroughly able to take in the whole performance. Instead of being at a great disadvantage in comparison with the mass of the audience, they were here *the* audience, for whose accommodation the place was made. We believe this to be one great cause of the success of these speculations. In whatever way the common people are addressed, whether in churches, chapels, schools, lecture-rooms, or theatres, to be successfully addressed they must be directly appealed to. No matter how good the feast, they will not come to it on mere sufferance. If, on looking round us, we find that the only things plainly and personally addressed to them, from quack medicines upwards, be bad or very defective things, — so much the worse for them and for all of us, and so much the more unjust and absurd the system which has haughtily abandoned a strong ground to such occupation.

We will add that we believe these people have a right to be

amused. A great deal that we consider to be unreasonable, is written and talked about not licensing these places of entertainment. We have already intimated that we believe a love of dramatic representations to be an inherent principle in human nature. In most conditions of human life of which we have any knowledge, from the Greeks to the Bosjesmen, some form of dramatic representation has always obtained. We have a vast respect for county magistrates, and for the Lord Chamberlain; but we render greater deference to such extensive and immutable experience, and think it will outlive the whole existing court and commission. We would assuredly not bear harder on the fourpenny theatre, than on the four shilling theatre, or the four guinea theatre; but we would decidedly interpose to turn to some wholesome account the means of instruction which it has at command, and we would make that office of Dramatic Licenser, which, like many other offices, has become a mere piece of Court favour and dandy conventionality, a real, responsible, educational trust. We would have it exercise a sound supervision over the lower drama, instead of stopping the career of a real work of art, as it did in the case of Mr. Chorley's play at the Surrey Theatre, but a few weeks since, for a sickly point of form.

To return to Mr. Whelks. The audience, being able to see and hear, were very attentive. They were so closely packed, that they took a little time in settling down after any pause; but otherwise the general disposition was to lose nothing, and to check (in no choice language) any disturber of the business of the scene.

On our arrival, Mr. Whelks had already followed Lady Hatton the Heroine (whom we faintly recognized as a mutilated theme of the late Thomas Ingoldsby) to the "Gloomy Dell and Suicide's Tree," where Lady H. had encountered the "apparition of the dark man of doom," and heard the "fearful story of the Suicide." She had also "signed the compact in her own Blood"; beheld "the Tombs rent asunder"; seen "skeletons start from their graves, and gibber Mine, mine, for ever!" and undergone all these little experiences (each set forth in a separate line in the bill) in the compass of one act. It was not yet over, indeed, for we found a remote king of England of the name of "Enerry," refreshing himself with the spectacle of a dance in a Garden, which was interrupted by the "thrilling appearance of the Demon." This "superhuman cause" (with black eyebrows slanting up into his temples, and red-foil cheekbones), brought the Drop-Curtain down as we took possession of our Shower-Bath.

It seemed, on the curtain's going up again, that Lady Hatton had sold herself to the Powers of Darkness, on very high terms, and was now overtaken by remorse, and by jealousy too; the latter passion being excited by the beautiful Lady Rodolpha, ward to the king. It was to urge Lady Hatton on to the murder of this young female (as well as we could make out, but both we and Mr. Whelks found the incidents complicated) that the Demon appeared "once again in all his terrors." Lady Hatton hesitating to accept this trifle from Tartarus, the Demon, for certain subtle reasons of his own, proceeded to entertain her with a view of the "gloomy court-yard of a convent," and the apparitions of the "Skeleton Monk," and the "King of Terrors." Against these superhuman causes, another superhuman cause, to wit, the ghost of Lady H.'s mother came into play, and greatly confounded the Powers of Darkness, by waving the "sacred emblem" over the head of the else devoted Rodolpha, and causing her to sink unto the earth. Upon this the Demon, losing his temper, fiercely invited Lady Hatton to "Be-old the tortures of the damned!" and straightway conveyed her to a "grand and awful view of Pandemonium, and Lake of Transparent Rolling Fire," whereof, and also of "Prometheus chained, and the Vulture gnawing at his liver," Mr. Whelks was exceedingly derisive.

The Demon still failing, even there, and still finding the ghost of the old lady greatly in his way, exclaimed that these vexations had such a remarkable effect upon his spirit as to "sear his eyeballs," and that he must go "deeper down," which he accordingly did. Hereupon it appeared that it was all a dream on Lady Hatton's part, and that she was newly married and uncommonly happy. This put an end to the incongruous heap of nonsense, and set Mr. Whelks applauding mightily; for, except with the lake of transparent rolling fire (which was not half infernal enough for him), Mr. Whelks was infinitely contented with the whole of the proceedings.

Ten thousand people, every week, all the year round, are estimated to attend this place of amusement. If it were closed to-morrow — if there were fifty such, and they were all closed to-morrow — the only result would be to cause that to be privately and evasively done, which is now publicly done; to render the harm of it much greater, and to exhibit the suppressive power of the law in an oppressive and partial light. The people who now resort here, *will be* amused somewhere. It is of no use to blink that fact, or to make pretences to the contrary. We had far better apply ourselves to improving the character of their amusement. It would not be exacting much, or exacting anything very difficult, to require that the pieces represented in these Theatres should have, at least, a good, plain, healthy purpose in them.

To the end that our experiences might not be supposed to be partial or unfortunate, we went, the very next night, to the Theatre where we saw *May Morning*, and found Mr. Whelks engaged in the study of an "Original old English Domestic and Romantic Drama," called *Eva the Betrayed*, or *The Ladye of Lambythe*. We proceed to develop the incidents which gradually unfolded themselves to Mr. Whelks's understanding.

One Geoffrey Thornley the younger, on a certain fine morning, married his father's ward, Eva the Betrayed, the Ladye of Lambythe. She had become the betrayed, in right — or in wrong — of designing Geoffrey's machinations; for that corrupt individual, knowing her to be under promise of marriage to Walter More, a young mariner (of whom he was accustomed to make slighting mention as "a minion"), represented the said More to be no more, and obtained the consent of the too trusting Eva to their immediate union.

Now, it came to pass, by a singular coincidence, that on the identical morning of the marriage, More came home, and was taking a walk about the scenes of his boyhood — a little faded since that time — when he rescued "Wilbert the Hunchback" from some very rough treatment. This misguided person, in return, immediately fell to abusing his preserver in round terms, giving him to understand that he (the preserved) hated "manerkind, wither two eckerceptions," one of them being the deceiving Geoffrey, whose retainer he was, and for whom he felt an unconquerable attachment; the other, a relative, whom, in a similar redundancy of emphasis, adapted to the requirements of Mr. Whelks, he called his "assister." This misanthrope also made the cold-blooded declaration, "There was a timer when I loved my fellow keretures, till they deserpised me. Now, I live only to witness man's disergherace and woman's misery!" In furtherance of this amiable purpose of existence, he directed More to where the bridal procession was coming home from church, and

Eva recognised More, and More reproached Eva, and there was a great to-do, and a violent struggling, before certain social villagers who were celebrating the event with morris-dances. Eva was borne off in a tearing condition, and the bill very truly observed that the end of that part of the business was "despair and madness."

Geoffrey, Geoffrey, why were you already married to another! Why could you not be true to your lawful wife Katherine, instead of deserting her, and leaving her to come tumbling into public-houses (on account of weakness) in search of you! You might have known what it would end in, Geoffrey Thornley! You might have known that she would come up to your house on your wedding day with her marriage-certificate in her pocket, determined to expose you. You might have known beforehand, as you now very composedly observe, that you would have "but one course to pursue." That course clearly is to wind your right hand in Katherine's long hair, wrestle with her, stab her, throw down the body behind the door (cheers from Mr. Whelks), and tell the devoted Hunchback to get rid of it. On the devoted Hunchback's finding that it is the body of his "assister," and taking her marriage-certificate from her pocket and denouncing you, of course you have still but one course to pursue, and that is to charge the crime upon him, and have him carried off with all speed into the "deep and massive dungeons beneath Thornley Hall."

More having, as he was rather given to boast, "a goodly vessel on the lordly Thames," had better have gone away with it, weather permitting, than gone after Eva. Naturally, he got carried down to the dungeons, too, for lurking about, and got put into the next dungeon to the Hunchback, then expiring from poison. And there they were, hard and fast, like two wild beasts in dens, trying to get glimpses of each other through the bars, to the unutterable interest of Mr. Whelks.

But when the Hunchback made himself known, and when More did the same; and when the Hunchback said he had got the certificate which rendered Eva's marriage illegal; and when More raved to have it given to him, and when the Hunchback (as having some grains of misanthropy in him to the last) persisted in going into his dying agonies in a remote corner of his cage, and took unheard-of trouble not to die anywhere near the bars that were within More's reach; Mr. Whelks applauded to the echo. At last the Hunchback was persuaded to stick the certificate on the point of a dagger, and hand it in; and that done, died extremely hard, knocking himself violently about, to the very last gasp, and certainly making the most of all the life that was in him.

Still, More had yet to get out of his den before he could turn this certificate to any account. His first step was to make such a violent uproar as to bring into his presence a certain "Norman Free Lance" who kept watch and ward over him. His second, to inform this warrior, in the style of the Polite Letter-Writer, that "circumstances had occurred" rendering it necessary that he should be immediately let out. The warrior declining to submit himself to the force of these circumstances, Mr. More proposed to him, as a gentleman and a man of honour, to allow him to step out into the gallery, and there adjust an old feud subsisting between them, by single combat. The unwary Free Lance, consenting to this reasonable proposal, was shot from behind by the comic man, whom he bitterly designated as "a snipe" for that action, and then died exceedingly game.

All this occurred in one day — the bridal day of the Ladye of Lambythe; and now Mr. Whelks concentrated all his energies into a focus, bent forward, looked straight in front of him, and held his breath. For, the night of the eventful day being come, Mr. Whelks was admitted to the "bridal chamber of the Ladye of Lambythe," where he beheld a toilet table, and a particularly large and desolate four-post bedstead. Here the Ladye, having dismissed her bridesmaids, was interrupted in deploring her unhappy fate, by the entrance of her husband; and matters, under these circumstances, were proceeding to very desperate extremities, when the Ladye (by this time aware of the existence of the certificate) found a dagger on the dressing-table, and said, "Attempt to enfold me in thy pernicious embrace, and this poignard — !" etc. He did attempt it, however, for all that, and he and the Ladye were dragging one another about like wrestlers, when Mr. More broke open the door, and entering with the whole domestic establishment and a Middlesex magistrate, took him into custody and claimed his bride.

It is but fair to Mr. Whelks to remark on one curious fact in this entertainment. When the situations were very strong indeed, they were very like what some favourite situations in the Italian Opera would be to a profoundly deaf spectator. The despair and madness at the end of the first act, the business of the long hair, and the struggle in the bridal chamber, were as like the conventional passion of the Italian singers, as the orchestra was unlike the opera band, or its "hurries" unlike the music of the great composers. So do extremes meet; and so is there some hopeful congeniality between what will excite Mr. Whelks, and what will rouse a Duchess.

Dukes and the Drama

[*Bulwer Lytton had invited Dickens's amateurs to be his guests at Knebworth, his Hertfordshire estate, before an audience of his aristocratic county neighbors. The performances took place on the evenings of November 18, 19, and 20, 1850, the carriages of the invited guests — "Dukes, Duchesses, and the like," Dickens said mischievously — rolling into the great rectangular court with its gargoyle-surmounted walls.*]

To Sir Edward Bulwer Lytton

Twenty-Sixth July, 1850

In the matter of the Play — which stirs my blood like a trumpet — I have not yet had conference with Forster, who has been sitting, since his return from you, with a touzled head, a dirty blouse, and extraordinarily dishevelled pantaloons, anathematising Henry, in an equable state of distraction. The last time I saw him, his eyebrows were just visible above a dirty sea of proofs. I should suppose that he may be expected to emerge, tomorrow, and, after conference holden, I shall report myself to you touching Bobadil. . . .

When I come to see you, I must compare notes with you about an idea that has occurred to me, generally, for a comedy — which I am NOT going to write.

Third September, 1850

I have had the long contemplated talk with Forster about the Play, and write to assure you that I shall be delighted to come down to Knebworth and do Bobadil or anything else, provided it would suit your convenience to hold the great Dramatic Festival in the last week of October. The concluding number of Copperfield will prevent me from leaving here until Saturday the 26th of that month. If I were at my own disposal, I hope I need not say I should be at yours.

Forster will tell you with what men we could do the Play, and what laurels we would propose to leave for the gathering of men aspirants, of whom I hope you have a reasonable stock in your part of the country.

Do you know Mary Boyle, the Hon. Mary, daughter of the old Admiral? Because she is the very best actress I ever saw off the stage, and immeasurably better than a great many I have seen on it. I have acted with her in a country house in Northamptonshire, and am going to do so again, next November. If you know her, I think she would be more than pleased to play; and by giving her something good in a farce, we could get her to do Mrs. Kitely. In that case, my little sister-in-law would "go on" for the second lady, and you could do without actresses — besides giving the thing a particular grace and interest.

But maybe you know nothing about the said Mary? and in that case I should like to know what you would think of doing. . . .

If we could get Mary Boyle, we would do Used Up — which is a delightful piece — as the farce.

To Miss Mary Boyle

Sixteenth September, 1850

Your letter having arrived in time for me to write a line by the evening post, I came out of a paroxysm of Copperfield, to say that I am *perfectly delighted* to read it, and to know that we are going to act together in that merry party. We dress Every Man in Queen Elizabeth's time. The acting copy is much altered from the old play, but we still smooth down phrases when needful. I don't remember any one that is changed. Georgina says she can't describe the dress Mrs. Kitely used to wear. I shall be in town on Saturday, and will then get Maclise to make me a little sketch of it, carefully explained, which I will post to you. At the same time I will send you the book. After consideration of farces, it has occurred to me (old Ben being, I daresay, "rare"; but I *do* know rather heavy here and there) that Mrs. Inchbald's Animal Magnetism, which we have often played, will "go" with a greater laugh than anything else. That book I will send you on Saturday too. You will find your part (Lisette, I think it is called, but it is a waiting-maid) a most admirable one; and I have seen people laugh at the piece until they have hung over the front of the boxes like ripe fruit. You may dress the part to please yourself after reading it. We wear powder. I will take care (bringing a theatrical hair-dresser for the company) of your wig! We will rehearse the two pieces when we go down, or at least anything with which you have to do, over and over again. You will find my company so well used to it, and so accustomed to consider it a grave matter of business, as to make it easy. I am now awaiting the French books with a view to Rockingham, and I hope to report of that too, when I write to you on Saturday. . . .

Twentieth September, 1850

I enclose you the book of Animal Magnetism, and the book of Every Man in his Humours. Also a sketch by Mr. Maclise of a correct and picturesque Mrs. Kitely. Mr. Forster is Kitely — Mr. Lemon, Brainworm — Mr. Leech, Master Matthew — Mr. Jerrold, Master Stephen — Mr. Stone, Downright. Kitely's dress is a very plain purple gown, like a Bluecoat-boy's. Downright's dress is also very sober, chiefly brown and gray. All the rest of us are very bright. I am flaming red.

Georgina will write you about your colours and hers in Animal Magnetism. The gayer the better. I am the Doctor — in black with red stockings. Mr. Lemon (an excellent actor), the valet — as far as I can remember in blue and yellow, and a chintz waistcoat. Mr. Leech is the Marquess — and Mr. Egg the one-eyed servant.

What do you think of doing Animal Magnetism as the last piece (we may play three in all, I think) at Rockingham? Is your brother equal to the Valet, and would he do it? If so, we might make Quin the one-eyed servant — and beat up, with Mrs. Watson, for a Marquess. Will you tell me what you think of this, addressed to Broadstairs.

I have not heard from Bulwer again — I daresay I have crossed a letter from him by coming up to-day — but I have every reason to believe that the last week in October is the time. . . .

This is quite a managerial letter, which I write with all manner of appointments and business-discussions going on about me — having my pen on the paper and my eye on "Household Words" — my head on Copperfield — and my ear nowhere particularly.

P.S. I will let you know about A Day after the Wedding. I have sent for the book — on Monday.

Twenty-Fourth September, 1850

All is going on, briskly, at Knebworth. I receive constant reports of the preparations. Mrs. Kitely's dress, extremely good (I will get one of the "County Men" who are to do the small parts, into canary color) but won't Lisette's color (lemon) be too like Mrs. Kitely's (canary)??? I ask this, in mild and timid ignorance.

As to Rockingham. The Marquess is very important, and moreover his words (to a novice) are not easy to learn (having no coherence in them) and his "business" (like the business of the whole piece) is enormous. We must consider what to do. Your brother we will book. And I will send Mrs. Watson Quin's part. With a patch over his eye, and a lame leg, he ought to be brilliant!

I know the two pieces your brother mentions — both very good — but I have a piece in my mind that I once saw done at the Haymarket; of which I don't remember the plot — or the story — or the situations — or anything whatever — except that I have a general impression of Webster and Celeste at a table, in some easy thing that had a melo-dramatic interest in it, (I don't think more than 3 parts) and was very picturesque. It may have been some anecdote of the French Revolution — I don't know — I think a pistol was fired in it — perhaps it was only a bell rung — I can't say. They send me word from the Theatre, on these lively recollections of mine, that the piece was called Louison, and was only played once. Madame Celeste has the manuscript, and will be in town next week. I have written to her, to give it to me then.

Animal Magnetism will utterly kill anything else in the Laughing Way; and it requires, besides, fresh spirits in the audience. Therefore I think if we could get something with an interest, between a Day after the Wedding, and that — say in this order

> Day after the Wedding
> Louison
> Animal Magnetism

— we should present each piece at an advantage. Don't you think so?

I have a wild dream that in this mysterious piece (one scene, one act) somebody was hid somewhere on account of something. But I

can't say who, or why, or when, or on what occasion — and very likely
I shall find that nothing of the sort is in it! . . .

To Mrs. Watson

First October, 1850

I have made minute enquiries into the construction and dimensions
of Mr. Hewitt's Theatre, and I think I now understand it — for the
first time. It cannot be used in part, it seems, but must be set up, altogether, — I mean the scenic part — and that is, unhappily, too large
for your rooms, being, at the smallest, *twenty feet high.* In depth and
width it would exactly do, — precisely do, — but its height appears to
be altogether fatal to any idea of using it at Rockingham. It must be
set up as it is made, because what we stage managers professionally
call the "rollers of the cloths" — that is, the piece of wood on which
each scene that drops, winds and unwinds itself, requires its own particular support and place. In short it is a perfect little mechanical
structure, of which one part cannot be used without another. The different pieces screw and fit like cabinet-work, and fill a waggon!

In right of my trusteeship for all the strolling actors in England, I
know a good many strange people in the vagabond way, who would
do anything in an honest direction to please me. If the worst came to
the worst, I think I know three scenes (we should hardly want more)
that I last heard of in the market place at Uxbridge, and which are
perpetually travelling about to fairs and small theatres — which I
could lay hold of, and bring down, to be erected by our own ingenuity.
But I think I have a better idea still. One Nathan, in Titchborne
Street Haymarket, a "costume-maker," has dressed all my company's
plays — dresses Everyman in His Humour, and Animal Magnetism —
and goes to Knebworth with us. . . . He has scenery, expressly for
rooms and country houses, I *know*; and it strikes me, all at once, that
he would fit you up a little boudoir stage and take it away again, with
great ease, very neatly, and at small cost. If you would like to know
further about him (which I don't at all assume without hearing from
you) I would send him down to you bodily by Railroad, and *you* could
judge for *your*self, and he could judge for *him*self directly. He stands
in great awe of my managerial ferocity (of which he has had great
experience) and would be as quiet and tractable as any Lamb.

Understand, — when I use the word "stage," I merely mean a curtain, scene-lights, and scenes. Nothing else.

I am turning over all sorts of things in my mind, to see whether Miss Boyle and I couldn't do something particularly applicable to the farmers on the second night — something in the agricultural line, with a country boy and girl in it. . . . I expect Bulwer to emigrate, before *his* play takes place. He is building a stage, and taking appalling steps.

To Miss Boyle

Seventh October, 1850

I send you, now,

LOUISON!!!

I have only received it an hour or so. Consequently, I send it with all the Prompter's absurd mistakes and short comings in the copying way. It is not much to read, *but I see great capacity in it*. The gun, I consider a sure thing. The eating and drinking should go off, even better than the gun. I see you (in my mind's eye) unable to eat, looking nervously at the place where the Marquis (another Marquis!) is concealed; and I see myself as Michel, watching you; and I see a vast amount of Business, over the half fowl and bottle of wine, only to be appreciated, and discerned afar off by practised actors like ourselves. Also, I behold you with a bright handkerchief on your head, and large ear-rings in your ears — and when I think of myself, in a red cap and with a gunpowdery face . . . I am transported beyond the ignorant Copperfieldian present, and soar into the Rockinghamian future!

The Prompter is copying the parts. If you will send me back the piece (by return of post, if you can read it so soon) I will send you your part, as soon as I get it. Very likely, the two documents will cross. We can have brilliant rehearsals of Louison in Devonshire Terrace.

Now, about My Grandmother. I have not the least objection to substitute it for Animal Magnetism, but I am quite confident — have not what Brougham calls the shadow of a shade of a doubt — of its being, in every respect, stupendously inferior, and failing to "go" one twenty thousandth part as well. Besides the excruciating nature of the Dialogue — which makes me feel as if I were being rubbed down with a gigantic Baker's-rasp — and the hoary-headed jokes, . . . — it is not a piece in which Animal spirits can tell *at all*. Briskness and animal spirits would carry Animal Magnetism anywhere. I am quite sure your brother would feel the part after rehearsing it. It can be all made so delightfully rapid, and the situations are so wonderfully good! As to my making what Mrs. Malaprop calls "caparisons," that wild apprehension can only originate in his modesty; and he *cannot* be modest and an actor — so I dismiss it.

Pray let him know what I think about it. I will willingly do the old gentleman (the phrase has quite a diabolical appearance, I find as I write it!) if he be bent, on fresh consideration, on that piece of My Grandmother. But I am certain it will never tell, and can never tell, and never might, could, would, or should, ever tell, like Mrs. Inchbald's farce. I think I can see exactly what can be done with my Grandmother, and I *know* what can be done with Animal Magnetism — wherefore I stand by the latter, and vote for it with three obstinate cheers.

On the second night at Knebworth, we play Turning the Tables. I send you the book and cast.

You will please — I now become strictly managerial — to consider yourself "called" for two Rehearsals in London, to wit on the 1st and 2nd of November. You are further requested to be "easy in the words" of Mrs. Kitely, Lisette, and Patty Larkins.

To Sir Edward Bulwer Lytton

Seventh November, 1850

On the principle of postponing nothing connected with the great scheme, I have been to Ollivier's, where I found our friend the choremusicon in a very shattered state, under repair; his mouth wide open, the greater part of his teeth out, his bowels disclosed to the public eyes, and his whole system frightfully disordered. In this condition he was speechless. I cannot, therefore, report, touching his eloquence, but I find he is a piano as well as a choremusicon; that he requires to pass through no intermediate stage between choremusicon and piano, and therefore that he can easily and certainly accompany songs. I have enquired into the window seat matter, and they (Ollivier and Moss) are decidedly of opinion that he can be hoisted into the window: a temporary scaffolding or stooling being made for Lewis Moss to sit upon.

If the Great Northern take carriages (which I suppose they do) they will take the choremusicon. It would come in a van, which would be put on a truck. It could come by the first train on Monday morning — would only require to be met at Stevenage by one horse in harness, and could be adjusted, set up, &c. &c. by Lewis Moss, assisted by our carpenters. The choremusicon will recover its usual health and spirits within a week.

Now, will you have it? I have promised to let them know, on Saturday morning. I am inclined to believe that on the whole it is the best thing, and I think we could so arrange it as not to obstruct the view. But I haven't heard it, and can't hear it. They are extremely confident of its being better than three musicians.

Ninth November, 1850

The choremusicon has surprisingly recovered. I saw him to-day, looking remarkedly well, with an immense crimson silk waistcoat on.

Ollivier has ascertained that the Great Northern (or Direct Northern, or whatever it is — I mean your railway) will bring him. Tidings of the precise train by which that service will be performed I will bring with me on Thursday evening.

The Theatre will (as I expected) take "full" two days putting up — which I suppose means three. It will be at Knebworth on *Tuesday* evening, and your carpenter and two assistants who were to have been ready for it on Thursday morning, must now be ready for it on *Wednesday morning*. Will you let Gilbert know this?

I have not heard of anything more having happened to anybody.

"A Fiery Cross Through England"

[*Out of the Knebworth theatricals grew the idea of the Guild of Literature and Art, and Lytton's costume drama,* Not So Bad as We Seem, *with its royal first night at Devonshire House in Piccadilly, on May 16, 1851, and its brilliant career of performances all over England for the entire following year.*]

To Sir Edward Bulwer Lytton

Fifth January, 1851

I am so sorry to have missed you! I had gone down to Forster, comedy in hand.

I think it *most admirable.* Full of character, strong in interest, rich in capital situations, and *certain to go nobly.* You know how highly I thought of Money, but I sincerely think these three acts finer. I did not think of the slight suggestions you make, but I said, *en passant,* that perhaps the drunken scene might do better on the stage a little concentrated. I don't believe it would require even that, with the leading-up which you propose. I cannot say too much of the comedy to express what I think and feel concerning it; and I look at it, too, remember, with the yellow eye of an actor! I should have taken to it (need I say so!) *con amore* in any case, but I should have been jealous of your reputation, exactly as I appreciate your generosity. If I had a misgiving of ten lines I should have scrupulously mentioned it.

Stone will look the Duke capitally; and I will answer for his being got into doing it *very well.* Looking down the perspective of a few winter evenings here, I am confident about him. Forster will be thoroughly sound and real. Lemon is so surprisingly sensible and trustworthy on the stage, that I don't think any actor could touch his part as he will; and I hope you will have opportunities of testing the accuracy of this prediction. Egg ought to do the Author to absolute perfection. As to Jerrold — there he stands in the play! I would propose Leech (well made up) for Easy. He is a good name, and I see nothing else for him.

This brings me to my own part. If we had anyone, or could get anyone, for Wilmot, I could do (I think) something so near your meaning in Sir Gilbert that I let him go with a pang. Assumption has charms for me — I hardly know for how many wild reasons — so delightful that I feel a loss of, oh! I can't say what exquisite foolery, when I lose a chance of being someone in voice, etc. not at all like myself. But — I speak quite freely, knowing you will not mistake me — I know from experience that we could find nobody to hold the play together in Wilmot if I didn't do it. I think I could touch the gallant, generous, careless pretence, with the real man at the bottom of it, so as to take the audience with him from the first scene. I am quite sure I understand your meaning; and I am absolutely certain that as Jerrold, Forster, and Stone come in, I could, as a mere little bit of mechanics, present them better by doing that part, and paying as much attention to their points as my own, than another amateur actor could. Therefore I throw up my cap for Wilmot, and hereby devote myself to him, heart and head!

I ought to tell you that in a play we once rehearsed and never played (but rehearsed several times, and very carefully), I saw Lemon do a piece of reality with a rugged pathos in it, which I felt, as I stood on the stage with him, to be extraordinarily good. In the serious part of Sir Gilbert he will surprise you. And he has an intuitive discrimination in such things which will just keep the suspicious part from being too droll at the outset — which will just shew a glimpse of something in the depths of it.

The moment I come back to town (within a fortnight, please God!) I will ascertain from Forster where you are. Then I will propose to you that we call our company together, agree upon our general plan of action, and that you and I immediately begin to see and book our Vice-Presidents, etc. Further, I think we ought to see about the Queen. I would suggest our playing first about three weeks before the opening of the Exhibition, in order that it may be the town talk before the country people and foreigners come. Macready thinks with me that a very large sum of money may be got in London.

I propose (for cheapness and many other considerations) to make a theatre expressly for the purpose, which we can put up and take down — say in the Hanover Square Rooms — and move into the country. As Watson wanted something of a theatre made for his forthcoming Little Go, I have made it a sort of model of what I mean, and shall be able to test its working powers before I see you. Many things that, for portability, were to be avoided in Mr. Hewitt's theatre, I have replaced with less expensive and weighty contrivances.

IN RE TUCKER

I have looked carefully over the bill. It appears very large, but I had not come far short of that amount in my mind. An immensity was done to every lamp of any consequence in your house, with the best workmanship, in the shortest time. They were all wrong, and Mr. Payne did not spare the opportunity — nor could it really have been spared. Mind! I *saw* the men at work. It is not pretended, observe, that 32 chimnies were broken; but that certain of that number were supplied to your lamps, and certain others to the Theatre's. Now, as to the former, I assuredly did see the men (having my eye upon them) fitting such glasses to your lamps; and as to the latter I know there were a good many broken. It always happens in a theatre even with gas, which is more handy and manageable — and the rollers of the scenes, and the heat, broke a good many to my knowledge. I don't think the man would exaggerate the quantity of oil consumed (which could be so very easily estimated to a certainty) and the quality was made, with my sanction, very good, in order that there might be no smell. If it were my case — considering that the work was undeniably well done, and very cheerfully done under difficulties, and that it extended by degrees all over your house — I should not dispute the bill, as one applying to a special occasion. But I want to impress two considerations upon you in saying this. First, that it is not a part of what you once called my "large way," because I oblige my other half to be very careful in all such matters, concerning which we hold solemn weekly councils when I consider it my bounden duty to break a chair or so, as a frugal demonstration. Secondly, that I should not have the least shadow of uncomfortable feeling as regards Mr. Tucker, if you *did* dispute the bill.

Now, my dear Bulwer, I have come to the small hours, and am writing alone here, as if *I* were writing something to do what your comedy will. At such a time the temptation is strong upon me to say a great deal more, but I will only say this — in mercy to you — that I do devoutly believe that this plan carried, will entirely change the status of the literary man in England, and make a revolution in his position, which no Government, no power on earth but his own, could ever effect. I have implicit confidence in the scheme — so splendidly begun — if we carry it out with a stedfast energy. I have a strong conviction that we hold in our hands the peace and honour of men of letters for centuries to come, and that you are destined to be their best and most enduring benefactor.

Oh! what a procession of New Years might walk out of all this, after we are very dusty! . . .

P.S. — I have forgotten something. I suggest this title: Knowing the World; or, Not So Bad as We Seem.

To Augustus Egg

Eighth March, 1851

I think *you* told *me* that Mr. Wilkie Collins would be glad to play any part in Bulwer's Comedy; and I think *I* told *you* that I considered him a very desirable recruit. There is a Valet, called (as I remember) Smart — a small part — but, what there is of it, decidedly good — he opens the play — which I should be delighted to assign to him, and in which he would have an opportunity of dressing your humble servant — frothing some chocolate with an obsolete milling-machine that must be revived for the purpose — arranging the room, and dispatching other similar "business," dear to actors. Will you undertake to ask him if I shall cast him in this part? If yes, I will call him to the reading on Wednesday; have the pleasure of leaving my card for him (say where), and beg him to favour us with his company at dinner on Wednesday evening. I knew his father well, and should be very glad to know him.

To Miss Coutts

Twentieth March 1851

. . . The maze of bewilderment into which I have got myself with carpenters, painters, tailors, machinists, and others, in consequence — to say nothing of two nights every week when the whole company are drilled for five hours, the undersigned presiding — or of this trifling addition to my usual occupations — is of the most entangled description; but, if I could help to set right what is wrong here and what I see every day to be so unhappily wrong, I should be munificently recompensed . . .

To David Roberts

Twentieth March, 1851

. . . For the representation of the new comedy Bulwer has written for us, to start this scheme, I am having an ingenious theatre made by Webster's people, for erection on certain nights in the Hanover Square Rooms. But it will first be put up in the Duke of Devonshire's house, where the first representation will take place before a brilliant company, including (I believe) the Queen.

Now, will you paint us a scene — the scene of which I enclose Bulwer's description from the prompter's book? It will be a cloth with a set-piece. It should be sent to your studio or put up in a theatre painting-room, as you would prefer. I have asked Stanny to do another scene, Edwin Landseer, and Louis Haghe. The Devonshire House performance will probably be on Monday, the Twenty-eighth of April. I should want to have the scenery complete by the twentieth, as it would require to be elaborately worked and rehearsed. *You* could do it in no time after sending in your pictures, and will you?

What the value of such aid would be I need not say. I say no more of the reasons that induce me to ask it, because if they are not in the prospectus they are nowhere.

On Monday and Tuesday nights I shall be in town for rehearsal, but until then I shall be here. Will you let me have a line from you in reply? . . .

Description of the Scene proposed:
STREETS OF LONDON IN THE TIME OF GEORGE I.

In perspective, an alley inscribed DEADMAN'S LANE; a large, old-fashioned, gloomy, mysterious house in the corner, marked No. 1. (*This No. 1 Deadman's Lane, has been constantly referred to in the play as the abode of a mysterious female figure, who enters masked, and passes into this house on the scene being disclosed.*) It is night, and there are moonlight mediums.

TO SIR EDWARD BULWER LYTTON

Twenty-Third March 1851
The amount of business and correspondence that I have to attend to in connexion with the play, is about (I should imagine) equal to the business of the Home Office. As the time approaches, it will enormously increase, for the Duke throws the whole collection and arrangement of the audience upon us, to prevent himself (which I can conceive to be very necessary) from giving offence to two or three hundred very particular and very sensitive friends. Carpenters, scene painters, tailors, bootmakers, musicians, all kinds of people, require my constant attention. Stone in himself is a Millstone — I shall have to go over that part with him (out of rehearsal) at least fifty times — round my neck.

Twenty-Eighth April, 1851
Everyone is greatly improved. I wrote an earnest note to Forster a few days ago on the subject of his being too loud and violent. He has since subdued himself with the most admirable pains, and improved the part a thousand per cent. All the points are gradually being worked and smoothed out with the utmost neatness all through the play. They are all most heartily anxious and earnest, and, upon the least hitch, will do the same thing twenty times over. The scenery, furniture, etc. are rapidly advancing towards completion, and will be beautiful. The dresses are a perfect blaze of colour, and there is not a pocket-flap or a scrap of lace that has not been made according to Egg's drawings to the quarter of an inch. Every wig has been made from an old print or picture. From the Duke's snuff-box to

Will's Coffee-house, you will find everything in perfect truth and
keeping. I have resolved that whenever we come to a weak place in
the acting, it must, somehow or other, be made a strong one. The
places that I used to be most afraid of are among the best points
now.

Fifteenth February, 1852

I left Liverpool at four o'clock this morning, and am so blinded
by excitement, gas, and waving hats and handkerchiefs, that I can
scarcely see to write, but I cannot go to bed without telling you what
a triumph we have had. Allowing for the necessarily heavy expenses
of all kinds, I believe we can scarcely fund less than a Thousand
Pounds out of this trip alone. And, more than that, the extraordinary
interest taken in the idea of the Guild by "this grand people of England" down in those vast hives, and the enthusiastic welcome they
give it, assure me that we may do what we will if we will only be
true and faithful to our design. There is a social recognition of it
which I cannot give you the least idea of. I sincerely believe that we
have the ball at our feet, and may throw it up to the very Heaven
of Heavens. And I don't speak for myself alone, but for all our people, and not least of all for Forster, who has been absolutely stunned
by the tremendous earnestness of these great places.

To tell you (especially after your affectionate letter) what I would
have given to have had you there would be idle. But I can most seriously say that all the sights of the earth turned pale in my eyes, before the sight of three thousand people with one heart among them,
and no capacity in them, in spite of all their efforts, of sufficiently
testifying to you how they believe you to be right, and feel that they
cannot do enough to cheer you on. They understood the play (*far
better acted by this time than ever you have seen it*) as well as you
do. They allowed nothing to escape them. They rose up, when it
was over, with a perfect fury of delight, and the Manchester people
sent a requisition after us to Liverpool to say that if we will go back
there in May, when we act at Birmingham (as of course we shall)
they will joyfully undertake to fill the Free Trade Hall again. Among
the Tories of Liverpool the reception was equally enthusiastic. We
played, two nights running, to a hall crowded to the roof — more
like the opera at Genoa or Milan than anything else I can compare

it to. We dined at the Town Hall magnificently, and it made no difference in the response. I said what we were quietly determined to do (when the Guild was given as the toast of the night), and really they were so noble and generous in their encouragement that I should have been more ashamed of myself than I hope I ever shall be, if I could have felt conscious of having ever for a moment faltered in the work.

I will answer for Birmingham — for any great working town to which we choose to go. We have won a position for the idea which years upon years of labour could not have given it. I believe its worldly fortunes have been advanced in this last week fifty years at least. I feebly express to you what Forster (who couldn't be at Liverpool, and has not those shouts ringing in his ears) has felt from the moment he set foot in Manchester. Believe me we may carry a perfect fiery cross through the North of England, and over the Border, in this cause, if need be — not only to the enrichment of the cause, but to the lasting enlistment of the people's sympathy.

I have been so happy in all this that I could have cried on the shortest notice any time since Tuesday. And I do believe that our whole body would have gone to the North Pole with me if I had shown them good reason for it.

Sleary's Circus

[Highlighting the gritty smoke-blackened landscape and the dark utilitarian melodrama of Hard Times *with splashes of spangled color are the scenes in Sleary's Circus which epitomize all the pulsing human warmth Mr. Gradgrind's world ignores. Published in the weekly numbers of* Household Words *between April 1 and August 12, 1854, the novel is a violent attack on the ethos of industrialism. The contrasts between the sooty gloom of Coketown and the bright circus glitter are essentials to Dickens's design. The parts quoted are from Book I, Chapters 3 and 6, and Book III, Chapter 7. In this first scene Mr. Gradgrind, a retired hardware dealer, has been walking back to "his matter of fact home," appropriately named Stone Lodge.]*

He had reached the neutral ground upon the outskirts of the town, which was neither town nor country, and yet was either spoiled, when his ears were invaded by the sound of music. The clashing and banging band attached to the horse-riding establishment which had there set up its rest in a wooden pavilion was in full bray. A flag, floating from the summit of the temple, proclaimed to mankind that it was "Sleary's Horse-riding" which claimed their suffrages. Sleary himself, a stout modern statue with a money-box at its elbow, in an ecclesiastical niche of early Gothic architecture, took the money. Miss Josephine Sleary, as some very long and very narrow strips of printed bill announced, was then inaugurating the entertainments with her graceful equestrian Tyrolean flower-act. Among the other pleasing but always strictly moral wonders which must be seen to be believed, Signor Jupe was that afternoon to "elucidate the diverting accomplishments of his highly trained performing dog Merrylegs." He was also to exhibit "his astounding feat of throwing seventy-five hundred-

weight in rapid succession backhanded over his head, thus forming
a fountain of solid iron in mid-air, a feat never before attempted in
this or any other country, and which having elicited such rapturous
plaudits from enthusiastic throngs it cannot be withdrawn." The
same Signor Jupe was to "enliven the varied performances at frequent intervals with his chaste Shaksperean quips and retorts."
Lastly, he was to wind them up by appearing in his favourite character of Mr. William Button, of Tooley Street, in "the highly novel
and laughable hippo-comedietta of The Tailor's Journey to Brent-
ford."

[*Mr. Gradgrind and Mr. Bounderby, the banker and industrialist,
have accompanied little Sissy Jupe, the daughter of a clown, to the
tavern where the circus performers are staying.*]

The name of the public-house was the Pegasus's Arms. The Pegasus's legs might have been more to the purpose; but, underneath the
winged horse upon the signboard, the Pegasus's Arms was inscribed
in Roman letters. Beneath that inscription again, in a flowing scroll,
the painter had touched off the lines:

> Good malt makes good beer,
> Walk in, and they'll draw it here;
> Good wine makes good brandy,
> Give us a call, and you'll find it handy.

Framed and glazed upon the wall behind the dingy little bar, was
another Pegasus — a theatrical one — with real gauze let in for his
wings, golden stars stuck on all over him, and his ethereal harness
made of red silk.

. . . A young man appeared at the door, and introducing himself
with the words, "By your leaves, gentlemen!" walked in with his
hands in his pockets. His face, close-shaven, thin, and sallow, was
shaded by a great quantity of dark hair, brushed into a roll all round
his head, and parted up the centre. His legs were very robust, but
shorter than legs of good proportions should have been. His chest
and back were as much too broad, as his legs were too short. He was
dressed in a Newmarket coat and tight-fitting trousers; wore a shawl
round his neck; smelt of lamp-oil, straw, orange-peel, horses' prov-

ender, and sawdust; and looked a most remarkable sort of Centaur, compounded of the stable and the play-house. Where the one began, and the other ended, nobody could have told with any precision. This gentleman was mentioned in the bills of the day as Mr. E. W. B. Childers, so justly celebrated for his daring vaulting act as the Wild Huntsman of the North American Prairies; in which popular performance, a diminutive boy with an old face, who now accompanied him, assisted as his infant son: being carried upside down over his father's shoulder, by one foot, and held by the crown of his head, heels upwards, in the palm of his father's hand, according to the violent paternal manner in which wild huntsmen may be observed to fondle their offspring. Made up with curls, wreaths, wings, white bismuth, and carmine, this hopeful young person soared into so pleasing a Cupid as to constitute the chief delight of the maternal part of the spectators; but in private, where his characteristics were a precocious cutaway coat and an extremely gruff voice, he became of the Turf, turfy.

"By your leaves, gentlemen," said Mr. E. W. B. Childers, glancing round the room. "It was you, I believe, that were wishing to see Jupe!"

"It was," said Mr. Gradgrind. "His daughter has gone to fetch him, but I can't wait; therefore, if you please, I will leave a message for him with you."

"You see, my friend," Mr. Bounderby put in, "we are the kind of people who know the value of time, and you are the kind of people who don't know the value of time."

"I have not," retorted Mr. Childers, after surveying him from head to foot, "the honour of knowing you, — but if you mean that you can make more money of your time than I can of mine, I should judge from your appearance, that you are about right."

"And when you have made it, you can keep it too, I should think," said Cupid.

"Kidderminster, stow that!" said Mr. Childers. (Master Kidderminster was Cupid's mortal name.)

"What does he come here cheeking us for, then?" cried Master Kidderminster, showing a very irascible temperament. "If you want to cheek us, pay your ochre at the doors and take it out."

"Kidderminster," said Mr. Childers, raising his voice, "stow that!

— Sir," to Mr. Gradgrind, "I was addressing myself to you. You may or you may not be aware (for perhaps you have not been much in the audience), that Jupe has missed his tip very often, lately."

"Has — what has he missed?" asked Mr. Gradgrind, glancing at the potent Bounderby for assistance.

"Missed his tip."

"Offered at the Garters four times last night, and never done 'em once," said Master Kidderminster. "Missed his tip at the banners, too, and was loose in his ponging."

"Didn't do what he ought to do. Was short in his leaps and bad in his tumbling," Mr. Childers interpreted.

"Oh!" said Mr. Gradgrind, "that is tip, is it?"

"In a general way that's missing his tip," Mr. E. W. B. Childers answered.

"Nine oils, Merrylegs, missing tips, garters, banners, and Ponging, eh!" ejaculated Bounderby, with his laugh of laughs. "Queer sort of company, too, for a man who has raised himself."

"Lower yourself, then," retorted Cupid. "Oh Lord! if you've raised yourself so high as all that comes to, let yourself down a bit."

"This is a very obtrusive lad!" said Mr. Gradgrind, turning, and knitting his brows on him.

"We'd have had a young gentleman to meet you, if we had known you were coming," retorted Master Kidderminster, nothing abashed. "It's a pity you don't have a bespeak, being so particular. You're on the Tight-Jeff, ain't you?"

"What does this unmannerly boy mean," asked Mr. Gradgrind, eyeing him in a sort of desperation, "by Tight-Jeff?"

"There! Get out, get out!" said Mr. Childers, thrusting his young friend from the room, rather in the prairie manner. "Tight-Jeff or Slack-Jeff, it don't much signify: it's only tight-rope and slack-rope. You were going to give me a message for Jupe?"

"Yes, I was."

"Then," continued Mr. Childers, quickly, "my opinion is, he will never receive it. Do you know much of him?"

"I never saw the man in my life."

"I doubt if you ever *will* see him now. It's pretty plain to me, he's off."

"Do you mean that he has deserted his daughter?"

"Ay! I mean," said Mr. Childers, with a nod, "that he has cut. He was goosed last night, he was goosed the night before last, he was goosed to-day. He has lately got in the way of being always goosed, and he can't stand it."

"Why has he been — so very much — Goosed?" asked Mr. Gradgrind, forcing the word out of himself, with great solemnity and reluctance.

"His joints are turning stiff, and he is getting used up," said Childers. "He has his points as a Cackler still, but he can't get a living out of *them*."

"A Cackler!" Bounderby repeated. "Here we go again!"

"A speaker, if the gentleman likes it better," said Mr. E. W. B. Childers, superciliously throwing the interpretation over his shoulder, and accompanying it with a shake of his long hair — which all shook at once. "Now, it's a remarkable fact, sir, that it cut that man deeper, to know that his daughter knew of his being goosed, than to go through with it."

"Good!" interrupted Mr. Bounderby. "This is good, Gradgrind! A man so fond of his daughter, that he runs away from her! This is devilish good! Ha! ha! Now, I'll tell you what, young man. I haven't always occupied my present station of life. I know what these things are. You may be astonished to hear it, but my mother ran away from *me*."

E. W. B. Childers replied pointedly, that he was not at all astonished to hear it. . . .

Meanwhile, the various members of Sleary's company gradually gathered together from the upper regions, where they were quartered, and, from standing about, talking in low voices to one another and to Mr. Childers, gradually insinuated themselves and him into the room. There were two or three handsome young women among them, with their two or three husbands, and their two or three mothers, and their eight or nine little children, who did the fairy business when required. The father of one of the families was in the habit of balancing the father of another of the families on the top of a great pole; the father of a third family often made a pyramid of both those fathers, with Master Kidderminster for the apex, and himself for the base; all the fathers could dance upon rolling casks, stand upon bottles, catch knives and balls, twirl hand-basins, ride upon anything, jump over everything, and stick at nothing. All the mothers could (and did) dance, upon the slack wire and the tight rope, and perform rapid acts on bare-backed steeds; none of them were at all particular in respect of showing their legs; and one of them, alone in a Greek chariot, drove six in hand into every town they came to. They all assumed to be mighty rakish and knowing, they were not very tidy in their private dresses, they were not at all orderly in their domestic arrangements, and the combined literature of the whole company would have produced but a poor letter on any subject. Yet there was a remarkable gentleness and childishness about these people, a special inaptitude for any kind of sharp practice, and an untiring readiness to help and pity one another, deserving often of as much respect, and always of as much generous construction, as the every-day virtues of any class of people in the world.

Last of all appeared Mr. Sleary: a stout man as already mentioned, with one fixed eye, and one loose eye, a voice (if it can be called so) like the efforts of a broken old pair of bellows, a flabby surface, and a muddled head which was never sober and never drunk.

"Thquire!" said Mr. Sleary, who was troubled with asthma, and whose breath came far too thick and heavy for the letter s, "Your thervant! Thith ith a bad piethe of bithnith, thith ith. You've heard of my Clown and hith dog being thuppothed to have morrithed?"

He addressed Mr. Gradgrind, who answered "Yes."

"Well, Thquire," he returned, taking off his hat, and rubbing the lining with his pocket-handkerchief, which he kept inside for the purpose. "Ith it your intenthion to do anything for the poor girl, Thquire?"

"I shall have something to propose to her when she comes back," said Mr. Gradgrind.

"Glad to hear it, Thquire. Not that I want to get rid of the child, any more than I want to thtand in her way. I'm willing to take her prentith, though at her age ith late. My voithe ith a little huthky, Thquire, and not eathy heard by them ath don't know me; but if you'd been chilled and heated, heated and chilled, chilled and heated in the ring when you wath young, ath often ath I have been, *your* voithe wouldn't have lathted out, Thquire, no more than mine."

"I dare say not," said Mr. Gradgrind.

"What thall it be, Thquire, while you wait? Thall it be Therry? Give it a name, Thquire!" said Mr. Sleary, with hospitable ease.

"Nothing for me, I thank you," said Mr. Gradgrind.

"Don't thay nothing, Thquire. What doth your friend thay? If you haven't took your feed yet, have a glath of bitterth."

Here his daughter Josephine — a pretty fair-haired girl of eighteen, who had been tied on a horse at two years old, and had made a will at twelve, which she always carried about with her, expressive of her dying desire to be drawn to the grave by the two piebald ponies — cried, "Father, hush! she has come back!" Then came Sissy Jupe, running into the room as she had run out of it. And when she saw them all assembled, and saw their looks, and saw no father there, she broke into a most deplorable cry, and took refuge on the bosom of the most accomplished tight-rope lady (herself in the family-way), who knelt down on the floor to nurse her, and to weep over her.

"Ith an infernal thame, upon my soul it ith," said Sleary.

"O my dear father, my good kind father, where are you gone? You are gone to try to do me some good, I know! You are gone away for my sake, I am sure! And how miserable and helpless you will be without me, poor, poor father, until you come back!" It was so pathetic to hear her saying many things of this kind, with her face turned upward, and her arms stretched out as if she were trying to stop his departing shadow and embrace it, that no one spoke a word until Mr. Bounderby (growing impatient) took the case in hand.

"Now, good people all," said he, "this is wanton waste of time. Let the girl understand the fact. Let her take it from me, if you like, who have been run away from myself. Here, what's your name! Your father has absconded — deserted you — and you mustn't expect to see him again as long as you live."

They cared so little for plain Fact, these people, and were in that advanced state of degeneracy on the subject, that instead of being impressed by the speaker's strong common sense, they took it in extraordinary dudgeon. The men muttered "Shame!" and the women "Brute!" and Sleary, in some haste, communicated the following hint, apart to Mr. Bounderby.

"I tell you what, Thquire. To thpeak plain to you, my opinion ith that you had better cut it thort, and drop it. They're a very good natur'd people, my people, but they're accuthtomed to be quick in their movementh; and if you don't act upon my advithe, I'm damned if I don't believe they'll pith you out o' winder."

Mr. Bounderby being restrained by this mild suggestion, Mr. Gradgrind found an opening for his eminently practical exposition of the subject.

"It is of no moment," said he, "whether this person is to be expected back at any time, or the contrary. He is gone away, and there is no present expectation of his return. That, I believe, is agreed on all hands."

"Thath agreed, Thquire. Thick to that!" From Sleary.

"Well then. I, who came here to inform the father of the poor girl, Jupe, that she could not be received at the school any more, in consequence of there being practical objections, into which I need not enter, to the reception there of the children of persons so employed, am prepared in these altered circumstances to make a proposal. I am willing to take charge of you, Jupe, and to educate you, and provide for you. The only condition (over and above your good behaviour) I make is, that you decide now, at once, whether to accompany me or remain here. Also, that if you accompany me now, it is understood that you communicate no more with any of your friends who are here present. These observations comprise the whole of the case."

"At the thame time," said Sleary, "I mutht put in my word, Thquire, tho that both thides of the banner may be equally theen. If you like, Thethilia, to be prentitht, you know the natur of the work and you know your companionth. Emma Gordon, in whothe lap you're a lying at prethent, would be a mother to you, and Jo-th'phine would be a thithter to you. I don't pretend to be of the angel breed mythelf, and I don't thay but what, when you mith'd your tip, you'd find me cut up rough, and thwear an oath or two at you. But what I thay, Thquire, ith, that good tempered or bad tempered, I never did a horthe a injury yet, no more than thwearing at him went, and that I don't expect I thall begin otherwithe at my time of life, with a rider. I never wath much of a Cackler, Thquire, and I have thed my thay."

The latter part of this speech was addressed to Mr. Gradgrind, who received it with a grave inclination of his head, and then remarked:

"The only observation I will make to you, Jupe, in the way of influencing your decision, is, that it is highly desirable to have a sound practical education, and that even your father himself (from what I understand) appears, on your behalf, to have known and felt that much."

The last words had a visible effect upon her. She stopped in her wild crying, a little detached herself from Emma Gordon, and turned her face full upon her patron. The whole company perceived the force of the change, and drew a long breath together, that plainly said, "she will go!"

The women sadly bestirred themselves to get the clothes together — it was soon done, for they were not many — and to pack them in a basket which had often travelled with them. Sissy sat all the time, upon the ground, still sobbing, and covering her eyes. Mr. Gradgrind and his friend Bounderby stood near the door, ready to take her away. Mr. Sleary stood in the middle of the room, with the male members of the company about him, exactly as he would have stood in the centre of the ring during his daughter Josephine's performance. He wanted nothing but his whip.

The basket packed in silence, they brought her bonnet to her, and smoothed her disordered hair, and put it on. Then they pressed about her, and bent over her in very natural attitudes, kissing and embracing her: and brought the children to take leave of her; and were a tender-hearted, simple, foolish set of women altogether.

"Now, Jupe," said Mr. Gradgrind. "If you are quite determined, come!"

But she had to take her farewell of the male part of the company yet, and every one of them had to unfold his arms (for they all assumed the professional attitude when they found themselves near Sleary), and give her a parting kiss — Master Kidderminster excepted, in whose young nature there was an original flavour of the misanthrope, who was also known to have harboured matrimonial views, and who moodily withdrew. Mr. Sleary was reserved until the last. Opening his arms wide he took her by both her hands, and would have sprung her up and down, after the riding-master manner

of congratulating young ladies on their dismounting from a rapid act;
but there was no rebound in Sissy, and she only stood before him
crying.

"Good bye, my dear!" said Sleary. "You'll make your fortun, I
hope, and none of our poor folkth will ever trouble you, I'll pound
it. I with your father hadn't taken hith dog with him; ith a ill-
conwenienth to have the dog out of the billth. But on thecond
thoughth, he wouldn't have performed without hith mathter, tho ith
ath broad ath ith long!"

With that he regarded her attentively with his fixed eye, surveyed
his company with his loose one, kissed her, shook his head, and
handed her to Mr. Gradgrind as to a horse. . . .

"Farewell, Thethilia! My latht wordth to you ith thith, Thtick to
the termth of your engagement, be obedient to the Thquire, and forget uth. But if, when you're grown up and married and well off, you
come upon any horthe-riding ever, don't be hard upon it, don't be
croth with it, give it a Bethpeak if you can, and think you might do
wurth. People must be amuthed, Thquire, somehow," continued
Sleary, rendered more pursy than ever, by so much talking; "they
can't be alwayth a working, nor yet they can't be alwayth a learning.
Make the betht of uth; not the wurtht. I've got my living out of the
horthe-riding all my life, I know; but I conthider that I lay down
the philothophy of the thubject when I thay to you, Thquire, make
the betht of uth: not the wurtht!"

The Sleary philosophy was propounded as they went downstairs;
and the fixed eye of Philosophy — and its rolling eye, too — soon
lost the three figures and the basket in the darkness of the street.

[*With Mr. Gradgrind and his daughter Louisa, Sissy, now grown to
young womanhood, pays a visit to her old circus friends.*]

The first thing they saw on entering the town was the skeleton of
Sleary's Circus. The company had departed for another town more
than twenty miles off, and had opened there last night. The connection between the two places was by a hilly turnpike-road, and
the travelling on that road was very slow. Though they took but a
hasty breakfast, and no rest (which it would have been in vain to
seek under such anxious circumstances), it was noon before they be-

gan to find the bills of Sleary's Horseriding on barns and walls, and one o'clock when they stopped in the market-place.

A Grand Morning Performance by the Riders, commencing at that very hour, was in course of announcement by the bellman as they set their feet upon the stones of the street. . . .

The flag with the inscription SLEARY'S HORSERIDING, was there; and the Gothic niche was there; but Mr. Sleary was not there. Master Kidderminster, grown too maturely turfy to be received by the wildest credulity as Cupid any more, had yielded to the invincible force of circumstances (and his beard), and, in the capacity of a man who made himself generally useful, presided on this occasion over the ex-chequer — having also a drum in reserve, on which to expend his leisure moments and superfluous forces. In the extreme sharpness of his look-out for base coin, Mr. Kidderminster, as at present situated, never saw anything but money; so Sissy passed him unrecognised, and they went in.

The Emperor of Japan, on a steady old white horse stencilled with black spots, was twirling five wash-hand basins at once, as it is the favourite recreation of that monarch to do. Sissy, though well acquainted with his Royal line, had no personal knowledge of the present Emperor, and his reign was peaceful. Miss Josephine Sleary, in her celebrated graceful Equestrian Tyrolean Flower-Act, was then announced by a new clown (who humorously said Cauliflower Act), and Mr. Sleary appeared, leading her in.

Mr. Sleary had only made one cut at the Clown with his long whip-lash, and the Clown had only said, "If you do it again, I'll throw the horse at you!" when Sissy was recognised both by father and daughter. But they got through the Act with great self-possession; and Mr. Sleary, saving for the first instant, conveyed no more expression into his locomotive eye than into his fixed one. The performance seemed a little long to Sissy and Louisa, particularly when it stopped to afford the Clown an opportunity of telling Mr. Sleary (who said "Indeed, sir!" to all his observations in the calmest way, and with his eye on the house), about two legs sitting on three legs looking at one leg, when in came four legs, and laid hold of one leg, and up got two legs, caught hold of three legs, and threw 'em at four legs, who ran away with one leg. For, although an ingenious Allegory re-lating to a butcher, a three-legged stool, a dog, and a leg of mutton, this narrative consumed time; and they were in great suspense. At last, however, little fair-haired Josephine made her curtsey amid great applause; and the Clown, left alone in the ring, had just warmed himself, and said, "Now, *I'll* have a turn!" when Sissy was touched on the shoulder, and beckoned out.

She took Louisa with her; and they were received by Mr. Sleary in a very little private apartment, with canvas sides, a grass floor, and a wooden ceiling all aslant, on which the box company stamped their approbation, as if they were coming through. "Thethilia," said Mr. Sleary, who had brandy and water at hand, "it doth me good to thee you. You wath alwayth a favourite with uth, and you've done uth credith thinth the old timeth I'm thure. You mutht thee our people, my dear, afore we thpeak of bithnith, or they'll break their hearth — ethpethially the women. Here'th Jothphine hath been and got married to E. W. B. Childerth, and thee hath got a boy, and though he'th only three yearth old, he thtickth on to any pony you can bring againtht him. He'th named The Little Wonder of Thcolathtic Equitation; and if you don't hear of that boy at Athley'th, you'll hear of him at Parith. And you recollect Kidderminthter, that wath thought to be rather thweet upon yourthelf? Well. He'th married too. Married a widder. Old enough to be hith mother. Thee wath Tightrope, thee wath, and now thee'th nothing — on accounth of fat. They've got two children, tho we're thtrong in the Fairy bithnith and the Nurthery dodge. If you wath to thee our Children in the Wood, with their father and mother both a dyin' on a horthe — their uncle a rethieving of 'em ath hith wardth, upon a horthe — themthelvth both a goin' a blackberryin' on a horthe — and the Robinth a coming in to cover 'em with leavth, upon a horthe — you'd thay it wath the completetht thing ath ever you thet your eyeth on! And you remember Emma Gordon, my dear, ath wath a'moth a mother to you? Of courthe you do; I needn't athk. Well! Emma, thee lotht her huthband. He wath throw'd a heavy backfall off a Elephant in a thort of a Pagoda thing ath the Thultan of Indieth, and he never got the better of it; and thee married a thecond time — married a Cheethemonger ath fell in love with her from the front — and he'th a Overtheer and makin' a fortun."

These various changes, Mr. Sleary, very short of breath now, related with great heartiness, and with a wonderful kind of innocence, considering what a bleary and brandy-and-watery old veteran he was. Afterwards he brought in Josephine, and E. W. B. Childers (rather deeply lined in the jaws by daylight), and the Little Wonder of Scholastic Equitation, and in a word, all the company. Amazing creatures they were in Louisa's eyes, so white and pink of complexion, so scant of dress, and so demonstrative of leg; but it was very agreeable to see them crowding about Sissy, and very natural in Sissy to be unable to refrain from tears.

Parisian Drama-Going Again

[*Repeatedly throughout the middle of the 1850's Dickens was in Paris, where he seldom failed to see the leading plays of the season. The letters that follow are a representative selection. Among them we have inserted one letter phrased as a high-spirited parody of Sheridan's style in* The Rivals.]

To W. C. MACREADY

Boulogne, Twenty-Fourth July, 1853

I saw The Midsummer Night's Dream of the Opéra Comique done here (very well) last night. The way in which a poet named Willyim Shay Kes Peer gets drunk in company with Sir John Foll Stayffe, fights with a noble knight, Lor Latimeer (who is in love with a maid of honour you may have read of in history, called Mees Oleevia), and promises not to do so any more on observing symptoms of love for him in the Queen of England, is very remarkable. Queen Elizabeth, too, in the profound and impenetrable disguise of a black velvet mask, two inches deep by three broad, following him into taverns and worse places, and enquiring of persons of doubtful reputation for "the sublime Williams," was inexpressibly ridiculous. And yet the nonsense was done with a sense quite admirable.

To MISS MARY BOYLE

Sixteenth January, 1854

It is all very well to pretend to love me as you do — Ah! If you loved as I love, Mary! but, when my breast is tortured by the perusal of such a letter as yours, Falkland, Falkland, madam, becomes my part in The Rivals, and I play it with desperate earnestness. As thus:

FALKLAND (*to Acres*). Then you see her, Sir, sometimes?

ACRES. See her! Odds beams and sparkles, yes. See her acting! Night after night.

FALKLAND (*aside and furiously*). Death and the Devil! Acting, and I not there! Pray, Sir (*with constrained calmness*), what does she act?

ACRES. Odds, monthly nurses and babbies! Sairey Gamp and Betsey Prig, "which, wotever it is, my dear (*mimicking*), I likes it brought reg'lar and draw'd mild!" *That's* very like her.

FALKLAND. Confusion! Laceration! Perhaps, Sir, perhaps she some-times acts — ha! ha! perhaps she sometimes acts, I say — eh! sir? — a — ha, ha, ha! a Fairy? (*with great bitterness.*)

ACRES. Odds, gauzy pinions and spangles, yes! You should hear her sing as a Fairy. You should see her dance as a Fairy. Tol de rol lol — la — lol — liddle diddle. (*Sings and dances.*) *That's* very like her.

FALKLAND. Misery! while I, devoted to her image, can scarcely write a line now and then, or pensively read aloud to the people of Birmingham (*to him*). And they applaud her, no doubt they ap-plaud her, Sir. And she — I see her! Curtsies and smiles! And they — curses on them! they laugh and — ha, ha, ha! and clap their hands — and say it's very good. Do they not say it's very good, Sir? Tell me. Do they not?

ACRES. Odds, thunderings and pealings, of course they do! and the third fiddler, little Tweaks, of the county town, goes into fits. "Ho, ho, ho, I can't bear it" (*mimicking*) "take me out! Ha, ha, ha! O what a one she is! She'll be the death of me. Ha, ha, ha, ha!" *That's* very like her!

FALKLAND. Damnation! Heartless Mary! (*Rushes out.*)

Scene opens and discloses coals of fire, heaped up into form of let-ters, representing the following inscription:

> *When the praise thou meetest*
> *To thine ear is sweetest,*
> *O then*
>   REMEMBER JOE!

(*Curtain falls.*)

To Miss Georgina Hogarth

Paris, Sixteenth February, 1855

The theatres are not particularly good, but I have seen Lemaître act in the most wonderful and astounding manner. I am afraid we must go to the Opéra Comique on Sunday. To-morrow we dine with Régnier, and to-day with the Olliffes.

La Joie fait Peur, at the Français, delighted me. Exquisitely played and beautifully imagined altogether. Last night we went to the Porte St. Martin to see a piece (English subject) called Jane Osborne, which the characters pronounce "Ja Nosbornnne." The seducer was Lord Nottingham. The comic Englishwoman's name (she kept lodgings and was a very bad character) was Missees Christmas. She had begun to get into great difficulties with a gentleman of the name of Meestair Cornhill, when we were obliged to leave, at the end of the first act, by the intolerable stench of the place. The whole theatre must be standing over some vast cess-pool. It was so alarming that I instantly rushed into a café and had brandy.

My ear has gradually become so accustomed to French, that I understand the people at the theatres (for the first time) with perfect ease and satisfaction. I walked about with Régnier for an hour and a half yesterday, and received many compliments on my angelic manner of speaking the celestial language. There is a winter Franconi's now, high up on the Boulevards, just like the round theatre on the Champs Élysées, and as bright and beautiful. A clown from Astley's is all in high favour there at present. He talks slang English (being evidently an idiot,) as if he felt a perfect confidence that everybody understands him. His name is Boswell, and the whole cirque rang last night with cries for Boz Zwilllll! Boz Zweellll! Boz Zwuallll! etc. etc. etc. etc.

To John Forster

[Paris, February 1855]

. . . Incomparably the finest acting I ever saw, I saw last night at the Ambigu. They have revived that old piece, once immensely popular in London under the name of Thirty Years of a Gambler's Life.

Old Lemaître plays his famous character, and never did I see anything, in art, so exaltedly horrible and awful. In the earlier acts he
was so well made up, and so light and active, that he really looked
sufficiently young. But in the last two, when he had grown old
and miserable, he did the finest things, I really believe, that are
within the power of acting. Two or three times, a great cry of horror
went all round the house. When he met, in the inn yard, the traveller
whom he murders, and first saw his money, the manner in which the
crime came into his head — and eyes — was as truthful as it was terrific. This traveller, being a good fellow, gives him wine. You should
see the dim remembrance of his better days that comes over him as
he takes the glass, and in a strange dazed way makes as if he were going to touch the other man's, or do some airy thing with it; and then
stops and flings the contents down his hot throat, as if he were pouring it into a lime-kiln. But this was nothing to what follows after he
has done the murder, and comes home, with a basket of provisions, a
ragged pocket full of money, and a badly-washed bloody right hand
— which his little girl finds out. After the child asked him if he had
hurt his hand, his going aside, turning himself round, and looking
over all his clothes for spots, was so inexpressibly dreadful that it
really scared one. He called for wine, and the sickness that came
upon him when he saw the colour, was one of the things that brought
out the curious cry I have spoken of, from the audience. Then he
fell into a sort of bloody mist, and went on to the end groping about,
with no mind for anything, except making his fortune by staking
this money, and a faint dull kind of love for the child. It is quite impossible to satisfy one's-self by saying enough of this magnificent
performance. I have never seen him come near its finest points, in
anything else. He said two things in a way that alone would put him
far apart from all other actors. One to his wife, when he has exultingly
shewn her the money and she has asked him how he got it — "I
found it" — and the other to his old companion and tempter, when
he was charged by him with having killed that traveller, and suddenly went headlong mad and took him by the throat and howled
out, "It wasn't I who murdered him — it was Misery!" And such a
dress; such a face; and, above all, such an extraordinary guilty wicked
thing as he made of a knotted branch of a tree which was his walking-stick, from the moment when the idea of the murder came into

his head! I could write pages about him. It is an impression quite ineffaceable. He got half-boastful of that walking-staff to himself, and half-afraid of it; and didn't know whether to be grimly pleased that it had the jagged end, or to hate it and be horrified of it. He sat at a little table in the inn-yard, drinking with the traveller; and this horrible stick got between them like the Devil, while he counted on his fingers the uses he could put the money to. . . .

[Paris, 1855]

Delightful music, an excellent story, immense stage tact, capital scenic arrangements, and the most delightful little prima donna ever seen or heard, in the person of Marie Cabel. It is called Manon Lescaut — from the old romance — and is charming throughout. She sings a laughing song in it which is received with madness, and which is the only real laughing song that ever was written. Auber told me that when it was first rehearsed, it made a great effect upon the orchestra; and that he could not have had a better compliment upon its freshness than the musical director paid him, in coming and clapping him on the shoulder with "Bravo, jeune homme! Cela promet bien!"

[The play mentioned below is Paul Foucher's La Joconde.]

[Paris, November 1855]

Of course the interest of it turns upon a flawed piece of living china (*that* seems to be positively essential), but as in most of these cases, if you will accept the position in which you find the people, you have nothing more to bother your morality about. . . . There is a dreary classicality at that establishment calculated to freeze the marrow. Between ourselves, even one's best friends there are at times very aggravating. One tires of seeing a man, through any number of acts, remembering everything by patting his forehead with the flat of his hand, jerking out sentences by shaking himself, and piling them up in pyramids over his head with his right forefinger. And they have a generic small comedy-piece, where you see two sofas and three little tables, to which a man enters with his hat on, to talk to another man — and in respect of which you know exactly when he will get up from one sofa to sit on the other, and take his hat off one table to put it upon the other — which strikes one quite as ludicrously as a good farce. . . . There seems to be a good piece at the Vaudeville, on the idea of the Town and Country Mouse. It is too respectable and inoffensive for me to-night, but I hope to see it before I leave. . . . I have a horrible idea of making friends with Franconi, and sauntering when I am at work into their sawdust green-room. . . .

[*The performance on which Dickens comments in the second paragraph below is Alexandre Dumas's version of* Orestes.]

[*January 1856*]

On Wednesday we went to the Odéon to see a new piece, in four acts and in verse, called Michel Cervantes. I suppose such an infernal dose of ditch water never was concocted. But there were certain passages, describing the suppression of public opinion in Madrid, which were received with a shout of savage application to France that made one stare again! And once more, here again, at every pause, steady, compact, regular as military drums, the Ça Ira! . . .

. . . Nothing have I ever seen so weighty and so ridiculous. If I had not already learnt to tremble at the sight of classic drapery on the human form, I should have plumbed the utmost depths of terrified boredom in this achievement. The chorus is not preserved otherwise than that bits of it are taken out for characters to speak. It is really so bad as to be almost good. Some of the Frenchified classical anguish struck me so unspeakably ridiculous that it puts me on the broad grin as I write. . . .

I was at the Porte St. Martin last night, where there is a rather good melodrama called Sang Melé, in which one of the characters is an English Lord — Lord William Falkland — who is called throughout the piece Milor Williams Fack Lorn, and is a hundred times described by others and described by himself as Williams. He is admirably played; and there is something positively vicious in their utter want of truth. One "set," where the action of a whole act is supposed to take place in the great wooden verandah of a Swiss hotel overhanging a mountain ravine, is the best piece of stage carpentering I have seen in France. Next week we are to have at the Ambigu Paradise Lost, with the murder of Abel, and the Deluge. The wildest rumours are afloat as to the un-dressing of our first parents. . . .

To W. Wilkie Collins

Nineteenth January, 1856

At the Porte St. Martin they are doing the Orestes, put into French verse by Alexandre Dumas. Really one of the absurdest things I ever saw. The scene of the tomb, with all manner of classical females, in black, grouping themselves — on the lid, and on the steps, and on each other, and in every conceivable aspect of obtrusive impossibility — is just like the window of one of those artists in hair, who address the friends of deceased persons. Tomorrow week a fête is coming off at the Jardin d'Hiver, next door but one here, which I must certainly go to and which I should think can hardly fail to attract all the Lorettes in Paris — the fête of the company of the Folies Nouvelles! The ladies of the company are to keep stalls, and are to sell to Messieurs the Amateurs orange-water and lemonade. Paul le Grand is to promenade among the company, dressed as Pierrot. Kelm, the big-faced comic singer, is to do the like, dressed as "a Russian Cossack." The entertainments are to conclude with La Polka des Bêtes féroces, par la Troupe entière des Folies Nouvelles.

[*Dickens is commenting below on the rivalry of Elizabeth Rachel and Adelaide Ristori, and the latter's performance in* Medea.]

To John Forster

Paris, April 1856

The papers have all been in fits respecting the sublimity of the performance, and the genuineness of the applause — particularly of the bouquets; which were thrown on at the most preposterous times in the midst of agonizing scenes, so that the characters had to pick their way among them, and a certain stout gentleman who played King Creon was obliged to keep a wary eye, all night, on the proscenium boxes, and dodge them as they came down. Now Scribe, who dined here next day (and who follows on the Ristori side, being offended, as everybody has been, by the insolence of Rachel), could not resist the temptation of telling us, that, going round at the end of the first act to offer his congratulations, he met all the bouquets coming back in men's arms to be thrown on again in the second act.

[April 1856]

We were rung in (out of the café below the Ambigu) at 8, and the play was over at half-past 1: the waits between the acts being very much longer than the acts themselves. The house was crammed to excess in every part, and the galleries awful with Blouses, who again, during the whole of the waits, beat with the regularity of military drums the revolutionary tune of famous memory — Ça Ira! The play is a compound of Paradise Lost and Byron's Cain; and some of the controversies between the archangel and the devil, when the celestial power argues with the infernal in conversational French, as "Eh bien! Satan, crois-tu donc que notre Seigneur t'aurait exposé aux tourments que t'endures à présent, sans avoir prévu," &c. &c. are very ridiculous. All the supernatural personages are alarmingly natural (as theatre nature goes), and walk about in the stupidest way. Which has occasioned Collins and myself to institute a perquisition whether the French ever have shown any kind of idea of the supernatural; and to decide this rather in the negative. The people are very well dressed, and Eve very modestly. All Paris and the provinces had been ransacked for a woman who had brown hair that would fall to the calves of her legs — and she was found at last at the Odéon. There was nothing attractive until the 4th act, when there was a pretty good scene of the Children of Cain dancing in, and desecrating, a temple, while Abel and his family were hammering hard at the Ark, outside, in all the pauses of the revel. The Deluge in the fifth act was up to about the mark of a drowning scene at the Adelphi; but it had one new feature. When the rain ceased, and the ark drove in on the great expanse of water, then lying waveless as the mists cleared and the sun broke out, numbers of bodies drifted up and down. These were all real men and boys, each separate, on a new kind of horizontal float. They looked horrible and real. Altogether, a really dull business; but I dare say it will go for a long while.

To Wilkie Collins

April Thirteenth, 1856

Macready went on Friday to the Rehearsal of Comme il vous plaira which was produced last night. His account of it was absolutely stunning. The speech of the Seven Ages delivered as a Light comedy joke; — Jacques at the Court of the Reigning Duke instead of the banished one, and winding up the thing by marrying Celia! Everything as wide of Shakespeare as possible . . .

To John Forster

[April 1856]

As I have no news, I may as well tell you about the tag that I thought so pretty to the Mémoires du Diable; in which piece by the way, there is a most admirable part, most admirably played, in which a man says merely "Yes" or "No" all through the piece, until the last scene. A certain M. Robin has got hold of the papers of a deceased lawyer, concerning a certain estate which has been swindled away from its rightful owner, a Baron's widow, into other hands. They disclose so much roguery that he binds them up into a volume lettered Mémoires du Diable. The knowledge he derives from these papers not only enables him to unmask the hypocrites all through the piece (in an excellent manner), but induces him to propose to the Baroness that if he restores to her her estate and good name — for even her marriage to the deceased Baron is denied — she shall give him her daughter in marriage. The daughter herself, on hearing the offer, accepts it; and a part of the plot is, her going to a masked ball, to which he goes as the Devil, to see how she likes him (when she finds, of course, that she likes him very much). The country people about the Château in dispute, suppose him to be really the Devil, because of his strange knowledge, and his strange comings and goings; and he, being with this girl in one of its old rooms, in the beginning of the 3rd act, shews her a little coffer on the table with a bell in it. "They suppose," he tells her, "that whenever this bell is rung, I appear and obey the summons. Very ignorant, isn't it? But, if *you* ever want me particularly — very particularly — ring the little bell and try." The plot proceeds to its development. The wrongdoers are exposed; the missing document, proving the marriage, is found; everything is finished; they are all on the stage; and M. Robin hands the paper to the Baroness. "You are reinstated in your rights, Madame; you are happy; I will not hold you to a compact made when you didn't know me; I release you and your fair daughter; the pleasure of doing what I have done, is my sufficient reward; I kiss your hand and take my leave. Farewell!" He backs himself courteously out; the piece seems concluded, everybody wonders, the girl (little Mdlle. Luther) stands amazed; when she suddenly remembers the little bell. In the prettiest way possible, she runs to the coffer on the table, takes out the little bell, rings it, and he comes rushing back and folds her to his heart. I never saw a prettier thing in my life. It made me laugh in that most delightful of ways, with the tears in my eyes; so that I can never forget it, and must go and see it again.

To Wilkie Collins

Twenty-Second April, 1856

Last Friday I took Mrs. Dickens, Georgina, and Mary and Katey, to dine at the Trois Frères. We then, Sir, went off to the Française to see Comme il vous plaira — which is a kind of Theatrical Representation that I think might be got up, with great completeness, by the Patients in the Asylum for Idiots. Dreariness is no word for it, vacancy is no word for it, gammon is no word for it, there *is* no word for it. Nobody has anything to do but to sit upon as many grey stones as he can. When Jacques had sat upon seventy-seven stones and forty-two roots of trees (which was at the end of the second act), we came away. He had by that time been made violent love to by Celia, had shown himself in every phase of his existence to be utterly unknown to Shakespeare, had made the speech about the Seven Ages out of its right place, and apropos of nothing on earth, and had in all respects conducted himself like a brutalized, benighted, and besotted Beast.

Gaslight Fairies

[*This piece was published in* Household Words, *February 2, 1855.*]

Fancy an order for five-and-thirty Fairies! Imagine a mortal in a loose-sleeved great-coat, with the mud of London streets upon his legs, commercially ordering, in the commonplace, raw, foggy forenoon, "five-and-thirty more Fairies"! Yet I, the writer, heard the order given. "Mr. Vernon, let me have five-and-thirty more Fairies tomorrow morning — and take care they are good ones."

Where was it that, towards the close of the year one thousand eight hundred and fifty-four, on a dark December morning, I overheard this astonishing commission given to Mr. Vernon, and by Mr. Vernon accepted without a word of remonstrance and entered in a note-book? It was in a dark, deep gulf of a place, hazy with fog — at the bottom of a sort of immense well without any water in it; remote crevices and chinks of daylight faintly visible on the upper rim; dusty palls enveloping the sides; gas flaring at my feet; hammers going, in invisible workshops; groups of people hanging about, trying to keep their toes and fingers warm, what time their noses were dimly seen through the smoke of their own breath. It was in the strange conventional world where the visible people only, never advance; where the unseen painter learns and changes; where the unseen tailor learns and changes; where the unseen mechanist adapts to his purpose the striding ingenuity of the age; where the electric light comes, in a box that is carried under a man's arm; but, where the visible flesh and blood is so persistent in one routine that, from the waiting-woman's apron-pockets (with her hands in them), upward to the smallest retail article in the "business" of mad Lear with straws in his wig, and downward to the last scene but one of the pantomime, where, for about one hundred years last past, all the characters have entered groping, in exactly the same way, in identically the same places, under precisely the same circumstances, and without the smallest reason — I say, it was in that strange world where the visible population have so completely settled their so-potent art, that when I pay my money at the door I know before-hand everything that can possibly happen to me, inside. It was in the Theatre, that I heard this order given for five-and-thirty Fairies.

And hereby hangs a recollection, not out of place, though not of a Fairy. Once, on just such another December morning, I stood on the same dusty boards, in the same raw atmosphere, intent upon a pantomime-rehearsal. A massive giant's castle arose before me, and the giant's body-guard marched in to comic music; twenty grotesque creatures, with little arms and legs, and enormous faces moulded into twenty varieties of ridiculous leer. One of these faces in particular — an absurdly radiant face, with a wink upon it, and its tongue in its cheek — elicited much approving notice from the authorities, and a ready laugh from the orchestra, and was, for a full half minute, a special success. But, it happened that the wearer of the beaming visage carried a banner; and, not to turn a banner as a procession moves, so as always to keep its decorated side towards the audience, is one of the deadliest sins a banner-bearer can commit. This radiant goblin, being half-blinded by his mask, and further disconcerted by partial suffocation, three distinct times omitted the first duty of man, and petrified us by displaying, with the greatest ostentation, mere sackcloth and timber, instead of the giant's armorial bearings. To crown which offence he couldn't hear when he was called to, but trotted about in his richest manner, unconscious of threats and imprecations. Suddenly, a terrible voice was heard above the music, crying, "Stop!" Dead silence, and we became aware of Jove in the boxes. "Hatchway," cried Jove to the director, "who is that man? Show me that man." Hereupon Hatchway (who had a wooden leg), vigorously apostrophising the defaulter as an "old beast," stumped straight up to the body-guard now in line before the castle, and taking the radiant countenance by the nose, lifted it up as if it were a saucepan-lid, and disclosed below, the features of a bald, superannuated, aged person, very much in want of shaving, who looked in the forlornest way at the spectators, while the large face aslant on the top of his head mocked him. "What! It's *you*, is it?" said Hatchway, with dire contempt. "I thought it was you." "I knew it was that man!" cried Jove. "I told you yesterday, Hatchway, he was not fit for it. Take him away, and bring another." He was ejected with every mark of ignominy, and the inconstant mask was just as funny on another man's shoulders immediately afterwards. To the present day, I never see a very comic pantomime-mask but I wonder whether this wretched old man can possibly have got behind it; and I never think of him as dead and buried (which is far more likely), but I make that absurd countenance a part of his mortality, and picture it to myself as gone the way of all the winks in the world.

Five-and-thirty more Fairies, and let them be good ones. I saw them next day. They ranged from an anxious woman of ten, learned in the prices of victual and fuel, up to a conceited young lady of five times that age, who always persisted in standing on one leg longer than was necessary, with the determination (as I was informed), "to make a Part of it." This Fairy was of long theatrical descent — centuries, I believe — and had never had an ancestor who was entrusted to communicate one word to a British audience. Yet, the whole race had lived and died with the fixed idea of "making a Part of it"; and she, the last of the line, was still unchangeably resolved to go down on one leg to posterity. Her father had fallen a victim to the family ambition; having become in course of time so extremely difficult to "get off," as a villager, seaman, smuggler, or what not, that it was at length considered unsafe to allow him to "go on." Consequently, those neat confidences with the public in which he had displayed the very acme of his art — usually consisting of an explanatory tear, or an arch hint in dumb show of his own personal determination to perish in the attempt then on foot — were regarded as superfluous, and came to be dispensed with, exactly at the crisis when he himself foresaw that he would "be put into Parts" shortly. I had the pleasure of recognising in the character of an Evil Spirit of the Marsh, overcome by this lady with one (as I should else have considered purposeless) poke of a javelin, an actor whom I had formerly encountered in the provinces under circumstances that had fixed him agreeably in my remembrance. The play represented to a nautical audience, was *Hamlet*; and this gentleman having been killed with much credit as Polonius, reappeared in the part of Osric: provided against recognition by the removal of his white wig, and the adjustment round his waist of an extremely broad belt and buckle. He was instantly recognised, notwithstanding these artful precautions, and a solemn impression was made upon the spectators for which I could not account, until a sailor in the Pit drew a long breath, said to himself in a deep voice, "Blowed if here an't another Ghost!" and composed himself to listen to a second communication from the tomb. Another personage whom I recognised as taking refuge under the wings of Pantomime (she was not a Fairy, to be sure, but she kept the cottage to which the Fairies came, and lived in a neat upper bedroom, with her legs obviously behind the street door), was a country manager's wife — a most estimable woman of about fifteen stone, with a larger family than I had ever been able to count: whom I had last seen in Lincolnshire, playing Juliet, while her four youngest children (and nobody else) were in the boxes — hanging out of window, as it were, to trace with their forefingers the pattern on the front, and making all Verona uneasy by their imminent peril of falling into the Pit. Indeed, I had seen this excellent woman in the whole round of Shakesperian beauties, and had much admired her way of getting through the text. If anybody made any remark to her, in reference to which any sort of answer occurred to her mind, she made that answer; otherwise, as a character in the drama, she preserved an impressive silence, and, as an individual, was heard to murmur to the unseen person next in order of appearance, "Come on!" I found her, now, on good motherly terms with the Fairies, and kindly disposed to chafe and warm the fingers of the younger of that race. Out of Fairy-land, I suppose that so many shawls and bonnets of a peculiar limpness were never assembled together. And, as to shoes and boots, I heartily wished that "the good people" were better shod, or were as little liable to take cold as in the sunny days when they were received at Court as Godmothers to Princesses.

Twice a-year, upon an average, these gaslight Fairies appear to us; but, who knows what becomes of them at other times? You are sure to see them at Christmas, and they may be looked for hopefully at Easter; but, where are they through the eight or nine long intervening months? They cannot find shelter under mushrooms, they cannot live upon dew; unable to array themselves in supernatural green, they must even look to Manchester for cotton stuffs to wear. When they become visible, you find them a traditionary people, with a certain conventional monotony in their proceedings which prevents their surprising you very much, save now and then when they appear in company with Mr. Beverley. In a general way, they have been sliding out of the clouds, for some years, like barrels of beer delivering at a public-house. They sit in the same little rattling stars, with glorious corkscrews twirling about them and never drawing anything, through a good many successive seasons. They come up in the same shells out of the same three rows of gauze water (the little ones lying down in front, with their heads diverse ways); and you resign yourself to what must infallibly take place when you see them armed with garlands. You know all you have to expect of them by moonlight. In the glowing day, you are morally certain that the gentleman with the muscular legs and the short tunic (like the Bust at the Hairdresser's, completely carried out), is coming, when you see them "getting over" to one side, while the surprising phenomenon is presented on the landscape of a vast mortal shadow in a hat of the present period, violently directing them so to do. You are acquainted with all these peculiarities of the gaslight Fairies, and you know by heart everything that they will do with their arms and legs, and when they will do it. But, as to the same good people in their invisible condition, it is a hundred to one that you know nothing, and never think of them.

I began this paper with, perhaps, the most curious trait, after all, in the history of the race. They are certain to be found when wanted. Order Mr. Vernon to lay on a hundred and fifty gaslight Fairies next Monday morning, and they will flow into the establishment like so many feet of gas. Every Fairy can bring other Fairies; her sister Jane, her friend Matilda, her friend Matilda's friend, her brother's young family, her mother — if Mr. Vernon will allow that respectable person to pass muster. Summon the Fairies, and Drury Lane, Soho, Somers' Town, and the neighbourhood of the obelisk in St. George's Fields, will become alike prolific in them. Poor, good-humoured, patient, fond of a little self-display, perhaps (sometimes, but far from always), they will come trudging through the mud, leading brother and sister lesser Fairies by the hand, and will hover about in the dark stage-entrances, shivering and chattering in their shrill way, and earning their little money hard, idlers and vagabonds though we may be pleased to think them. I wish, myself, that we were not so often pleased to think ill of those who minister to our amusement. I am far from having satisfied my heart that either we or they are a bit the better for it.

Nothing is easier than for any one of us to get into a pulpit, or upon a tub, or a stump, or a platform, and blight (so far as with our bilious and complacent breath we can), any class of small people we may choose to select. But, it by no means follows that because it is easy and safe, it is right. Even these very gaslight Fairies, now. Why should I be bitter on them because they are shabby personages, tawdrily dressed for the passing hour, and then to be shabby again? I have known very shabby personages indeed — the shabbiest I ever heard of — tawdrily dressed for public performances of other kinds, and performing marvellously ill too, though transcendently rewarded: yet whom none disparaged! In even-handed justice, let me render these little people their due.

Ladies and Gentlemen. Whatever you may hear to the contrary (and may sometimes have a strange satisfaction in believing), there is no lack of virtue and modesty among the Fairies. All things considered, I doubt if they be much below our own high level. In respect of constant acknowledgement of the claims of kindred, I assert for the Fairies, that they yield to no grade of humanity. Sad as it is to say, I have known Fairies even to fall, through this fidelity of theirs. As to young children, sick mothers, dissipated brothers, fathers unfortunate and fathers undeserving, Heaven and Earth, how many of these have I seen clinging to the spangled skirts, and contesting for the nightly shilling or two, of one little lop-sided, weak-legged Fairy!

Let me, before I ring the curtain down on this short piece, take a single Fairy, as Sterne took his Captive, and sketch the Family-Picture. I select Miss Fairy, aged three-and-twenty, lodging within cannon range of Waterloo Bridge, London — not alone, but with her mother, Mrs. Fairy, disabled by Chronic rheumatism in the knees; and with her father, Mr. Fairy, principally employed in lurking about a public-house, and waylaying the theatrical profession for twopence wherewith to purchase a glass of old ale, that he may have something warming on his stomach (which has been cold for fifteen years); and with Miss Rosina Fairy, Miss Angelica Fairy, and Master Edmund Fairy, aged respectively, fourteen, ten, and eight. Miss Fairy has an engagement of twelve shillings a week — sole means of preventing

the Fairy family from coming to a dead lock. To be sure, at this time
of year the three young Fairies have a nightly engagement to come
out of a Pumpkin as French soldiers; but, its advantage to the house-
keeping is rendered nominal, by that dreadful old Mr. Fairy's making
it a legal formality to draw the money himself every Saturday — and
never coming home until his stomach is warmed, and the money
gone. Miss Fairy is pretty too, makes up very pretty. This is a trying
life at the best, but very trying at the worst. And the worst is, that
that always beery old Fairy, the father, hovers about the Stagedoor
four or five nights a week, and gets his cronies among the carpenters
and footmen to carry in messages to his daughter (he is not admitted himself), representing the urgent coldness of his stomach and
his parental demand for twopence; failing compliance with which,
he creates disturbances; and getting which, he becomes maudlin and
waits for the manager, to whom he represents with tears that his
darling child and pupil, the pride of his soul, is "kept down in the
Theatre." A hard life this for Miss Fairy, I say, and a dangerous! And
it is good to see her, in the midst of it, so watchful of Rosina Fairy,
who otherwise might come to harm one day. A hard life this, I say
again, even if John Kemble Fairy, the brother, who sings a good
song, and when he gets an engagement always disappears about the
second week or so and is seen no more, had not a miraculous property
of turning up on a Saturday without any heels to his boots, firmly
purposing to commit suicide, unless bought off with half-a-crown.
And yet — so curious is the gaslighted atmosphere in which these
Fairies dwell! — through all the narrow ways of such an existence,
Miss Fairy never relinquishes the belief that that incorrigible old
Fairy, the father, is a wonderful man! She is immovably convinced
that nobody ever can, or ever could, approach him in Rolla. She has
grown up in this conviction, will never correct it, will die in it. If,
through any wonderful turn of fortune, she were to arrive at the
emolument and dignity of a Free Benefit to-morrow, she would
"put up" old Fairy, red nosed, stammering and imbecile — with delirium tremens shaking his very buttons off — as the noble Peruvian,
and would play Cora herself, with a profound belief in his taking
the town by storm at last.

The Lighthouse

[*Wilkie Collins's "regular old-style melodrama," The Lighthouse, was privately performed in the schoolroom at Dickens's home, Tavistock House, before wildly enthusiastic invited audiences on the evenings of June 15, 16, 18, and 19, 1855. The production created such a furore that Dickens gave it again on July 10 at Campden House, Kensington, for the benefit of the Bournemouth Sanatorium for Consumptives.*]

To Clarkson Stanfield

Twentieth May, 1855

I have a little lark in contemplation, if you will help it to fly.

Collins has done a melodrama (a regular old-style melodrama), in which there is a very good notion. I am going to act it, as an experiment, in the children's theatre here — I, Mark, Collins, Egg, and my daughter Mary, the whole *dram. pers.*; our families and yours the whole audience; for I want to make the stage large and shouldn't have room for above five-and-twenty spectators. Now, there is only one scene in the piece, and that, my tarry lad, is the inside of a lighthouse. Will you come and paint it for us one night, and we'll all turn to and help? It is a mere wall, of course, but Mark and I have sworn that you must do it. If you will say yes, I should like to have the tiny flats made, after you have looked at the place, and not before. On Wednesday in this week I am good for a steak and the play, if you will make your own appointment here; or any day next week except Thursday. Write me a line in reply. We mean to burst on an astonished world with the melodrama, without any note of preparation. So don't say a syllable to Forster if you should happen to see him.

Twenty-Second May, 1855

I only wait your instructions to get the little canvases made. O, what a pity it is not the outside of the Light-'us, with the sea a-rowling agin it! Never mind, we'll get an effect out of the inside, and there's a storm and shipwreck "off;" and the great ambition of my life will be achieved at last, in the wearing of a pair of very coarse petticoat trousers. So hooroar for the salt sea, Mate, and bowse up!

To Mark Lemon

Twenty-Third May, 1855

Stanny says he is only sorry it is not the outside of the lighthouse with a raging sea and a transparent light. He enters into the project with the greatest delight, and I think we shall make a capital thing of it.

It now occurs to me that we may as well do a farce too. I should like to get in a little part for Katey, and also for Charley, if it were practicable. What do you think of Animal Mag.? You and I in our old parts; Collins, Jeffrey; Charley, the Markis; Katey and Mary (or Georgina), the two ladies? Can you think of anything merry that is better? It ought to be broad, as a relief to the melodrama, unless we could find something funny with a story in it too. I rather incline myself to Animal Mag. Will you come round and deliver your sentiments?

To Miss Coutts

Nineteenth June, 1855

The audience were not so *demonstrative* last night as on Saturday, and the Corps Dramatique were disposed to think them "flat." I observed however that they were crying vigorously, and I think they were quite as much moved and pleased as on Saturday, though they did not cheer the actors on so much — except in the Farce. Everybody played exactly as on the previous night — including Mr. Forster, who buffeted the guests (I am informed) in the same light and airy manner. Mrs. Stanfield was mollified, and certainly seemed to have been hustled out of the house on Saturday Night, like a species of pick-pocket. Lady Becher was evidently very much impressed and surprised, and Mrs. Yates said (with a large, red circle round each eye), "O Mr. Dickens what a pity it is you can do anything else!" Longman the bookseller was seen to cry dreadfully — and I don't know that anything could be said beyond that!

Little Dorrit and the Ballet

[Little Dorrit *was published in monthly installments between De-*
cember 1855 and June 1857. Amy Dorrit, the "Little Dorrit" of the
story, and her sister Fanny are the daughters of a gentleman confined
in the Marshalsea for debt, and have spent their lives surrounded by
its prisoners. The scenes given are from Book I, Chapters 7 and 20.]

Once, among the heterogeneous crowd of inmates there appeared
a dancing-master. Her sister had a great desire to learn the dancing-
master's art, and seemed to have a taste that way. At thirteen years
old, the Child of the Marshalsea presented herself to the dancing-
master, with a little bag in her hand, and preferred her humble pe-
tition.

"If you please, I was born here, sir."

"Oh! You are the young lady, are you?" said the dancing-master,
surveying the small figure and uplifted face.

"Yes, sir."

"And what can I do for you?" said the dancing-master.

"Nothing for me, sir, thank you," anxiously undrawing the strings
of the little bag; "but if, while you stay here, you could be so kind as
to teach my sister cheap —"

"My child, I'll teach her for nothing," said the dancing-master,
shutting up the bag. He was as good-natured a dancing-master as
ever danced to the Insolvent Court, and he kept his word. The sister
was so apt a pupil, and the dancing-master had such abundant leisure
to bestow upon her (for it took him a matter of ten weeks to set to his
creditors, lead off, turn the Commissioners, and right and left back to
his professional pursuits), that wonderful progress was made. Indeed
the dancing-master was so proud of it, and so wishful to display it be-

fore he left, to a few select friends among the collegians, that at six
o'clock on a certain fine morning, a minuet de la cour came off in the
yard — the college-rooms being of too confined proportions for the
purpose — in which so much ground was covered, and the steps were
so conscientiously executed, that the dancing-master, having to play
the kit besides, was thoroughly blown. . . .

The sister became a dancer. There was a ruined uncle in the family
group — ruined by his brother, the Father of the Marshalsea, and
knowing no more how than his ruiner did, but accepting the fact as
an inevitable certainty — on whom her protection devolved. Naturally a retired and simple man, he had shown no particular sense of
being ruined, at the time when that calamity fell upon him, further
than that he left off washing himself when the shock was announced,
and never took to that luxury any more. He had been a very indifferent musical amateur in his better days; and when he fell with his
brother, resorted for support to playing a clarionet as dirty as himself
in a small Theatre Orchestra. It was the theatre in which his niece
became a dancer; he had been a fixture there a long time when she
took her poor station in it; and he accepted the task of serving as
her escort and guardian, just as he would have accepted an illness, a
legacy, a feast, starvation — anything but soap.

Little Dorrit was almost as ignorant of the ways of theatres as of
the ways of gold mines, and when she was directed to a furtive sort
of door, with a curious up-all-night air about it, that appeared to be
ashamed of itself and to be hiding in an alley, she hesitated to approach it; being further deterred by the sight of some half-dozen
close-shaved gentlemen, with their hats very strangely on, who were
lounging about the door, looking not at all unlike Collegians. On her
applying to them, reassured by this resemblance, for a direction to
Miss Dorrit, they made way for her to enter a dark hall — it was more
like a great grim lamp gone out than anything else — where she
could hear the distant playing of music and the sound of dancing
feet. A man so much in want of airing that he had a blue mould
upon him, sat watching this dark place from a hole in a corner, like a
spider; and he told her that he would send a message up to Miss Dorrit by the first lady or gentleman who went through. The first lady
who went through had a roll of music, half in her muff and half out
of it, and was in such a tumbled condition altogether, that it seemed

as if it would be an act of kindness to iron her. But as she was very good-natured, and said "Come with me; I'll soon find Miss Dorrit for you," Miss Dorrit's sister went with her, drawing nearer and nearer at every step she took in the darkness, to the sound of music and the sound of dancing feet.

At last they came into a maze of dust, where a quantity of people were tumbling over one another, and where there was such a confusion of unaccountable shapes of beams, bulkheads, brick walls, ropes, and rollers, and such a mixing of gaslight and daylight, that they seemed to have got on the wrong side of the pattern of the universe. Little Dorrit, left to herself, and knocked against by somebody every moment, was quite bewildered when she heard her sister's voice.

"Why, good gracious, Amy, what ever brought you here?"

"I wanted to see you, Fanny dear; and as I am going out all day to-morrow, and knew you might be engaged all day to-day, I thought —"

"But the idea, Amy, of *you* coming behind! I never did!" As her sister said this in no very cordial tone of welcome, she conducted her to a more open part of the maze, where various golden chairs and tables were heaped together, and where a number of young ladies were sitting on anything they could find, chattering. All these young ladies wanted ironing, and all had a curious way of looking everywhere while they chattered.

Just as the sisters arrived here, a monotonous boy in a Scotch cap put his head round a beam on the left, and said, "Less noise there, ladies!" and disappeared. Immediately after which, a sprightly gentleman with a quantity of long black hair looked round a beam on the right, and said, "Less noise there, darlings!" and also disappeared.

"The notion of you among professionals, Amy, is really the last thing I could have conceived!" said her sister. "Why, how did you ever get here?"

The monotonous boy put his head round the beam on the left, and said, "Look out there, ladies!" and disappeared. The sprightly gentleman with the black hair as suddenly put his head round the beam on the right, and said, "Look out there, darlings!" and also disappeared. Thereupon all the young ladies rose, and began shaking their skirts out behind. . . .

"Now, ladies!" said the boy in the Scotch cap. "Now, darlings!"

said the gentleman with the black hair. They were every one gone in a moment, and the music and the dancing feet were heard again.

Little Dorrit sat down in a golden chair, made quite giddy by these rapid interruptions. Her sister and the rest were a long time gone; and during their absence a voice (it appeared to be that of the gentleman with the black hair) was continually calling out through the music, "One, two, three, four, five, six — go! One, two, three, four, five, six — go! Steady, darlings! One, two, three, four, five, six — go!" Ultimately the voice stopped, and they all came back again, more or less out of breath, folding themselves in their shawls, and making ready for the streets. "Stop a moment, Amy, and let them get away before us," whispered Fanny. They were soon left alone; nothing more important happening, in the meantime, than the boy looking round his old beam, and saying, "Everybody at eleven to-morrow, ladies!" and the gentleman with the black hair looking round his old beam, and saying, "Everybody at eleven to-morrow, darlings!" each in his own accustomed manner.

The Frozen Deep

[*Wilkie Collins wrote this play between April and October 1856, William Telbin painted the scenery for the first act and Clarkson Stanfield that for the succeeding two. Dickens acted the principal part and Collins the supporting one of Frank Aldersley. The four private performances at Tavistock House in January 1857 were followed by the wild whirl of the Jerrold benefits — before the Queen and then for the general public at the Gallery of Illustration in London during July, and still later ones that August in the Free Trade Hall at Manchester. In his angry disillusion with the world and the deepening misery of his marital unhappiness, Dickens flung himself into the anguished role of Richard Wardour with an excitement hardly short of frenzy. This last of Dickens's performances on the theatrical stage was the climax of his triumphs as a play-actor.*]

To W. H. WILLS

Sixth April, 1856

CHRISTMAS.

Collins and I have a mighty original notion (mine in the beginning) for another Play at Tavistock House. I purpose opening on Twelfth Night, the theatrical season of that great establishment. But now a tremendous question. Is

Mrs. Wills!

game to do a Scotch Housekeeper, in a supposed country-house with Mary, Katey, Georgina, &c. If she can screw her courage up to saying

Yes, that country house opens the piece in a singular way, and that Scotch housekeeper's part shall flow from the present pen. If she says No (but she won't), no Scotch Housekeeper can be. The Tavistock House Season of 4 nights pauses for a reply. Scotch song (new and original) of Scotch Housekeeper, would pervade the piece.

To W. C. MACREADY

Thirteenth December, 1856

You may faintly imagine, my venerable friend, the occupation of these also gray hairs, between Golden Marys, Little Dorrits, Household Wordses, four stage-carpenters entirely boarding on the premises, a carpenter's shop erected in the back-garden, size always boiling over on all the lower fires, Stanfield perpetually elevated on planks and splashing himself from head to foot, Telbin requiring impossibilities of swart gasmen, and a legion of prowling nondescripts for ever shirking in and out. Calm amidst the wreck, your aged friend glides away on the Dorrit stream, forgetting the uproar for a stretch of hours, refreshing himself with a ten or twelve miles' walk, pitches headforemost into foaming rehearsals, placidly emerges for editorial purposes, smokes over buckets of distemper with Mr. Stanfield aforesaid, — again calmly floats upon the Dorrit waters.

To W. F. DE CERJAT

Seventeenth January, 1857

Workmen are now battering and smashing down my theatre here, where we have just been acting a new play of great merit, done in what I may call (modestly speaking of the getting-up, and not of the acting) an unprecedented way. I believe that anything so complete has never been seen. We had an act at the North Pole, where the slightest and greatest thing the eye beheld were equally taken from the books of the Polar voyagers. Out of thirty people, there were certainly not two who might not have gone straight to the North Pole itself, completely furnished for the winter! And now it is a mere chaos of scaffolding, ladders, beams, canvases, paint-pots, sawdust, artificial snow, gas-pipes, and ghastliness. I have taken such pains with it for these ten weeks in all my leisure hours, that I feel now shipwrecked — as if I had never been without a play on my hands before.

To Miss Mary Boyle

Seventh February, 1857

For about ten minutes after his death, on each occasion of that event occurring, — Richard Wardour was in a floored condition. And one night, to the great terror of Devonshire, the Arctic Regions, and Newfoundland (all of which localities were afraid to speak to him, as his ghost sat by the kitchen fire in its rags), he very nearly did what he never did — went and fainted off, dead — again. But he always plucked up, on the turn of ten minutes, and became facetious.

Likewise he chipped great pieces out of all his limbs (solely, as I imagine, from moral earnestness and concussion of passions, for I never knew him to hit himself in any way) and terrified Aldersley to that degree, by lunging at him to carry him into the cave, that the said Aldersley always shook like a mould of jelly, and muttered. "This is an awful thing!"

To Mrs. Watson

Seventh December, 1857

All last summer I had a transitory satisfaction in rending the very heart out of my body by doing that Richard Wardour part. It was a good thing to have a couple of thousand people all rigid and frozen together, in the palm of one's hand — as at Manchester — and to see the hardened Carpenters at the sides crying and trembling at it night after night. Which reminds me of a pretty little story about it. We engaged for Manchester a young lady from Kean's Theatre — Miss Maria Ternan — born on the stage, and inured to it from the days when she was a little child in Pizarro. She had been brought to the Gallery of Illustration in town, to see the Play; and when she came on to me in the morning at Manchester, I said, "Why my dear, how cold your hand is, and what a tremble you are in! This won't do at night."—"Oh, Mr. Dickens," she said, "I am so afraid I can't bear it, that I hope you'll be very gentle with me this morning. I cried so much when I saw it, that I have a dread of it, and I don't know what to do." She had to take my head up as I was dying, and to put it in her lap, and give me her face to hold between my two hands. All of which I showed her elaborately (as Mary had done it before), that morning. When we came to that point at night, her tears fell down my face, down my beard (excuse my mentioning that hateful appenage), down my ragged dress — poured all over me like Rain, so that it was as much as I could do to speak for them. I whispered to her, "My dear child, it will be over in two minutes. Pray, compose yourself." — "It's no comfort to me that it will be soon over," she answered. "Oh it is so sad, it is so dreadfully sad. Oh don't die! Give me time, give me a little time! Don't take leave of me in this terrible way — pray, pray, pray!!" Whereupon Lemon, the softest-hearted of men, began to cry too, and then they all went at it together. I think I never saw such a pretty little genuine emotion in my life. And if you had seen the poor little thing, when the Curtain fell, put in a chair behind it — with her mother and sister taking care of her — and your humble servant drying her eyes and administering Sherry (in Rags so horrible that they would scarcely hold together), and the people in front all blowing their noses, and our own people behind standing about in corners and getting themselves right again, you would have remembered it for a long, long time.

Marston's *A Hard Struggle* and Marie Wilton as a Boy

[These two theater-letters of the year 1858 need no explanation, but one might note, as an evidence of the psychological perception Dickens brought to the drama, his protest against a man's crushing in his hand a letter from the woman he loves.]

To John Forster

Third February, 1858

I beg to report two phenomena:

1. An excellent little play in one act, by Marston, at the Lyceum; title, A Hard Struggle; as good as La Joie fait Peur, though not at all like it.

2. Capital acting in the same play, by Mr. Dillon. Real good acting, in imitation of nobody, and honestly made out by himself!!

I went (at Marston's request) last night, and cried till I sobbed again. I have not seen a word about it from Oxenford. But it is as wholesome and manly a thing altogether as I have seen for many a day. (I would have given a hundred pounds to have played Mr. Dillon's part.)

To Dr. Westland Marston

Third February, 1858

I most heartily and honestly congratulate you on your charming little piece. It moved me more than I could easily tell you, if I were to try. Except La Joie fait Peur, I have seen nothing nearly so good, and there is a subtlety in the comfortable presentation of the child who is to become a devoted woman for Reuben's sake, which goes a long way beyond Madame de Girardin. I am at a loss to let you know how much I admired it last night, or how heartily I cried over it. A touching idea, most delicately conceived and wrought out by a true artist and poet, in a spirit of noble, manly generosity, that no one should be able to study without great emotion.

It is extremely well acted by all concerned; but Mr. Dillon's performance is really admirable, and deserving of the highest commendation. It is good in these days to see an actor taking such pains, and expressing such natural and vigorous sentiment. There is only one thing I should have liked him to change. I am much mistaken if any man — least of all any such man — would crush a letter written by the hand of the woman he loved. Hold it to his heart unconsciously and look about for it the while, he might; or he might do anything with it that expressed a habit of tenderness and affection in association with the idea of her; but he would never crush it under any circumstances. He would as soon crush her heart.

You will see how closely I went with him by my minding so slight an incident in so fine a performance. There is no one who could approach him in it; and I am bound to add that he surprised me as much as he pleased me.

I think it might be worth while to try the people at the Français with the piece. They are very good in one-act plays; such plays take well there, and this seems to me well suited to them. If you would like Samson or Régnier to read the play (in English) I know them well, and would be very glad indeed to tell them that I sent it with your sanction because I had been so much struck by it.

To John Forster

17th December 1858

I escaped at half-past seven, and went to the Strand Theatre: having taken a stall beforehand, for it is always crammed. I really wish you would go, between this and next Thursday, to see the Maid and the Magpie burlesque there. There is the strangest thing in it that ever I have seen on the stage. The boy, Pippo, by Miss Wilton. While it is astonishingly impudent (must be, or it couldn't be done at all), it is so stupendously like a boy, and unlike a woman, that it is perfectly free from offence. I never have seen such a thing. Priscilla Horton, as a boy, not to be thought of beside it. She does an imitation of the dancing of the Christy Minstrels — wonderfully clever — which, in the audacity of its thorough-going, is surprising. A thing that you *can not* imagine a woman's doing at all; and yet the manner, the appearance, the levity, impulse, and spirits of it, are so exactly like a boy that you cannot think of anything like her sex in association with it. It begins at 8, and is over by a quarter-past 9. I never have seen such a curious thing, and the girl's talent is unchallengeable. I call her the cleverest girl I have ever seen on the stage in my time, and the most singularly original.

Wopsle and the Decline of the Drama

[Great Expectations *appeared in Dickens's weekly,* All the Year Round, *between December 1, 1859, and August 3, 1860. Pip's "great expectations" and their disappointment are echoed with variations in the blighted plans of many other characters in the novel — notably Mr. Wopsle, once the clerk at their little village church, has gone on and grotesquely counterpointed in the frustration of Wopsle's hopes of "reviving the drama." Our three scenes are from Chapter 27, Chapters 30 and 31, and Chapter 47. The first opens with Joe Gargery, the country blacksmith, coming to London and bringing Pip word that Mr. Wopsle, once the clerk at their little village church, has gone on the stage and is appearing in* Hamlet.]

"Wopsle: he's had a drop." . . .

"Had a drop, Joe?"

"Why yes," said Joe, lowering his voice, "he's left the Church and went into the playacting. Which the playacting have likewise brought him to London along with me. And his wish were," said Joe, getting the bird's-nest under his left arm for the moment, and groping in it for an egg with his right; "if no offence, as I would 'and you that."

I took what Joe gave me, and found it to be the crumpled playbill of a small metropolitan theatre, announcing the first appearance, in that very week, of "the celebrated Provincial Amateur of Roscian renown, whose unique performance in the highest tragic walk of our National Bard has lately occasioned so great a sensation in local dramatic circles."

"Were you at his performance, Joe?" I inquired.

"I *were*," said Joe, with emphasis and solemnity.

"Was there a great sensation?"

"Why," said Joe, "yes, there certainly were a peck of orangepeel. Partickler when he see the ghost. Though I put it to yourself, sir, whether it were calc'lated to keep a man up to his work with a good hart, to be continiwally cutting in betwixt him and the Ghost with 'Amen!' A man may have had a misfortun' and been in the Church," said Joe, lowering his voice to an argumentative and feeling tone, "but that is no reason why you should put him out at such a time. Which I meantersay, if the ghost of a man's own father cannot be allowed to claim his attention, what can, Sir? Still more, when his mourning 'at is unfortunately made so small as that the weight of the black feathers brings it off, try to keep it on how you may."

[*Not until some time later, when Pip is talking in their chambers with his friend and roommate Herbert Pocket, does he find the theatrical handbill Joe gave him.*]

As we contemplated the fire . . . I put my hands in my pockets. A folded piece of paper in one of them attracting my attention, I opened it and found it to be the playbill I had received from Joe, relative to the celebrated provincial amateur of Roscian renown. "And bless my heart," I involuntarily added aloud, "it's to-night!"

This changed the subject in an instant, and made us hurriedly resolve to go to the play. So . . . we blew out our candles, made up our fire, locked our door, and issued forth in quest of Mr. Wopsle and Denmark.

On our arrival in Denmark, we found the king and queen of that country elevated in two arm-chairs on a kitchen-table, holding a Court. The whole of the Danish nobility were in attendance; consisting of a noble boy in the wash-leather boots of a gigantic ancestor, a venerable Peer with a dirty face, who seemed to have risen from the people late in life, and the Danish chivalry with a comb in its hair and a pair of white silk legs, and presenting on the whole a feminine appearance. My gifted townsman stood gloomily apart, with folded arms, and I could have wished that his curls and forehead had been more probable.

Several curious little circumstances transpired as the action proceeded. The late king of the country not only appeared to have been troubled with a cough at the time of his decease, but to have taken it with him to the tomb, and to have brought it back. The royal phantom also carried a ghostly manuscript round its truncheon, to which it had the appearance of occasionally referring, and that, too, with an air of anxiety and a tendency to lose the place of reference which were suggestive of a state of mortality. It was this, I conceive, which led to the Shade's being advised by the gallery to "turn over!" — a recommendation which it took extremely ill. It was likewise to be noted of this majestic spirit that whereas it always appeared with an air of having been out a long time and walked an immense distance, it perceptibly came from a closely-contiguous wall. This occasioned its terrors to be received derisively. The Queen of Denmark, a very buxom lady, though no doubt historically brazen, was considered by the public to have too much brass about her; her chin being attached to her diadem by a broad band of that metal (as if she had a gorgeous toothache), her waist being encircled by another, and each of her arms by another, so that she was openly mentioned as "the kettledrum." The noble boy in the ancestral boots, was inconsistent; representing himself, as it were in one breath, as an able seaman, a strolling actor, a gravedigger, a clergyman, and a person of the utmost importance at a Court fencing-match, on the authority of whose practised eye and nice discrimination the finest strokes were judged. This gradually led to a want of toleration for him, and even — on his being detected in holy orders, and declining to perform the funeral service — to the general indignation taking the form of nuts. Lastly, Ophelia was a prey to such slow musical madness, that when, in course of time, she had taken off her white muslin scarf, folded it up, and buried it, a sulky man who had been long cooling his impatient nose against an iron bar in the front row of the gallery, growled, "Now the baby's put to bed, let's have supper!" Which, to say the least of it, was out of keeping.

Upon my unfortunate townsman all these incidents accumulated with playful effect. Whenever that undecided Prince had to ask a question or state a doubt, the public helped him out with it. As for example; on the question whether 'twas nobler in the mind to suffer, some roared yes, and some no, and some inclining to both opinions said "toss up for it;" and quite a Debating Society arose. When he asked what should such fellows as he do crawling between earth and

heaven, he was encouraged with loud cries of "Hear, hear!" When he
appeared with his stocking disordered (its disorder expressed, according to usage, by one very neat fold in the top, which I suppose to be
always got up with a flat iron), a conversation took place in the gallery respecting the paleness of his leg, and whether it was occasioned
by the turn the ghost had given him. On his taking the recorders —
very like a little black flute that had just been played in the orchestra
and handed out at the door — he was called upon unanimously for
Rule Britannia. When he recommended the player not to saw the air
thus, the sulky man said, "And don't *you* do it, neither; you're a deal
worse than *him!*" And I grieve to add that peals of laughter greeted
Mr. Wopsle on every one of these occasions.

But his greatest trials were in the churchyard: which had the appearance of a primeval forest, with a kind of small ecclesiastical washhouse on one side, and a turnpike gate on the other. Mr. Wopsle, in
a comprehensive black cloak, being descried entering at the turnpike,
the gravedigger was admonished in a friendly way, "Look out! Here's
the undertaker a coming, to see how you're getting on with your
work!" I believe it is well known in a constitutional country that Mr.
Wopsle could not possibly have returned the skull, after moralising
over it, without dusting his fingers on a white napkin taken from his
breast; but even that innocent and indispensable action did not pass
without the comment "Wai-ter!" The arrival of the body for inter-
ment (in an empty black box with the lid tumbling open), was the
signal for a general joy which was much enhanced by the discovery,
among the bearers, of an individual obnoxious to identification. The
joy attended Mr. Wopsle through his struggle with Laertes on the
brink of the orchestra and the grave, and slackened no more until he
had tumbled the king off the kitchen-table, and had died by inches
from the ankles upward.

We had made some pale efforts in the beginning to applaud Mr.
Wopsle; but they were too hopeless to be persisted in. Therefore we
had sat, feeling keenly for him, but laughing, nevertheless, from ear
to ear. I laughed in spite of myself all the time, the whole thing was
so droll; and yet I had a latent impression that there was something
decidedly fine in Mr. Wopsle's elocution — not for old associations'
sake, I am afraid, but because it was very slow, very dreary, very up-
hill and down-hill, and very unlike any way in which any man in any

natural circumstances of life or death ever expressed himself about anything. When the tragedy was over, and he had been called for and hooted, I said to Herbert, "Let us go at once, or perhaps we shall meet him."

We made all the haste we could downstairs, but we were not quick enough either. Standing at the door was a Jewish man with an un-natural heavy smear of eyebrow, who caught my eyes as we advanced, and said, when we came up with him:

"Mr. Pip and friend?"

Identity of Mr. Pip and friend confessed.

"Mr. Waldengarver," said the man, "would be glad to have the honour."

"Waldengarver?" I repeated — when Herbert murmured in my ear, "Probably Wopsle."

"Oh!" said I. "Yes. Shall we follow you?"

"A few steps, please." When we were in a side alley, he turned and asked, "How do you think he looked? — I dressed him."

I don't know what he had looked like, except a funeral; with the addition of a large Danish sun or star hanging round his neck by a blue ribbon, that had given him the appearance of being insured in some extraordinary Fire Office. But I said he had looked very nice.

"When he come to the grave," said our conductor, "he showed his cloak beautiful. But, judging from the wing, it looked to me that when he see the ghost in the queen's apartment, he might have made more of his stockings."

I modestly assented, and we all fell through a little dirty swing door, into a sort of hot packing-case immediately behind it. Here Mr. Wopsle was divesting himself of his Danish garments, and here there was just room for us to look at him over one another's shoulders, by keeping the packing-case door, or lid, wide open.

"Gentlemen," said Mr. Wopsle, "I am proud to see you. I hope, Mr. Pip, you will excuse my sending round. I had the happiness to know you in former times, and the Drama has ever had a claim which has ever been acknowledged, on the noble and the affluent."

Meanwhile, Mr. Waldengarver, in a frightful perspiration, was trying to get himself out of his princely sables.

"Skin the stockings off, Mr. Waldengarver," said the owner of that property, "or you'll bust 'em. Bust 'em and you'll bust five-and-thirty shillings. Shakspeare never was complimented with a finer pair. Keep quiet in your chair now, and leave 'em to me."

With that, he went upon his knees, and began to flay his victim; who, on the first stocking coming off, would certainly have fallen over backward with his chair, but for there being no room to fall anyhow.

I had been afraid until then to say a word about the play. But then, Mr. Waldengarver looked up at us complacently, and said:

"Gentlemen, how did it seem to you, to go, in front?"

Herbert said from behind (at the same time poking me), "capitally." So I said "capitally."

"How did you like my reading of the character, gentlemen?" said Mr. Waldengarver, almost, if not quite, with patronage.

Herbert said from behind (again poking me), "massive and concrete." So I said boldly, as if I had originated it, and must beg to insist upon it, "massive and concrete."

"I am glad to have your approbation, gentlemen," said Mr. Waldengarver, with an air of dignity, in spite of his being ground against the wall at the time, and holding on by the seat of the chair.

"But I'll tell you one thing, Mr. Waldengarver," said the man who was on his knees, "in which you're out in your reading. Now mind! I don't care who says contrary; I tell you so. You're out in your reading of Hamlet when you get your legs in profile. The last Hamlet as I dressed, made the same mistakes in his reading at rehearsal, till I got him to put a large red wafer on each of his shins, and then at that rehearsal (which was the last) I went in front, sir, to the back of the pit, and whenever his reading brought him into profile, I called out 'I don't see no wafers!' And at night his reading was lovely."

Mr. Waldengarver smiled at me, as much to say "a faithful dependent — I overlook his folly;" and then said aloud, "My view is a little classic and thoughtful for them here; but they will improve, they will improve."

Herbert and I said together, Oh, no doubt they would improve.

"Did you observe, gentlemen," said Mr. Waldengarver, "that there was a man in the gallery who endeavoured to cast derision on the service — I mean, the representation?"

We basely replied that we rather thought we had noticed such a man. I added, "He was drunk, no doubt."

"Oh dear no, sir," said Mr. Wopsle, "not drunk. His employer would see to that, sir. His employer would not allow him to be drunk."

"You know his employer?" said I.

Mr. Wopsle shut his eyes, and opened them again; performing both ceremonies very slowly. "You must have observed, gentlemen," said he, "an ignorant and a blatant ass, with a rasping throat and a countenance expressive of low malignity, who went through — I will not say sustained — the rôle (if I may use a French expression) of Claudius King of Denmark. That is his employer, gentlemen. Such is the profession!"

Without distinctly knowing whether I should have been more sorry for Mr. Wopsle if he had been in despair, I was so sorry for him as it was, that I took the opportunity of his turning round to have his braces put on — which jostled us out at the doorway — to ask Herbert what he thought of having him home to supper? Herbert said he thought it would be kind to do so; therefore I invited him, and he went to Barnard's with us, wrapped up to the eyes, and we did our best for him, and he sat until two o'clock in the morning, reviewing his success and developing his plans. I forgot in detail what they were, but I have a general recollection that he was to begin with reviving the Drama, and to end with crushing it; inasmuch as his decease would leave it utterly bereft and without a chance or hope.

[*The last stage in Wopsle's tragic downfall takes place on a cold February night several years later.*]

As it was a raw evening and I was cold, I thought I would comfort myself with dinner at once; and as I had hours of dejection and solitude before me if I went home to the Temple, I thought I would afterwards go to the play. The theatre where Mr. Wopsle had achieved his questionable triumph, was in that water-side neighbourhood (it is nowhere now), and to that theatre I resolved to go.

I was aware that Mr. Wopsle had not succeeded in reviving the drama, but, on the contrary, had rather partaken of its decline. He had been ominously heard of, through the playbills, as a faithful Black, in connection with a little girl of noble birth, and a monkey. And Herbert had seen him as a predatory Tartar, of comic propensities, with a face like a red brick, and an outrageous hat all over bells.

I dined at what Herbert and I used to call a Geographical chop-house — where there were maps of the world in porter-pot rims on every half-yard of the table-cloths, and charts of gravy on every one of the knives — to this day there is scarcely a single chop-house within the Lord Mayor's dominions which is not Geographical — and wore out the time in dozing over crumbs, staring at gas, and baking in a hot blast of dinners. By-and-bye, I roused myself and went to the play.

There I found a virtuous boatswain in his Majesty's service — a most excellent man, though I could have wished his trousers not quite so tight in some places and not quite so loose in others — who knocked all the little men's hats over their eyes, though he was very generous and brave, and who wouldn't hear of anybody's paying taxes, though he was very patriotic. He had a bag of money in his pocket, like a pudding in the cloth, and on that property married a young person in bed-furniture, with great rejoicings; the whole population of Portsmouth (nine in number at the last Census) turning out on the beach, to rub their own hands, and shake everybody else's, and sing, "Fill, fill!" A certain dark-complexioned Swab, however, who wouldn't fill, or do anything else that was proposed to him, and whose heart was openly stated (by the boatswain) to be as black as his figure-head, proposed to two other Swabs to get all mankind into difficulties; which was so effectually done (the Swab family having considerable political influence) that it took half the evening to set things right, and then it was only brought about through an honest little grocer with a white hat, black gaiters, and red nose, getting into a clock, with a gridiron, and listening, and coming out, and knocking everybody down from behind with the gridiron whom he couldn't confute with what he had overheard. This led to Mr. Wopsle's (who had never been heard of before) coming in with a star and garter on, as a plenipotentiary of great power direct from the Admiralty, to say that the Swabs were all to go to prison on the spot, and that he had brought the boatswain down the Union Jack, as a slight acknowledgment of his public services. The boatswain, unmanned for the first time, respectfully dried his eyes on the Jack, and then cheering up and addressing Mr. Wopsle as Your Honour, solicited permission to take him by the fin. Mr. Wopsle conceding his fin with a gracious dignity, was immediately shoved into a dusty corner, while everybody danced a hornpipe; and from the corner, surveying the public with a discontented eye, became aware of me.

The second piece was the last new grand comic Christmas pantomime, in the first scene of which, it pained me to suspect that I detected Mr. Wopsle with red worsted legs under a highly magnified phosphoric countenance and a shock of red curtain-fringe for his hair, engaged in the manufacture of thunderbolts in a mine, and displaying great cowardice when his gigantic master came home (very hoarse) to dinner. But he presently presented himself under worthier circumstances; for, the Genius of Youthful Love being in want of assistance — on account of the parental brutality of an ignorant farmer who opposed the choice of his daughter's heart, by purposely falling upon the object in a flour sack, out of the first-floor window — summoned a sententious Enchanter; and he, coming up from the antipodes rather unsteadily, after an apparently violent journey, proved to be Mr. Wopsle in a high-crowned hat, with a necromantic work in one volume under his arm. The business of this enchanter on earth being principally to be talked at, sung at, butted at, danced at, and flashed at with fires of various colours, he had a good deal of time on his hands.

A Cheap Theatre

[*The following is part of an article, "Two Views of a Cheap Thea-tre," which appeared in* All the Year Round, *February 25, 1860.*]

As I shut the door of my lodging behind me, and came out into the streets at six on a drizzling Saturday evening in the last past month of January, all that neighbourhood of Covent-garden looked very desolate. It is so essentially a neighbourhood which has seen better days, that bad weather affects it sooner than another place which has not come down in the world. In its present reduced condition it bears a thaw almost worse than any place I know. It gets so dreadfully low-spirited when damp breaks forth. Those wonderful houses about Drury-lane Theatre, which in the palmy days of theatres were prosperous and long-settled places of business, and which now change hands every week, but never change their character of being divided and sub-divided on the ground floor into mouldy dens of shops where an orange and half-a-dozen nuts, or a pomatum-pot, one cake of fancy soap, and a cigar box, are offered for sale and never sold, were most ruefully contemplated that evening, by the statue of Shakespeare, with the rain-drops coursing one another down its innocent nose. Those inscrutable pigeon-hole offices, with nothing in them (not so much as an inkstand) but a model of a theatre before the curtain, where, in the Italian Opera season, tickets at reduced prices are kept on sale by nomadic gentlemen in smeary hats too tall for them, whom one occasionally seems to have seen on race-courses, not wholly unconnected with strips of cloth of various colours and a rolling ball — those Bedouin establishments, deserted by the tribe, and tenantless, except when sheltering in one corner an irregular row of ginger-beer-bottles, which would have made one shudder on such a night, but for its being plain that they had nothing in them, shrunk from the shrill cries of the newsboys at their Exchange in the kennel of Catherine-street, like guilty things upon a fearful summons. At the pipeshop in Great Russell-street, the Death's-head pipes were like theatrical memento mori, admonishing beholders of the decline of the playhouse as an Institution. I walked up Bow-street, disposed to be angry with the shops there, that were letting out theatrical secrets by exhibiting to work-a-day humanity the stuff of which diadems and robes of kings are made. I noticed that some shops which had once been in the dramatic line, and had struggled out of it, were not getting on prosperously — like some actors I have known, who took to business and failed to make it answer. In a word, those streets looked so dull, and, considered as theatrical streets, so broken and bankrupt, that the FOUND DEAD on the black board at the police station might have announced the decease of the Drama, and the pools of water outside the fire-engine makers at the corner of Long-acre might have been occasioned by his having brought out the whole of his stock to play upon its last smouldering ashes.

And yet, on such a night in so degenerate a time, the object of my journey was theatrical. And yet within half an hour I was in an immense theatre, capable of holding nearly five thousand people.

What Theatre? Her Majesty's? Far better. Royal Italian Opera? Far better. Infinitely superior to the latter for hearing in; infinitely superior to both, for seeing in. To every part of this Theatre, spacious fireproof ways of ingress and egress. For every part of it, convenient places of refreshment and retiring rooms. Everything to eat and drink carefully supervised as to quality, and sold at an appointed price; respectable female attendants ready for the commonest women in the audience; a general air of consideration, decorum, and supervision, most commendable; an unquestionably humanising influence in all the social arrangement of the place.

Surely a dear Theatre, then? Because there were in London (not very long ago) Theatres with entrance-prices up to half-a-guinea a head, whose arrangements were not half so civilised. Surely, therefore, a dear Theatre? Not very dear. A gallery at threepence, another gallery at fourpence, a pit at sixpence, boxes and pit-stalls at a shilling, and a few private-boxes at half-a-crown.

My uncommercial curiosity induced me to go into every nook of this great place, and among every class of the audience assembled in it — amounting that evening, as I calculated, to about two thousand and odd hundreds. Magnificently lighted by a firmament of sparkling chandeliers, the building was ventilated to perfection. My sense of smell, without being particularly delicate, has been so offended in some of the commoner places of public resort, that I have often been obliged to leave them when I have made an uncommercial journey expressly to look on. The air of this Theatre was fresh, cool, and wholesome. To help towards this end, very sensible precautions had been used, ingeniously combining the experience of hospitals and railway stations. Asphalt pavements substituted for wooden floors, honest bare walls of glazed brick and tile — even at the back of the boxes — for plaster and paper, no benches stuffed, and no carpeting or baize used; a cool material with a light glazed surface, being the covering of the seats.

These various contrivances are as well considered in the place in question as if it were a Fever Hospital; the result is, that it is sweet and healthful. It has been constructed from the ground to the roof, with a careful reference to sight and sound in every corner; the result is, that its form is beautiful, and that the appearance of the audience, as seen from the proscenium — with every face in it commanding the stage, and the whole so admirably raked and turned to that centre, that a hand can scarcely move in the great assemblage without the movement being seen from thence — is highly remarkable in its union of vastness with compactness. The stage itself, and all its appurtenances of machinery, cellarage height and breadth, are on a scale more like the Scala at Milan, or the San Carlo at Naples, or the Grand Opera at Paris, than any notion a stranger would be likely to form of the Britannia Theatre at Hoxton, a mile north of St. Luke's Hospital in the Old-street-road, Loudon. The Forty Thieves might be played here, and every thief ride his real horse, and the disguised captain bring in his oil jars on a train of real camels, and nobody be put out of the way. This really extraordinary place is the achievement of one man's enterprise, and was erected on the ruins of an inconvenient old building in less than five months, at a round cost of five-and-twenty thousand pounds. To dismiss this part of my subject, and still to render to the proprietor the credit that is strictly his due, I must add that his sense of the responsibility upon him to make the best of his audience, and to do his best for them, is a highly agreeable sign of these times.

As the spectators at this theatre, for a reason I will presently show, were the object of my journey, I entered on the play of the night as one of the two thousand and odd hundreds, by looking about me at my neighbours. We were a motley assemblage of people, and we had a good many boys and young men among us; we had also many girls and young women. To represent, however, that we did not include a very great number, and a very fair proportion of family groups, would be to make a gross misstatement. Such groups were to be seen in all parts of the house; in the boxes and stalls particularly, they were composed of persons of very decent appearance, who had many children with them. Among our dresses there were most kinds of shabby and greasy wear, and much fustian and corduroy that was neither sound nor fragrant. The caps of our young men were mostly of a limp character, and we who wore them, slouched, high-shouldered, into our places with our hands in our pockets, and occasionally twisted our cravats about our necks like eels, and occasionally tied them down our breasts like links of sausages, and occasionally had a screw in our hair over each cheekbone with a slight Thief-flavour in it. Besides prowlers and idlers, we were mechanics, dock-labourers, costermongers, petty tradesmen, small clerks, milliners, stay-makers, shoebinders, slop workers, poor workers in a hundred highways and byways. Many of us — on the whole, the majority — were not at all clean, and not at all choice in our lives or conversation. But we had all come together in a place where our convenience was well consulted, and where we were well looked after, to enjoy an evening's entertainment in common. We were not going to lose any part of what we had paid for through anybody's caprice, and as a community we had a character to lose. So, we were closely attentive, and kept excellent order; and let the man or boy who did otherwise instantly get out from this place, or we would put him out with the greatest expedition.

We began at half-past six with a pantomime — with a pantomime so long, that before it was over I felt as if I had been travelling for six weeks — going to India, say, by the Overland Mail. The Spirit of Liberty was the principal personage in the Introduction, and the Four Quarters of the World came out of the glove, glittering, and discoursed with the Spirit, who sang charmingly. We were delighted to understand that there was no liberty anywhere but among ourselves, and we highly applauded the agreeable fact. In an allegorical way, which did as well as any other way, we and the Spirit of Liberty got into a kingdom of Needles and Pins, and found them at war with a potentate who called in to his aid their old arch enemy Rust, and who would have got the better of them if the Spirit of Liberty had not in the nick of time transformed the leaders into Clown, Pantaloon, Harlequin, Columbine, Harlequina, and a whole family of Sprites, consisting of a remarkably stout father and three spineless sons. We all knew what was coming when the Spirit of Liberty addressed the king with a big face, and His Majesty backed to the side-scenes and began untying himself behind, with his big face all on one side. Our excitement at that crisis was great, and our delight unbounded. After this era in our existence, we went through all the incidents of a pantomime; it was not by any means a savage pantomime, in the way of burning or boiling people, or throwing them out of window, or cutting them up; was often very droll; was always liberally got up, and cleverly presented. I noticed that the people who kept the shops, and who represented the passengers in the thoroughfares, and so forth, had no conventionality in them, but were unusually like the real thing — from which I infer that you may take that audience in (if you wish to) concerning Knights and Ladies, Fairies, Angels, or such like, but they are not to be done as to anything in the streets. I noticed, also, that when two young men, dressed in exact imitation of the eel-and-sausage-cravated portion of the audience, were chased by policemen, and, finding themselves in danger of being caught, dropped so suddenly as to oblige the policemen to tumble over them, there was great rejoicing among the caps — as though it were a delicate reference to something they had heard of before.

The Pantomime was succeeded by a Melo-Drama. Throughout the evening I was pleased to observe Virtue quite as triumphant as she usually is out of doors, and indeed I thought rather more so. We all agreed (for the time) that honesty was the best policy, and we were as hard as iron upon Vice, and we wouldn't hear of Villainy getting on in the world — no, not on any consideration whatever.

Between the pieces, we almost all of us went out and refreshed. Many of us went the length of drinking beer at the bar of the neighbouring public-house, some of us drank spirits, crowds of us had sandwiches and ginger-beer at the refreshment-bars established for us in the Theatre. The sandwich — as substantial as was consistent with portability, and as cheap as possible — we hailed as one of our greatest institutions. It forced its way among us at all stages of the entertainment, and we were always delighted to see it; its adaptability to the varying moods of our nature was surprising; we could never weep so comfortably as when our tears fell on our sandwich; we could never laugh so heartily as when we choked with sandwich; Virtue never looked so beautiful or Vice so deformed as when we paused, sandwich in hand, to consider what would come of that resolution of Wickedness in boots, to sever Innocence in flowered chintz from Honest Industry in striped stockings. When the curtain fell for the night, we still fell back upon sandwich, to help us through the rain and mire, and home to bed.

Poor Mercantile Jack

[This is part of an article of the same title which appeared in All the Year Round *on March 10, 1860, dealing with the saloons, cabarets, gambling dens, and brothels that preyed on merchant sailors in seaports like Liverpool.]*

The uncommerical transaction which had brought me and Jack together, was this: — I had entered the Liverpool police-force, that I might have a look at the various unlawful traps which are every night set for Jack. As my term of service in that distinguished corps was short, and as my personal bias in the capacity of one of its members has ceased, no suspicion will attach to my evidence that it is an admirable force. Besides that it is composed, without favour, of the best men that can be picked, it is directed by an unusual intelligence. Its organisation against Fires, I take to be much better than the metropolitan system, and in all respects it tempers its remarkable vigilance with a still more remarkable discretion.

Jack had knocked off work in the docks some hours, and I had taken, for purposes of identification, a photograph-likeness of a thief, in the portrait-room at our head police office (on the whole, he seemed rather complimented by the proceeding), and I had been on police parade, and the small hand of the clock was moving on to ten, when I took up my lantern to follow Mr. Superintendent to the traps that were set for Jack. In Mr. Superintendent I saw, as anybody might, a tall well-looking well set-up man of a soldierly bearing, with a cavalry air, a good chest, and a resolute but not by any means ungentle face. He carried in his hand a plain black walkingstick of hard wood; and whenever and wherever, at any after-time of the night, he struck it on the pavement with a ringing sound, it instantly produced a whistle out of the darkness, and a policeman. To this remarkable stick, I refer an air of mystery and magic which pervaded the whole of my perquisition among the traps that were set for Jack.

We began by diving into the obscurest streets and lanes of the port. Suddenly pausing in a flow of cheerful discourse, before a dead wall, apparently some ten miles long, Mr. Superintendent struck upon the ground, and the wall opened and shot out, with military salute of hand to temple, two policemen — not in the least surprised themselves, not in the least surprising Mr. Superintendent.

"All right, Sharpeye?"

"All right, sir."

"All right, Trampfoot?"

"All right, sir."

"Is Quickear there?"

"Here am I, sir."

"Come with us."

"Yes, sir."

So Sharpeye went before, and Mr. Superintendent and I went next, and Trampfoot and Quickear marched as rear-guard. Sharpeye, I soon had occasion to remark, had a skilful and quite professional way of opening doors — opened every door he touched, as if he were perfectly confident that there was stolen property behind it — instantly insinuated himself, to prevent its being shut.

Sharpeye opened several doors of traps that were set for Jack, but Jack did not happen to be in any of them. They were all such miserable places that really, Jack, if I were you, I would give them a wider berth. In every trap, somebody was sitting over a fire, waiting for Jack. Now, it was a crouching old woman, like the picture of the Norwood Gipsy in the old sixpenny dream-books; now, it was a crimp of the male sex, in a checked shirt and without a coat, reading a newspaper; now, it was a man crimp and a woman crimp, who always introduced themselves as united in holy matrimony; now, it was Jack's delight, his (un)lovely Nan; but they were all waiting for Jack, and were all frightfully disappointed to see us.

"Who have you got up-stairs here?" says Sharpeye, generally. (In the Move-on tone.)

"Nobody, surr; sure not a blessed sowl!" (Irish feminine reply.)

"What do you mean by nobody? Didn't I hear a woman's step go up-stairs when my hand was on the latch?"

"Ah! sure thin you're right. surr, I forgot her! 'Tis on'y Betsy White, surr. Ah! you know Betsy, surr. Come down, Betsy darlin', and say the gintlemin."

Generally, Betsy looks over the banisters (the steep staircase is in the room) with a forcible expression in her protesting face, of an intention to compensate herself for the present trial by grinding Jack finer than usual when he does come. Generally, Sharpeye turns to Mr. Superintendent, and says, as if the subjects of his remarks were wax-work:

"One of the worst, sir, this house is. This woman has been indicted three times. This man's a regular bad one likewise. His real name is Pegg. Gives himself out as Waterhouse."

"Never had sitch a name as Pegg near me back, thin, since I was in this house, bee the good Lard!" says the woman.

Generally, the man says nothing at all, but becomes exceedingly round-shouldered, and pretends to read his paper with rapt attention. Generally, Sharpeye directs our observation with a look, to the prints and pictures that are invariably numerous on the walls. Always, Trampfoot and Quickear are taking notice on the doorstep. In default of Sharpeye being acquainted with the exact individuality of any gentleman encountered, one of these two is sure to proclaim from the outer air, like a gruff spectre, that Jackson is not Jackson, but knows himself to be Fogle; or that Canlon is Walker's brother, against whom there was not sufficient evidence; or that the man who says he never was at sea since he was a boy, came ashore from a voyage last Thursday, or sails to-morrow morning. "And that is a bad class of man, you see," says Mr. Superintendent, when he got out into the dark again, "and very difficult to deal with, who, when he has made this place too hot to hold him, enters himself for a voyage as steward or cook, and is out of knowledge for months, and then turns up again worse than ever."

When we had gone into many such houses, and had come out (always leaving everybody relapsing into waiting for Jack), we started off to a singing-house where Jack was expected to muster strong.

The vocalisation was taking place in a long low room up-stairs; at one end, an orchestra of two performers, and a small platform; across the room, a series of open pews for Jack, with an aisle down the middle; at the other end a larger pew than the rest, entitled SNUG, and reserved for mates and similar good company. About the room, some amazing coffee-coloured pictures varnished an inch deep, and some stuffed creatures in cases; dotted among the audience, in Snug and out of Snug, the "Professionals;" among them, the celebrated comic favourite Mr. Banjo Bones, looking very hideous with his blackened face and limp sugar-loaf hat; beside him, sipping rum-and-water, Mrs. Banjo Bones, in her natural colours — a little heightened.

It was a Friday night, and Friday night was considered not a good night for Jack. At any rate, Jack did not show in very great force even here, though the house was one to which he much resorts, and where a good deal of money is taken. There was British Jack, a little maudlin and sleepy, lolling over his empty glass, as if he were trying to read his fortune at the bottom; there was Loafing Jack of the Stars and Stripes, rather an unpromising customer with his long nose, lank cheek, high cheek-bones, and nothing soft about him but his cabbage-leaf hat; there was Spanish Jack, with curls of black hair, rings in his ears, and a knife not far from his hand, if you got into trouble with him; there were Maltese Jack, and Jack of Sweden, and Jack the Finn, looming through the smoke of their pipes, and turning faces that looked as if they were carved out of dark wood, towards the young lady dancing the hornpipe: who found the platform so exceedingly small for it, that I had a nervous expectation of seeing her, in the backward steps, disappear through the window. Still, if all hands had been got together, they would not have more than half-filled the room. Observe, however, said Mr. Licensed Victualler, the host, that it was Friday night, and, besides, it was getting on for twelve, and Jack had gone aboard. A sharp and watchful man, Mr. Licensed Victualler, the host, with tight lips and a complete edition of Cocker's arithmetic in each eye. Attended to his business himself, he said. Always on the spot. When he heard of talent, trusted nobody's account of it, but went off by rail to see it. If true talent, engaged it. Pounds a week for talent — four pound — five pound. Banjo Bones was undoubted talent. Hear this instrument that was going to play — it was real talent! In truth it was very good; a kind of piano-accordion, played by a young girl of a delicate prettiness of face, figure, and dress, that made the audience look coarser. She sang to the instrument, too; first, a song about village bells, and how they chimed; then a song about how I went to sea; winding up with an imitation of the bagpipes, which Mercantile Jack seemed to understand much the best. A good girl, said Mr. Licensed Victualler. Kept herself select. Sat in Snug, not listening to the blandishments of Mates. Lived with mother. Father dead. Once a merchant well to do, but over-speculated himself. On delicate inquiry as to salary paid for item of talent under consideration, Mr. Victualler's pounds dropped suddenly to shillings — still it was a very confortable thing for a young person like that, you know; she only went on six times a night, and was only required to be there from six at night to twelve. What was more conclusive was, Mr. Victualler's assurance that he "never allowed any language, and never suffered any disturbance." Sharpeye confirmed the statement, and the order that prevailed was the best proof of it that could have been cited. So, I came to the conclusion that poor Mercantile Jack might do (as I am afraid he does) much worse than trust himself to Mr. Victualler, and pass his evenings here.

But we had not yet looked, Mr. Superintendent — said Trampfoot, receiving us in the street again with military salute — for Dark Jack. True, Trampfoot. Ring the wonderful stick, rub the wonderful lantern, and cause the spirits of the stick and lantern to convey us to the Darkies.

There was no disappointment in the matter of Dark Jack; *he* was producible. The Genii set us down in the little first floor of a little public-house, and there, in a stiflingly close atmosphere, were Dark Jack, and Dark Jack's delight, his *white* unlovely Nan, sitting against the wall all around the room. More than that: Dark Jack's delight was the least unlovely Nan, both morally and physically, that I saw that night.

As a fiddle and tambourine band were sitting among the company, Quickear suggested why not strike up? "Ah, la'ads!" said a negro sitting by the door, "gib the jebblem a darnse. Tak' yah pardlers, jebblem, for 'um QUAD-rill."

This was the landlord, in a Greek cap, and a dress half Greek and half English. As master of the ceremonies, he called all the figures, and occasionally addressed himself parenthetically — after this manner. When he was very loud, I use capitals.

"Now den! Hoy! ONE. Right and left. (Put a steam on, gib 'um powder.) LA-dies' chail. BAL-loon say. Lemonade! Two. ADwarnse and go back (gib 'ell a breakdown, shake it out o' yerselbs, keep a movil). SWING-corners, BAL-loon say, and Lemonade! (Hoy!) THREE. GENT come for'ard with a lady and go back, hoppersite come for'ard and do what yer can. (Aeiohoy!) BAL-loon say, and leetle lemonade (Dat hair nigger by 'um fireplace 'hind a' time, shake it out o' yerselbs, gib 'ell a breakdown). Now den! Hoy! FOUR! Lemonade. BAL-loon say, and swing. FOUR ladies meets in 'um middle, FOUR gents goes round 'um ladies, FOUR gents passes out under 'um ladies' arms, SWING — and Lemonade till 'a moosic can't play no more! (Hoy, Hoy!)"

The male dancers were all blacks, and one was an unusually powerful man of six feet three or four. The sound of their flat feet on the floor was as unlike the sound of white feet as their faces were unlike white faces. They toed and heeled, shuffled, double-shuffled, double-double-shuffled, covered the buckle, and beat the time out, rarely, dancing with a great show of teeth, and with a childish good-humoured enjoyment that was very prepossessing. They generally kept together, these poor fellows, said Mr. Superintendent, because they were at a disadvantage singly, and liable to slights in the neighbouring streets. But, if I were Light Jack, I should be very slow to interfere oppressively with Dark Jack, for, whenever I have had to do with him I have found him a simple and a gentle fellow. Bearing this in mind, I asked his friendly permission to leave him restoration of beer, in wishing him good night, and thus it fell out that the last words I heard him say as I blundered down the worn stairs, were, "Jebblem's elth! Ladies drinks fust!"

The night was now well on into the morning, but, for miles and hours we explored a strange world, where nobody ever goes to bed, but everybody is eternally sitting up, waiting for Jack. This exploration was among a labyrinth of dismal courts and blind alleys, called Entries, kept in wonderful order by the police, and in much better order than by the corporation: the want of gaslight in the most dangerous and infamous of these places being quite unworthy of so spirited a town. I need describe but two or three of the houses in which Jack was waited for as specimens of the rest. Many we attained by noisome passages so profoundly dark that we felt our way with our hands. Not one of the whole number we visited, was without its show of prints and ornamented crockery; the quantity of the latter set forth on little shelves and in little cases, in otherwise wretched rooms, indicating that Mercantile Jack must have an extraordinary fondness for crockery, to necessitate so much of that bait in his traps.

Among such garniture, in one front parlour in the dead of the night, four women were sitting by a fire. One of them had a male child in her arms. On a stool among them was a swarthy youth with a guitar, who had evidently stopped playing when our footsteps were heard.

"Well! how do *you* do?" says Mr. Superintendent, looking about him.

"Pretty well, sir, and hope you gentlemen are going to treat us ladies, now you have come to see us."

"Order there!" says Sharpeye.

"None of that!" says Quickear.

Trampfoot, outside, is heard to confide to himself, "Meggisson's lot this is. And a bad 'un!"

"Well!" says Mr. Superintendent, laying his hand on the shoulder of the swarthy youth, "and who's this?"

"Antonio, sir."

"And what does *he* do here?"

"Come to give us a bit of music. No harm in that, I suppose?"

"A young foreign sailor?"

"Yes. He's a Spaniard. You're a Spaniard, ain't you, Antonio?"

"Me Spanish."

"And he don't know a word you say, not he; not if you was to talk to him till doomsday." (Triumphantly, as if it redounded to the credit of the house.)

"Oh, yes, if you like. Play something, Antonio. *You* ain't ashamed to play something; are you?"

The cracked guitar raises the feeblest ghost of a tune, and three of the women keep time to it with their heads, and the fourth with the child. If Antonio has brought any money in with him, I am afraid he will never take it out, and it even strikes me that his jacket and the tinkling of the instrument so change the place in a moment to a leaf out of Don Quixote, that I wonder where his mule is stabled, until he leaves off.

I am bound to acknowledge (as it tends rather to my uncommercial confusion), that I occasioned a difficulty in this establishment, by having taken the child in my arms. For, on my offering to restore it to a ferocious joker not unstimulated by rum, who claimed to be its mother, that unnatural parent put her hands behind her, and declined to accept it; backing into the fireplace, and very shrilly declaring, regardless of remonstrance from her friends, that she knowed it to be Law, that whoever took a child from its mother of his own will, was bound to stick to it. The uncommercial sense of being in a rather ridiculous position with the poor little child beginning to be frightened, was relieved by my worthy friend and fellow-constable, Trampfoot; who, laying hands on the article as if it were a Bottle, passed it on to the nearest woman, and bade her "take hold of that." As we came out the Bottle was passed to the ferocious joker, and they all sat down as before, including Antonio and the guitar. It was clear that there was no such thing as a nightcap to this baby's head, and that even he never went to bed, but was always kept up — and would grow up, kept up — waiting for Jack.

Later still in the night, we came (by the court "where the man was murdered," and by the other court across the street, into which his body was dragged) to another parlour in another Entry, where several people were sitting round a fire in just the same way. It was a dirty and offensive place, with some ragged clothes drying in it; but there was a high shelf over the entrance-door (to be out cf the reach of marauding hands, possibly) with two large white loaves on it, and a great piece of Cheshire cheese.

"Well!" says Mr. Superintendent, with a comprehensive look all round. "How do you do?"

"Not much to boast of, sir." From the curtseying woman of the house. "This is my good man, sir."

"You are not registered as a common Lodging House?"

"No, sir."

Sharpeye (in the Move-on tone) puts in the pertinent inquiry, "Then why ain't you?"

"Ain't got no one here, Mr. Sharpeye," rejoins the woman and my good man together, "but our own family."

"How many are you in family?"

The woman takes time to count, under pretence of coughing, and adds, as one scant of breath, "Seven, sir."

But she has missed one, so Sharpeye, who knows all about it, says: "Here's a young man here makes eight, who ain't of your family?"

"No, Mr. Sharpeye, he's a weekly lodger."

"What does he do for a living?"

The young man here, takes the reply upon himself, and shortly answers, "Ain't got nothing to do."

The young man here, is modestly brooding behind a damp apron pendent from a clothes-line. As I glance at him I become — but I don't know why — vaguely reminded of Woolwich, Chatham, Portsmouth, and Dover. When we get out, my respected fellow-constable Sharpeye addressing Mr. Superintendent, says:

"You noticed that young man, sir, in at Darby's?"

"Yes. What is he?"

"Deserter, sir."

Mr. Sharpeye further intimates that when we have done with his services, he will step back and take that young man. Which in course of time he does: feeling at perfect ease about finding him, and knowing for a moral certainty that nobody in that region will be gone to bed.

Later still in the night, we came to another parlour up a step or two from the street, which was very cleanly, neatly, even tastefully, kept, and in which, set forth on a draped chest of drawers masking the staircase, was such a profusion of ornamental crockery, that it would have furnished forth a handsome sale-booth at a fair. It backed up a stout old lady —HOGARTH drew her exact likeness more than once — and a boy who was carefully writing a copy in a copy-book.

"Well, ma'am, how do you do?"

Sweetly, she can assure the dear gentlemen, sweetly. Charmingly, charmingly. And overjoyed to see us!

"Why, this is a strange time for this boy to be writing his copy. In the middle of the night!"

"So it is, dear gentlemen, Heaven bless your welcome faces and send ye prosperous, but he has been to the Play with a young friend for his diversion, and he combinates his improvement with entertainment, by doing his school-writing afterwards, God be good to ye!"

The copy admonished human nature to subjugate the fire of every fierce desire. One might have thought it recommended stirring the fire, the old lady so approved it. There she sat, rosily beaming at the copy-book and the boy, and invoking showers of blessings on our heads, when we left her in the middle of the night, waiting for Jack.

Later still in the night, we came to a nauseous room with an earth floor, into which the refuse scum of an alley trickled. The stench of this habitation was abominable; the seeming poverty of it, diseased and dire. Yet, here again, was visitor or lodger — a man sitting before the fire, like the rest of them elsewhere, and apparently not distasteful to the mistress's niece, who was also before the fire. The mistress herself had the misfortune of being in jail.

Three weird old women of transcendent ghastliness, were at needlework at a table in the room. Says Trampfoot to First Witch, "What are you making?" Says she, "Money-bags."

"*What* are you making?" retorts Trampfoot, a little off his balance.

"Bags to hold your money," says the witch, shaking her head, and setting her teeth; "you as has got it."

She holds up a common cash-bag, and on the table is a heap of such bags. Witch Two laughs at us. Witch Three scowls at us. Witch sisterhood all, stitch, stitch. First Witch has a red circle round each eye. I fancy it like the beginning of the development of a perverted diabolical halo, and that when it spreads all round her head, she will die in the odour of devilry.

Trampfoot wishes to be informed what First Witch has got behind the table, down by the side of her, there? Witches Two and Three croak angrily, "Show him the child!"

She drags out a skinny little arm from a brown dustheap on the ground. Adjured not to disturb the child, she lets it drop again. Thus we find at least that there is one child in the world of Entries who goes to bed — if this be bed.

Mr. Superintendent asks how long are they going to work at those bags?

How long? First Witch repeats. Going to have supper presently. See the cups and saucers, and the plates.

"Late? Ay! But we has to 'arn our supper afore we eats it!" Both the other witches repeat this after First Witch, and take the Uncommercial measurement with their eyes, as for a charmed winding-sheet.

Some grim discourse ensues, referring to the mistress of the cave, who will be released from jail to-morrow. Witches pronounce Tramp-foot "right there," when he deems it a trying distance for the old lady to walk; she shall be fetched by niece in a spring-cart.

As I took a parting look at First Witch in turning away, the red marks round her eyes seemed to have already grown larger, and she hungrily and thirstily looked out beyond me into the dark doorway, to see if Jack were there. For, Jack came even here, and the mistress had got into jail through deluding Jack.

When I at last ended this night of travel and got to bed, I failed to keep my mind on comfortable thoughts of Seamen's Homes (not overdone with strictness), and improved dock regulations giving Jack greater benefit of fire and candle aboard ship, through my mind's wandering among the vermin I had seen. Afterwards the same vermin ran all over my sleep. Evermore, when on a breezy day I see Poor Mercantile Jack running into port with a fair wind under all sail, I shall think of the unsleeping host of devourers who never go to bed, and are always in their set traps waiting for him.

Pantomime and Opera

[*The letters dated 1862 and 1863 were all written from Paris. An-dalusia was Lady Molesworth; the picturesque drama in which Charles Fechter scored such a triumph was* The Duke's Motto.]

To Miss Mary Boyle

Twenty-Eighth December, 1860

I pass my time here (I am staying here alone) in working, taking physic, and taking a stall at the Theatre every night. On Boxing Night I was at Covent Garden. A dull pantomime was "worked" (as we say) better than I ever saw a heavy piece worked on a first night, until suddenly and without a moment's warning, every scene on that immense stage fell over on its face, and disclosed Chaos by Gaslight behind! There never was such a business — about sixty people who were on the stage being extinguished in the most re-markable manner. Not a soul was hurt. In the uproar, some moon-calf rescued a porter pot, six feet high (one of which the clown had been drinking when the accident happened), and stood it on the cushion of the lowest Proscenium Box, P.S., beside a lady and gentle-man, who were dreadfully ashamed of it. The moment the House knew that nobody was injured, they directed their whole attention to this gigantic porter pot in its genteel position (the lady and gentle-man trying to hide behind it), and roared with laughter. When a modest footman came from behind the curtain to clear it, and took it up in his arms like a Brobdingnagian Baby, we all laughed more than ever we had laughed in our lives. I don't know why. . . .

The poor actors waylay me in Bow Street to represent their necessities; and I often see one cut down a court when he beholds me coming — cut round Drury Lane to face me — and come up towards me near this door in the freshest and most accidental way; as if I was the last person he expected to see on the surface of this globe. The other day, there thus appeared before me (simultaneously with a scent of rum in the air) one aged and greasy man, with a pair of pumps under his arm. He said he thought if he could get down to somewhere (I think it was Newcastle), he would get "taken on" as Pantaloon, the existing Pantaloon being "a stick, sir — a mere muff." I observed that I was sorry times were so bad with him. "Mr. Dickens, you know our profession, Sir — no one knows it better, Sir — there is no right feeling in it. I was Harlequin on your own circuit, Sir, for five-and-thirty years, and was displaced by a boy, Sir — a boy!"

To John Forster

[November] 1862

Last night I saw Madame Viardot do Gluck's Orphée. It is a most extraordinary performance — pathetic in the highest degree, and full of quite sublime acting. Though it is unapproachably fine from first to last, the beginning of it, at the tomb of Eurydice, is a thing that I cannot remember at this moment of writing, without emotion. It is the finest presentation of grief that I can imagine. And when she has received hope from the Gods, and encouragement to go into the other world and seek Eurydice, Viardot's manner of taking the relinquished lyre from the tomb and becoming radiant again, is most noble. Also she recognizes Eurydice's touch, when at length the hand is put in hers from behind, like a most transcendant genius. And when, yielding to Eurydice's entreaties she has turned round and slain her with a look, her despair over the body is grand in the extreme. It is worth a journey to Paris to see, for there is no such Art to be otherwise looked upon. Her husband stumbled over me by mere chance, and took me to her dressing-room. Nothing could have happened better as a genuine homage to the performance, for I was disfigured with crying.

In the French-Flemish Country

[*This is part of an article of the same title which appeared in* All the Year Round, *September 12, 1863. Dickens does not identify the town, but during the previous February he had been in the north of France, and spent some time at Arras and Amiens.*]

Monsieur P. Salcy, "par permission de M. le Maire," had established his theatre in the whitewashed Hôtel de Ville, on the steps of which illustrious edifice I stood. And Monsieur P. Salcy, privileged director of such theatre, situate in "the first theatrical arrondissement of the department of the North," invited French-Flemish mankind to come and partake of the intellectual banquet provided by his family of dramatic artists, fifteen subjects in number. "La Famille P. Salcy, composée d'artistes dramatiques, au nombre de 15 sujets."

The members of the Family P. Salcy were so fat and so like one another — fathers, mothers, sisters, brothers, uncles, and aunts — that I think the local audience were much confused about the plot of the piece under representation, and to the last expected that everybody must turn out to be the long-lost relative of everybody else. The Theatre was established on the top story of the Hôtel de Ville, and was approached by a long bare staircase, whereon, in an airy situation, one of the P. Salcy Family — a stout gentleman imperfectly repressed by a belt — took the money. This occasioned the greatest excitement of the evening; for, no sooner did the curtain rise on the introductory Vaudeville, and reveal in the person of the young lover (singing a very short song with his eyebrows) apparently the very same identical stout gentleman imperfectly repressed by a belt, than

To Georgina Hogarth

Paris, First Februar

I forgot to tell Mamie that I went (with Andalusia) to hea
last night. It is a splendid work, in which that noble and sad
most nobly and sadly rendered; and it perfectly delighted me.
think it requires too much of the audience, to do for a London
House. The composer must be a very remarkable man indeed.
management of light throughout the story is also very poetical
fine. We had Carvalho's box. I could hardly bear the thing; it
fected me so, and sounded in my ears so like a mournful echo
things that lie in my own heart.

To W. C. Macready

Nineteenth February, 1863

Paris generally is about as wicked and extravagant as in the days of
the Regency. Madame Viardot in the Orphée, most splendid. An
opera of Faust, a very sad and noble rendering of that sad and noble
story. Stage management remarkable for some admirable, and really
poetical, effects of light. In the more striking situations, Mephistopheles surrounded by an infernal red atmosphere of his own.
Marguerite has taken the jewels placed in her way in the garden, a
weird evening draws on, and the bloom fades from the flowers, and
the leaves of the trees droop and lose their fresh green, and mournful
shadows overhang her chamber window, which was innocently bright
and gay at first. I couldn't bear it, and gave in completely.

Fechter doing wonders over the way here, with a picturesque
French drama. Miss Kate Terry, in a small part in it, perfectly charming. You may remember her making a noise, years ago, doing a boy
at an inn, in The Courier of Lyons? She has a tender love-scene in
this piece, which is a really beautiful and artistic thing. I saw her do
it at about three in the morning of the day when the theatre opened,
surrounded by shavings and carpenters, and (of course) with that inevitable hammer going; and I told Fechter: "That is the very best
piece of womanly tenderness I have ever seen on the stage, and you'll
find that no audience can miss it." It is a comfort to add that it was
instantly seized upon, and is much talked of.

To Georgina Hogarth

Paris, First February 1863

I forgot to tell Mamie that I went (with Andalusia) to hear Faust last night. It is a splendid work, in which that noble and sad story is most nobly and sadly rendered; and it perfectly delighted me. But I think it requires too much of the audience, to do for a London Opera House. The composer must be a very remarkable man indeed. Some management of light throughout the story is also very poetical and fine. We had Carvalho's box. I could hardly bear the thing; it affected me so, and sounded in my ears so like a mournful echo of things that lie in my own heart.

To W. C. Macready

Nineteenth February, 1863

Paris generally is about as wicked and extravagant as in the days of the Regency. Madame Viardot in the Orphée, most splendid. An opera of Faust, a very sad and noble rendering of that sad and noble story. Stage management remarkable for some admirable, and really poetical, effects of light. In the more striking situations, Mephistopheles surrounded by an infernal red atmosphere of his own. Marguerite has taken the jewels placed in her way in the garden, a weird evening draws on, and the bloom fades from the flowers, and the leaves of the trees droop and lose their fresh green, and mournful shadows overhang her chamber window, which was innocently bright and gay at first. I couldn't bear it, and gave in completely.

Fechter doing wonders over the way here, with a picturesque French drama. Miss Kate Terry, in a small part in it, perfectly charming. You may remember her making a noise, years ago, doing a boy at an inn, in The Courier of Lyons? She has a tender love-scene in this piece, which is a really beautiful and artistic thing. I saw her do it at about three in the morning of the day when the theatre opened, surrounded by shavings and carpenters, and (of course) with that inevitable hammer going; and I told Fechter: "That is the very best piece of womanly tenderness I have ever seen on the stage, and you'll find that no audience can miss it." It is a comfort to add that it was instantly seized upon, and is much talked of.

In the French-Flemish Country

[*This is part of an article of the same title which appeared in* All the Year Round, *September 12, 1863. Dickens does not identify the town, but during the previous February he had been in the north of France, and spent some time at Arras and Amiens.*]

Monsieur P. Salcy, "par permission de M. le Maire," had established his theatre in the whitewashed Hôtel de Ville, on the steps of which illustrious edifice I stood. And Monsieur P. Salcy, privileged director of such theatre, situate in "the first theatrical arrondissement of the department of the North," invited French-Flemish mankind to come and partake of the intellectual banquet provided by his family of dramatic artists, fifteen subjects in number. "La Famille P. Salcy, composée d'artistes dramatiques, au nombre de 15 sujets."

The members of the Family P. Salcy were so fat and so like one another — fathers, mothers, sisters, brothers, uncles, and aunts — that I think the local audience were much confused about the plot of the piece under representation, and to the last expected that everybody must turn out to be the long-lost relative of everybody else. The Theatre was established on the top story of the Hôtel de Ville, and was approached by a long bare staircase, whereon, in an airy situation, one of the P. Salcy Family — a stout gentleman imperfectly repressed by a belt — took the money. This occasioned the greatest excitement of the evening; for, no sooner did the curtain rise on the introductory Vaudeville, and reveal in the person of the young lover (singing a very short song with his eyebrows) apparently the very same identical stout gentleman imperfectly repressed by a belt, than everybody rushed out to the paying-place, to ascertain whether he could possibly have put on that dress-coat, that clear complexion, and those arched black vocal eyebrows, in so short a space of time. It then became manifest that this was another stout gentleman imperfectly repressed by a belt: to whom, before the spectators had recovered their presence of mind, entered a third stout gentleman imperfectly repressed by a belt, exactly like him. These two "subjects," making with the money-taker three of the announced fifteen, fell into conversation touching a charming young widow: who, presently appearing, proved to be a stout lady altogether irrepressible by any means — quite a parallel case to the American Negro — fourth of the fifteen subjects, and sister of the fifth who presided over the check-department. In good time the whole of the fifteen subjects were dramatically presented, and we had the inevitable Ma Mère, Ma Mère! and also the inevitable malédiction d'un père, and likewise the inevitable Marquis, and also the inevitable provincial young man, weakminded but faithful, who followed Julie to Paris, and cried and laughed and choked all at once. The story was wrought out with the help of a virtuous spinning-wheel in the beginning, a vicious set of diamonds in the middle, and a rheumatic blessing (which arrived by post) from Ma Mère towards the end; the whole resulting in a small sword in the body of one of the stout gentlemen imperfectly repressed by a belt, fifty thousand francs per annum and a decoration to the other stout gentleman imperfectly repressed by a belt, and an assurance from everybody to the provincial young man that if he were not supremely happy — which he seemed to have no reason whatever for being — he ought to be. This afforded him a final opportunity of crying and laughing and choking all at once, and sent the audience home sentimentally delighted. Audience more attentive or better behaved there could not possibly be, though the places of second rank in the Theatre of the Family P. Salcy were sixpence each in English money, and the places of first rank a shilling. How the fifteen subjects ever got so fat upon it, the kind Heavens know.

What gorgeous china figures of knights and ladies, gilded till they gleamed again, I might have bought at the Fair for the garniture of my home, if I had been a French-Flemish peasant, and had had the money! What shining coffee-cups and saucers I might have won at the turntables, if I had had the luck! Ravishing perfumery also, and sweetmeats, I might have speculated in, or I might have fired for prizes at a multitude of little dolls in niches, and might have hit the dolls, and won francs and fame. Or, being a French-Flemish youth, I might have been drawn in a hand-cart by my compeers, to tilt for municipal rewards at the water-quintain; which, unless I sent my lance clean through the ring, emptied a full bucket over me; to fend off which, the competitors wore grotesque old scarecrow hats. Or, being French-Flemish man or woman, boy or girl, I might have circled all night on my hobby-horse in a stately cavalcade of hobby-horses four abreast, interspersed with triumphal cars, going round and round and round and round, we the goodly company singing a ceaseless chorus to the music of the barrel-organ, drum, and cymbals. On the whole, not more monotonous than the Ring in Hyde Park, London, and much merrier; for when do the circling company sing chorus, *there*, to the barrel-organ, when do the ladies embrace their horses round the neck with both arms, when do the gentlemen fan the ladies with the tails of their gallant steeds? On all these revolving delights, and on their own especial lamps and Chinese lanterns revolving with them, the thoughtful weaver-face brightens, and the Hôtel de Ville sheds an illuminated line of gaslight: while above it, the Eagle of France, gas-outlined and apparently afflicted with the prevailing infirmities that have lighted on the poultry, is in a very undecided state of policy, and as a bird moulting. Flags flutter all around. Such is the prevailing gaiety that the keeper of the prison sits on the stone steps outside the prison-door, to have a look at the world that is not locked up; while that agreeable retreat, the wine-shop opposite to the prison in the prison-alley (its sign La Tranquillité, because of its charming situation), resounds with the voices of the shepherds and shepherdesses who resort there this festive night. And it reminds me that only this afternoon, I saw a shepherd in trouble, tending this way, over the jagged stones of a neighbouring street. A magnificent sight it was, to behold him in his blouse, a feeble little jog-trot rustic, swept along by the wind of two immense gendarmes, in cocked-hats for which the street was hardly wide enough, each carrying a bundle of stolen property that would not have held his shoulder-knot, and clanking a sabre that dwarfed the prisoner.

"Messieurs et Mesdames, I present to you at this Fair, as a mark

of my confidence in the people of this so-renowned town, and as an
act of homage to their good sense and fine taste, the Ventriloquist,
the Ventriloquist! Further, Messieurs et Mesdames, I present to you
the Face-Maker, the Physiognomist, the great Changer of Countenances, who transforms the features that Heaven has bestowed upon
him into an endless succession of surprising and extraordinary visages,
comprehending, Messieurs et Mesdames, all the contortions, energetic
and expressive, of which the human face is capable, and all the
passions of the human heart, as Love, Jealousy, Revenge, Hatred,
Avarice, Despair! Hi hi, Ho ho, Lu lu, Come in!" To this effect,
with an occasional smite upon a sonorous kind of tambourine —
bestowed with a will, as if it represented the people who don't come
in — holds forth a man of lofty and severe demeanour; a man in
stately uniform, gloomy with the knowledge he possesses of the inner
secrets of the booth. "Come in, come in! Your opportunity presents
itself to-night; to-morrow it will be gone for ever. To-morrow morning by the Express Train the railroad will reclaim the Ventriloquist
and the Face-Maker! Algeria will reclaim the Ventriloquist and the
Face-Maker! Yes! For the honour of their country they have accepted
propositions of a magnitude incredible, to appear in Algeria. See
them for the last time before their departure! We go to commence
on the instant. Hi hi! Ho ho! Lu lu! Come in! Take the money that
now ascends, Madame; but after that, no more, for we commence!
Come in!"

Nevertheless, the eyes both of the gloomy Speaker and of Madame
receiving sous in a muslin bower, survey the crowd pretty sharply
after the ascending money has ascended, to detect any lingering sous
at the turning-point. "Come in, come in! Is there any more money,
Madame, on the point of ascending? If so, we wait for it. If not, we
commence!" The orator looks back over his shoulder to say it, lashing
the spectators with the conviction that he beholds through the folds
of the drapery into which he is about to plunge, the Ventriloquist
and the Face-Maker. Several sous burst out of pockets, and ascend.
"Come up, then, Messieurs!" exclaims Madame in a shrill voice, and
beckoning with a bejewelled finger. "Come up! This presses. Monsieur
has commanded that they commence!" Monsieur dives into his Interior, and the last half-dozen of us follow. His Interior is comparatively severe; his Exterior also. A true Temple of Art needs nothing but

seats, drapery, a small table with two moderator lamps hanging over it, and an ornamental looking-glass let into the wall. Monsieur in uniform gets behind the table and surveys us with disdain, his forehead becoming diabolically intellectual under the moderators. "Messieurs et Mesdames, I present to you the Ventriloquist. He will commence with the celebrated Experience of the bee in the window. The bee, apparently the veritable bee of Nature, will hover in the window, and about the room. He will be with difficulty caught in the hand of Monsieur the Ventriloquist — he will escape — he will again hover — at length he will be recaptured by Monsieur the Ventriloquist, and will be with difficulty put into a bottle. Achieve then, Monsieur!" Here the proprietor is replaced behind the table by the Ventriloquist, who is thin and sallow, and of a weakly aspect. While the bee is in progress, Monsieur the Proprietor sits apart on a stool, immersed in dark and remote thought. The moment the bee is bottled, he stalks forward, eyes us gloomily as we applaud, and then announces, sternly waving his hand: "The magnificent Experience of the child with the whooping-cough!" The child disposed of, he starts up as before. "The superb and extraordinary Experience of the dialogue between Monsieur Tatambour in his dining-room, and his domestic, Jerome, in the cellar; concluding with the songsters of the grove, and the Concert of domestic Farm-yard animals." All this done, and well done, Monsieur the Ventriloquist withdraws, and Monsieur the Face-Maker bursts in, as if his retiring-room were a mile long instead of a yard. A corpulent little man in a large white waistcoat, with a comic countenance, and with a wig in his hand. Irreverent disposition to laugh, instantly checked by the tremendous gravity of the Face-Maker, who intimates in his bow that if we expect that sort of thing we are mistaken. A very little shaving-glass with a leg behind it is handed in, and placed on the table before the Face-Maker. "Messieurs et Mesdames, with no other assistance than this mirror and this wig, I shall have the honour of showing you a thousand characters." As a preparation, the Face-Maker with both hands gouges himself, and turns his mouth inside out. He then becomes frightfully grave again, and says to the Proprietor, "I am ready!" Proprietor stalks forth from baleful reverie, and announces "The Young Conscript!" Face-Maker claps his wig on, hind side before, looks in the glass, and appears above it as a conscript so very imbecile, and squinting so extremely hard, that I should think the State would never get any good of him. Thunders of applause. Face-Maker dips behind the looking-glass, brings his own hair forward, is himself again, is awfully grave. "A distinguished inhabitant of the Faubourg St. Germain." Face-Maker dips, rises, is supposed to be aged, blear-eyed, toothless, slightly palsied, supernaturally polite, evidently of noble birth. "The oldest member of the Corps of Invalides on the fête-day of his master." Face-Maker dips, rises, wears the wig on one side, has become the feeblest military bore in existence, and (it is clear) would lie frightfully about his past achievements, if he were not confined to pantomime. "The Miser!" Face-Maker dips, rises, clutches a bag, and every hair of the wig is on end to express that he lives in continual dread of thieves. "The Genius of France!" Face-Maker dips, rises, wig pushed back and smoothed flat, little cocked-hat (artfully concealed till now) put a-top of it, Face-Maker's white waistcoat much advanced, Face-Maker's left hand in bosom of white waistcoat, Face-Maker's right hand behind his back. Thunders. This is the first of three positions of the Genius of France. In the second position, the Face-Maker takes snuff; in the third, rolls up his right hand, and surveys illimitable armies through that pocket-glass. The Face-Maker then, by putting out his tongue, and wearing the wig nohow in particular, becomes the Village Idiot. The most remarkable feature in the whole of his ingenious performance, is, that whatever he does to disguise himself, has the effect of rendering him rather more like himself than he was at first.

There were peep-shows in this Fair, and I had the pleasure of recognising several fields of glory with which I became well acquainted a year or two ago as Crimean battles, now doing duty as Mexican victories. The change was neatly effected by some extra smoking of the Russians, and by permitting the camp followers free range in the foreground to despoil the enemy of their uniforms. As no British troops had ever happened to be within sight when the artist took his original sketches, it followed fortunately that none were in the way now.

The Fair wound up with a ball. Respecting the particular night of the week on which the ball took place, I decline to commit myself; merely mentioning that it was held in a stable-yard so very close to the railway, that it is a mercy the locomotive did not set fire to it. (In Scotland, I suppose it would have done so.) There, in a tent prettily decorated with looking-glasses and a myriad of toy flags, the people danced all night. It was not an expensive recreation, the price of a double ticket for a cavalier and lady being one and threepence in English money, and even of that small sum fivepence was reclaimable for "consommation;" which world I venture to translate into refreshments of no greater strength, at the strongest, than ordinary wine made hot, with sugar and lemon in it. It was a ball of great good humour and of great enjoyment, though very many of the dancers must have been as poor as the fifteen subjects of the P. Salcy Family.

Play Doctor

[*Dickens conceived a glowing admiration for the actor Charles Fechter, whom he first saw in Paris playing the role of Armand Duval in* La Dame aux Camélias. *Later, Fechter's passionate Hamlet, played with flaxen hair, thrilled by its fiery logic of conception, and his Iago brilliantly gulled his victims with plausible deception. The aid Dickens gave him in staging Bellew's* The King's Butterfly *in 1864 was only the first of his services in such ways; he also helped with J. Palgrave Simpson's dramatization of* The Bride of Lammermoor, *entitled* The Master of Ravenswood *and starring Carlotta Leclercq as Lucy Ashton, and later with Dion Boucicault's play* A Long Strike *and Fechter's highly successful revival of Lytton's romantic drama* The Lady of Lyons.]

To Miss Mary Boyle

Sixth January, 1866

I did not dramatise The Master of Ravenswood, though I did a good deal towards and about the Piece, having an earnest desire to put Scott — for once — upon the stage in his own gallant manner. It is *an enormous success*, and increases in attraction nightly. I have never seen the people in all parts of the house, so leaning forward, in lines sloping towards the stage, earnestly and intently attentive, as while the story gradually unfolds itself. But the astonishing circumstance of all is, that Carlotta, (never thought of for Lucy till all other Lucies had failed) is marvellously good, highly pathetic, and almost unrecognizable in person! What note it touches in her, always dumb until now, I do not pretend to say; but there is no one on the

Stage who could play the contract scene better, or more simply and naturally — and I find it impossible to see it without crying! . . . Almost everyone plays well, the whole is exceedingly picturesque, and there is scarcely a movement throughout, or a look, that is not indicated by Scott. So you get a Live Romance with beautiful illustrations, and I do not expect ever again to see a book take up its bed and walk in like manner.

To Charles Fechter

Fourth September, 1866

This morning I received the play to the end of the telegraph scene, and I have since read it twice.

I clearly see the *ground* of Mr. Boucicault's two objections; but I do not see their *force.*

First, as to the writing. If the characters did not speak in a terse and homely way, their idea and language would be inconsistent with their dress and station, and they would lose, as characters, before the audience. The dialogue seems to be exactly what is wanted. Its simplicity (particularly in Mr. Boucicault's part) is often very effective; and throughout there is an honest, straight-to-the-purpose ruggedness in it, like the real life and the real people.

Secondly, as to the absence of the comic element. I really do not see how more of it could be got into the story, and I think Mr. Boucicault underrates the pleasant effect of his own part. The very notion of a sailor, whose life is not among those little courts and machinery, but with the four wild winds, is a relief to me in reading the play. I am quite confident of its being an immense relief to the audience when they see the sailor before them, with an entirely different bearing, action, dress, complexion even, from the rest of the men. I would make him the freshest and airiest sailor that ever was seen; and through him I can distinctly see my way out of "the Black Country" into clearer air. (I speak as one of the audience, mind.) I should like something of this contrast to be expressed in the dialogue between the sailor and the Jew, in the second scene of the second act. Again, I feel Widdicomb's part (which is charming, and ought to make the whole house cry) most agreeable and welcome, much better than any amount in such a story, of mere comicality.

It is unnecessary to say that the play is done with a master's hand. Its closeness and movement are quite surprising. Its construction is admirable. I have the strongest belief in its making a great success. But I must add this proviso: I never saw a play so dangerously depending in critical places on strict natural propriety in the manner and perfection in the shaping of the small parts. Those small parts cannot take the play up, but they can let it down. I would not leave a hair on the head of one of them to the chance of the first night, but I would see, to the minutest particular, the make-up of every one of them at a night rehearsal.

Of course you are free to show this note to Mr. Boucicault, and I suppose you will do so; let me throw out this suggestion to him and you. Might it not ease the way with the Lord Chamberlain's Office, and still more with the audience, when there are Manchester champions in it, if instead of "Manchester" you used a fictitious name? When I did Hard Times I called the scene Coketown. Everybody knew what was meant, but every cotton-spinning town said it was the other cotton-spinning town.

Sixteenth September, 1867

Going over the prompt-book carefully, I see one change in your part to which (on Lytton's behalf) I positively object, as I am quite certain he would not consent to it. It is highly injudicious besides, as striking out the best known line in the play.

Turn to your part in Act III., the speech beginning

> Pauline, *by pride*
> *Angels have fallen ere thy time: by pride* —

You have made a passage farther on stand:

> *Then did I seek to rise*
> *Out of my mean estate. Thy bright image, etc.*

I must stipulate for your restoring it thus:

> Then did I seek to rise
> Out of the prison of my mean estate;
> And, with such jewels as the exploring mind
> Brings from the caves of knowledge, buy my ransom

From those twin jailers of the daring heart —
Low birth and iron fortune. Thy bright image, etc. etc.

The last figure has been again and again quoted; is identified with the play; is fine in itself; and above all, I KNOW that Lytton would not let it go. In writing to him to-day, fully explaining the changes in detail, and saying that I disapprove of nothing else, I have told him that I notice this change and that I immediately let you know that it must not be made.

(There will not be a man in the house from any newspaper who would not detect mutilations in that speech, moreover.)

To Lord Lytton

Sixteenth September 1867

I have your letter this morning, and I sit down to answer it, with the Prompt Book before me. The play is produced tonight. Of course the word absurdly made "yours" in the Telegram, was really "words."

Here follow the changes. All other changes are of scenic arrangement and stage management.

The play opens thus.

Scene. Exterior of a small village inn. Sign, the Golden Lion.

Beauséant (behind the scenes). Yes, you may bait the horses; we shall rest here an hour.

Enter Beauséant and Glavis. Glavis. Really my dear Beauséant! Consider! Consider that I have promised to spend a day or two with you at your château; that I am quite at your mercy for my entertainment; and yet you are as silent and gloomy as a mute at a funeral, or an Englishman at a party of pleasure — (then as the book goes; until in the book a servant brings in Beauséant's letter). Instead of which, Beauséant himself enters, and says "citizen Melnotte:" to which Melnotte replies "aside" (from "perhaps. — who are you?"). To which Beauséant rejoins: "young man I know thy secret," and speaks the letter word for word.

The Second Act ends with your original ending. Damas finishes his speech with Zounds! I envy you. Claude. Do you?

The first scene of the fifth act has only *two* speaking officers instead of *three.*

The following scene between Damas and Melnotte is slightly cut.

The contract scene is not otherwise touched, then that after Damas' speech about the Arab proverb, Beauséant gets off with "I wish you joy!" (in a burst of spite), and Glavis gets off with him. They then go straight to Melnotte's tag: "Ah the same love that tempts us into sin" — etc.

I noticed that in one of Melnotte's best speeches Fechter has erased three lines, including a passage I am very fond of:

> From those twin jailers of the daring heart,
> Low birth and iron fortune.

I have immediately told him that he must restore that passage, and that I insist (for you) on its being spoken.

Tomorrow I will write you another line, and tell you how the play is put upon the stage, and how the effects struck the audience. . . .

P. S. Fechter has throughout devoutly believed that you sanctioned at Knebworth the omission of your first scene. If I, on seeing it out of the Prompt Book today, had felt it safe, or indeed practicable, to get Pauline down to the Theatre and her wonder about the flowers restored, I should have done so — even at the risk of you yourself having actually considered the omission an improvement.

The mother is not touched. Therefore she is of course not reintroduced after you dismiss her.

The Black Crook

[*This famous and absurd piece of melodramatic hokum Dickens saw at Niblo's Gardens during his second American trip in 1867-1868.*]

To John Forster

New York, 14th December 1867

Niblo's great attraction, the Black Crook, has now been played every night for 16 months (!), and is the most preposterous peg to hang ballets on that was ever seen. The people who act in it have not the slightest idea of what it is about, and never had; but, after taxing my intellectual powers to the utmost, I fancy that I have discovered Black Crook to be a malignant hunchback leagued with the Powers of Darkness to separate two lovers; and that the Powers of Lightness coming (in no skirts whatever) to the rescue, he is defeated. I am quite serious in saying that I do not suppose there are two pages of All the Year Round in the whole piece (which acts all night); the whole of the rest of it being ballets of all sorts, perfectly unaccountable processions, and the Donkey out of last year's Covent Garden pantomime! At the other theatres, comic operas, melodramas, and domestic dramas prevail all over the city, and my stories play no inconsiderable part in them. I go nowhere, having laid down the rule that to combine visiting with my work would be absolutely impossible.

To W. C. Macready

Massachusetts, Twenty-first March 1868

To pass from Boston personal, to New York theatrical, I will mention here that one of the Proprietors of my New York Hotel is one of the Proprietors of Niblo's and the most active. Consequently, I have seen The Black Crook and The White Faun in majesty from an arm-chair in the first entrance P.S. more than once. Of these astonishing dramas, I beg to report (seriously) that I have found no human creature "behind," who has the slightest idea what they are about ('pon my honor, my Dearest Macready!) and that having some amiable small talk with a neat little Spanish woman who is the Première Danseuse, I asked her, in joke, to let me measure her skirt with my dress glove. Holding the glove by the tip of the fore-finger, I found the skirt to be just three gloves long — and yet its length was much in excess of the skirts of 200 other ladies whom the carpenters were, at that moment, getting into their places for a transformation scene — on revolving columns — on wire and travellers — in iron cradles — up in the flies down in the cellars — on every impossible description of float that Wilmot, gone distracted, could imagine.

No Thoroughfare

[*First written for the Christmas number of* All the Year Round *in 1867, of the original narrative Dickens had contributed the "Overture" and "Act III," Collins "Act II," and the two men had collaborated on "Act I" and "Act IV." But, as the titles suggest, the story was designed from the start to be adapted to the stage, and most of this work Collins did, although with countless suggestions from Dickens, carried on by mail even after he had embarked on his reading tour in the United States. The play opened at the Adelphi Theatre on December 26, 1867, with Fechter "magnificent" as the villainous Obenreizer. The play at once became an enormous success. "Charles Dickens and Wilkie Collins have made their dramatic hit at last!" wrote one reviewer. "In* No Thoroughfare *they are both at liberty to enjoy their triumph to the utmost." Entitled* L'Abîme, *it opened in Paris at the Vaudeville Theatre in June 1868, where it was no less enthusiastically received by French audiences.*]

To Wilkie Collins

Twelfth January, 1868

First, of the play. I am truly delighted to learn that it made so great a success, and I hope I may see it on the Adelphi boards. You have had a world of trouble and work with it, but I hope will be repaid in some degree by the pleasure of a triumph. Even for the alteration at the end of the 4th act (of which you tell me in your letter received yesterday), I was fully prepared, for I COULD NOT see the original effect in the reading of the play, and COULD NOT make it go. I agree with Webster in thinking it best that Obenreizer should die on the stage; but no doubt that point is disposed of. In reading the play before the representation, I felt that it was too long, and that there was a good deal of unnecessary explanation. Those points are, no doubt, disposed of too by this time.

To Mrs. James T. Fields

Twenty-Fifth May, 1868

No Thoroughfare is very shortly coming out in Paris, where it is now in active rehearsal. It is still playing here, but without Fechter, who has been very ill. The doctor's dismissal of him to Paris, however, and his getting better there, enables him to get up the play there. He and Wilkie missed so many pieces of stage-effect here, that, unless I am quite satisfied with his report, I shall go over and try my stage-managerial hand at the Vaudeville Theatre. I particularly want the drugging and attempted robbing in the bedroom scene at the Swiss inn to be done to the sound of a waterfall rising and falling with the wind. Although in the very opening of that scene they speak of the waterfall and listen to it, nobody thought of its mysterious music. I could make it, with a good stage carpenter, in an hour. Is it not a curious thing that they want to make me a governor of the Foundling Hospital, because, since the Christmas number, they have had such an amazing access of visitors and money?

To Alfred Harmant

Paris, 2 Juin, 1868

J'ai l'honneur de vous prier de vouloir bien présenter mes vrais remerciements aux artistes qui m'ont prêté leurs concours dans la représentation de *L'Abîme* ce soir; et de les assurer de ma haute et reconnaissante appréciation de leur puissante interprétation de mon drame.

Permettez-moi aussi de vous remercier de la libéralité avec laquelle vous avez mis les ressources de votre excellent Théatre au service d'un écrivain Anglais.

J'espère avant peu, Monsieur, vous exprimer ma gratitude, et remercier vos artistes, *en personne*; mais, forcé de retourner à Londres sans délais, je n'ai pu quitter Paris sans leur adresser, ainsi que vous,

Monsieur, l'expression de ma reconnaissance, et l'assurance de mon parfait dévouement.

To Wilkie Collins

Fourth June, 1868

I have been to Paris. The piece is a genuine and real success. They all agree that if it could have been done at the Porte St. Martin it would have gone 200 nights. I did not see it on the first night, being far too nervous and oppressed by a terrible sense of the helplessness of the situation. Fechter, too, was lead-coloured, and shaking from head to foot. So we took a ride in an open coach, and repaired at intervals to the Café Vaudeville, where Didier (the announced translator) came from act to act with his report. Joey Ladle knew nothing of his part, and made less than nothing of it — all the rest did well. Bertrand was loudly called at the end of the second act, and did his very utmost. There is no doubt whatever that it was a success from first to last. It was too late to make the change when I got to Paris, and Fechter had great faith in the retention of the scene besides; but I am quite certain that the piece would go better without Wilding's death scene. The audience are told (in the person of Vendale) that Wilding is dead, and that is quite enough. I saw our French Wilding after his decease, and could very clearly perceive that he had got mighty little out of it.

"A Theatre Under One Hat"

[*In the public readings of Dickens's last dozen years he attained to the very peak of his career as a dramatist and actor. The dramas and the comedies he himself enacted, alone on his own stage, were indeed dealt with according to his own pleasure and his own judgment, for he molded them out of his own writings, and the players, "a skilled and noble company," every member of which was his own protean self, were absolutely under his command. In essence, he had achieved his "cherished day-dream" of holding supreme authority over a great theater.*

That theater he controlled with a rigor even more relentless than any he had ever exercised over a cast of his fellow-actors. Ruthlessly he pruned away needless description, tightened up dialogue, subjecting his material to drastic cuts, conveying dramatic atmosphere and the appearance and mannerisms of his characters by sheer histrionic brilliance. The margins of his reading copies were punctuated by stage directions to himself in blue ink — "Snap your fingers," "Rising action," "Scrooge melted," "Soften very much," "Beckon down," "Shudder," "Cupboard action," "Bed stooping action," "Terror to the End." Every reading he practiced hundreds of times, striving for perfection of intonation, absolute mastery over every episode. Though for safety he kept the little reading books before him on the stand, he knew each reading by heart, and sometimes engaged in impromptu variations, "gagging" on sudden inspiration, magnetizing his listeners at will.

His reading-stand was one that he had especially designed for the purpose, with a top covered in dark wine-red velvet and a little shelf to the right for a glass and carafe of water and his white kid gloves. Behind rose a large violet-colored screen against which his figure was sharply defined in the glare of the gas flares overhead. Striding on the stage from the wings, the white of his linen silhouetted against the black of his evening dress, a red geranium in his lapel, he calmly waited for the tumultuous applause to die down, for the last latecomer to be seated. He was in no hurry; not until absolute hush had settled over the audience did he utter a word. Then the extraordinary performance began.

Nothing like it had ever been done. "People were taken off their legs"; "it was just one roar with me and them." "Those marvellous characters of his came forth one by one," wrote John Greenleaf Whittier, "real personages, as if their original creator had breathed new life into them. . . . Another such star-shower is not to be expected in one's lifetime." Said the German janitor at Steinway Hall when Dickens read in New York, "Mr. Digguns, you are gread, mein herr. There is no end to you." Then, reopening the door and sticking his head out, "Bedder und bedder," he added; "Wot negst!"

Dickens's repertory came to include sixteen readings all told, including A Christmas Carol, The Chimes, The Cricket on the Hearth, *and selections from* Pickwick, Nicholas Nickleby, Oliver Twist, Martin Chuzzlewit, Dombey and Son, *and* David Copperfield, *as well as some of his other, shorter stories. He also prepared and printed, but never performed, four others, one of which was drawn from* A Tale of Two Cities *and one from* Great Expectations.

His dramatic powers ranged from the pathos of little Paul Dombey's death to the wild courtroom travesty of the trial scene from Pickwick Papers, *and from the youthful romance of David Copperfield's courtship to the tremendous storm at Yarmouth in which Steerforth and Ham Peggotty are drowned. He rollicked in the grotesque farce-comedy of the* Nicholas Nickleby *scenes with the schoolmaster Squeers at Dotheboys Hall, the gasping and ungrammatical volubility of Mrs. Gamp, Bob Sawyer's raffish party and the termagant fury of his landlady Mrs. Raddle. He excited his listeners with the Christmas pantomime transformation of Scrooge, moved them to laughter and tears with* The Chimes. *The reading he carved out of* Oliver Twist — *with its brutal ferocity and the delirium of Sikes's haunted flight — left people blanched and horror-stricken.*

Like Henry Irving in such a melodrama as The Bells, *however, or George Arliss in* The Green Goddess, *Dickens could strike tears and*

*terror from his audiences with materials that sometimes read but
flatly in cold print. The murderous power of his "Sikes and Nancy,"
which at every performance left a trail of faintings in its wake, is dead
with the demonic performer. Despite its fame, therefore, though not
without reluctance, it has been omitted. Not only does it risk a note
of bathos, but it would end this volume on a somber chord out of
harmony with the genial and often comic spirit romping through
most of the selections.*

*But if Dickens was never entirely successful in donning the mask of
tragedy, he wore the mask of comedy with irresistible dash and aban-
don. People roared at the "Trial" from Pickwick, laughed till they
wept at Mr. Toots, rolled in their seats at Mrs. Gamp, howled at Bob
Sawyer. Even of these, of course, the printed texts cannot altogether
convey the towering heights to which Dickens soared in those tremendous displays of acting genius, but "Mr. Bob Sawyer's Party"
(first given in his 1862 series) may hint the hilarity of his comic
mask.]*

MR. BOB SAWYER'S PARTY

There is a repose about Lant Street, in the borough of Southwark
in the county of Surrey, which sheds a gentle melancholy upon the
soul. A house in Lant Street would not come within the denomina-
tion of a first-rate residence, in the strict acceptation of the term; but
if a man wished to abstract himself from the world, — to remove himself from the reach of temptation, — to place himself beyond the possibility of any inducement to look out of window, — he should by all
means go to Lant Street.

In this happy retreat are colonized a few clear-starchers, a sprin-
kling of journeymen bookbinders, one or two prison agents for the
Insolvent Court, several small housekeepers who are employed in the
Docks, a handful of milliners, and a seasoning of jobbing tailors. The
majority of the inhabitants either direct their energies to the letting
of furnished apartments, or devote themselves to the healthful pursuit
of mangling. The chief features in the still life of the street are green
shutters, lodging-bills, brass door-plates, and bell-handles; the principal specimens of animated nature are the pot-boy, the muffin youth,

and the baked-potato man. The population is migratory, usually disappearing on the verge of quarter-day, and generally by night. Her Majesty's revenues are seldom collected in this happy valley; the receipt of rent is dubious; and the water communication is frequently cut off.

Mr. Bob Sawyer embellished one side of the fire, in his first-floor front, early on the evening for which he had invited Mr. Pickwick to a friendly party; and his chum Mr. Ben Allen embellished the other side. The preparations for the reception of visitors appeared to be completed. The umbrellas in the passage had been heaped into the little corner outside the back-parlor door; the bonnet and shawl of the landlady's servant had been removed from the banisters; there were not more than two pairs of pattens on the street-door mat, and a kitchen candle, with a long snuff, burnt cheerfully on the ledge of the staircase window. Mr. Bob Sawyer had himself purchased the spirits, and had returned home in attendance on the bearer, to preclude the possibility of their being absconded with or delivered at the wrong house. The bottles were ready in the bedroom; a little table had been got from the parlor to play at cards on; and the glasses of the establishment, together with those which had been borrowed for the occasion from the public-house, were all drawn up in a tray on the floor of the landing outside the door.

Notwithstanding the highly satisfactory nature of these arrangements, there was a cloud on the countenance of Mr. Bob Sawyer, as he sat by the fire, and there was a sympathizing expression, too, in the features of Mr. Ben Allen, and melancholy in his voice, as he said, "Well, it *is* unlucky that your landlady Mrs. Raddle should have taken it in her head to turn sour, just on this occasion. She might at least have waited till to-morrow."

"That's her malevolence, that's her malevolence. She says that, if I can afford to give a party, I ought to be able to afford to pay her confounded 'little bill.' "

"How long has it been running?" A bill, by the by, is the most extraordinary locomotive engine that the genius of man ever produced. It would keep on running during the longest lifetime, without ever once stopping of its own accord.

"Only a quarter, and a month or so."

Ben Allen coughed, and directed a searching look between the two top bars of the stove.

"It'll be a deuced unpleasant thing if she takes it into her head to let out, when those fellows are here, won't it?"

"Horrible, horrible."

Here a low tap was heard at the room door, and Mr. Bob Sawyer looked expressively at his friend, and bade the tapper come in; whereupon a dirty slipshod girl, in black cotton stockings, thrust in her head, and said, "Please, Mister Sawyer, Missis Raddle wants to speak to *you*."

Before Mr. Bob Sawyer could return an answer, this young person suddenly disappeared with a jerk, as if somebody had given her a violent pull behind. This mysterious exit was no sooner accomplished, than there was another tap at the door.

Mr. Bob Sawyer glanced at his friend with a look of abject apprehension, and once more cried, "Come in."

The permission was not at all necessary, for, before Mr. Bob Sawyer had uttered the words, a little fierce woman bounced into the room, all in a tremble with passion, and pale with rage.

"Now, Mr. Sawyer, if you'll have the kindness to settle that little bill of mine I'll thank you, because I've got my rent to pay this afternoon, and my landlord's a waiting below now." Here the little woman rubbed her hands, and looked steadily over Mr. Bob Sawyer's head at the wall behind him.

"I am very sorry to put you to any inconvenience, Mrs. Raddle, but —"

"O, it isn't any inconvenience. I didn't want it particular before today; leastways, as it has to go to my landlord directly, it was as well for you to keep it as me. You promised me this afternoon, Mr. Sawyer, and every gentleman as has ever lived here has kept his word, sir, as of course anybody as calls himself a gentleman do." Mrs. Raddle tossed her head, bit her lips, rubbed her hands harder, and looked at the wall more steadily than ever.

"I am very sorry, Mrs. Raddle, but the fact is, that I have been disappointed in the City today."— Extraordinary place that city. Astonishing number of men always getting disappointed there.

"Well, Mr. Sawyer, and what is that to me, sir?"

"I — I — have no doubt, Mrs. Raddle," said Bob, blinking this last question, "that before the middle of next week we shall be able to set ourselves quite square, and go on, on a better system, afterwards."

This was all Mrs. Raddle wanted. She had bustled up to the apartment of the unlucky Bob, so bent upon going into a passion, that, in all probability, payment would have rather disappointed her. She was in excellent order for a little relaxation of the kind, having just exchanged a few introductory compliments with Mr. Raddle in the front kitchen.

"Do you suppose, Mr. Sawyer," elevating her voice for the information of the neighbors, — "do you suppose that I'm a going day after day to let a fellar occupy my lodgings as never thinks of paying his rent, nor even the very money laid out for the fresh butter and lump sugar that's bought for his breakfast, nor the very milk that's took in at the street door? Do you suppose as a hard-working and industrious woman which has lived in this street for twenty year (ten year over the way, and nine year and three quarter in this very house) has nothing else to do but to work herself to death after a parcel of lazy idle fellars, that are always smoking and drinking and lounging, when they ought to be glad to turn their hands to anything that would help 'em to pay their bills?"

"My good soul," interposed Mr. Benjamin Allen.

"Have the goodness to keep your observashuns to yourself, sir, I beg," suddenly arresting the rapid torrent of her speech, and addressing the third party with impressive slowness and solemnity. "I am not aweer, sir, that you have any right to address your conversation to me. I don't think I let these apartments to you, sir."

"No, you certainly did not."

"Very good sir. Then p'r'aps, sir, as a medical studint, you'll confine yourself to breaking the arms and legs of the poor people in the hospitals, and will keep yourself to yourself, sir, or there may be some persons here as will make you, sir."

"But you are such an unreasonable woman."

"I beg your parding, young man; but will you have the goodness to call me that again, sir?"

"I didn't make use of the word in any invidious sense, ma'am."

"I beg your parding, young man; but who do you call a woman? Did you make that remark to me, sir?"

"Why, bless my heart!"

"Did you apply that name to me, I ask of you, sir?"—with intense ferocity, and throwing the door wide open.

"Why, of course I did."

"Yes, of course you did," backing gradually to the door, and raising her voice, for the special behoof of Mr. Raddle in the kitchen, —"yes, of course you did! And everybody knows that they may safely insult me in my own house while my husband sits sleeping down stairs, and taking no more notice than if I was a dog in the streets. He ought to be ashamed of himself (sob) to allow his wife to be treated in this way by a parcel of young cutters and carvers of live people's bodies, that disgraces the lodgings (another sob), and leaving her exposed to all manner of abuse; a base, faint-hearted, timorous wretch, that's afraid to come up stairs and face the ruffinly creatures — that's afraid — that's afraid to come!" Mrs. Raddle paused to listen whether the repetition of the taunt had roused her better half; and, finding that it had not been successful, proceeded to descend the stairs with sobs innumerable, when there came a loud double-knock at the street door. Hereupon she burst into a fit of weeping, which was prolonged until the knock had been repeated six times, when, in an uncontrollable burst of mental agony, she threw down all the umbrellas, and disappeared into the back parlor.

"Does Mr. Sawyer live here?" said Mr. Pickwick, when the door was opened.

"Yes, first floor. It's the door straight afore you, when you gets to the top of the stairs." Having given this instruction, the handmaid, who had been brought up among the aboriginal inhabitants of Southwark, disappeared, with the candle in her hand, down the kitchen stairs.

Mr. Pickwick and his two friends stumbled up stairs, where they were received by the wretched Bob, who had been afraid to go down, lest he should be waylaid by Mrs. Raddle.

"How are you? Glad to see you, — take care of the glasses." This caution was addressed to Mr. Pickwick, who had put his foot in the tray.

"Dear me, I beg your pardon."

"Don't mention it, — don't mention it. I'm rather confined for room here, but you must put up with all that when you come to see a young bachelor. Walk in. You've seen Mr. Ben Allen before, I think?" Mr. Pickwick shook hands with Mr. Benjamin Allen, and his friends followed his example. They had scarcely taken their seats when there was another double-knock.

"I hope that's Jack Hopkins! Hush. Yes, it is. Come up, Jack; come up."

A heavy footstep was heard upon the stairs, and Jack Hopkins presented himself.

"You're late, Jack."

"Been detained at Bartholomew's."

"Anything new?"

"No, nothing particular. Rather a good accident brought into the casualty ward."

"What was that, sir?"

"Only a man fallen out of a four pair of stairs' window; but it's a very fair case, very fair case indeed."

"Do you mean that the patient is in a fair way to recover?"

"No; no, I should rather say he wouldn't. There must be a splendid operation though, to-morrow, — magnificent sight, if Slasher does it."

"You consider Mr. Slasher a good operator?"

"Best alive. Took a boy's leg out of the socket last week — boy ate five apples and a gingerbread cake — exactly two minutes after it was all over, boy said he wouldn't lie there to be made game of, and he'd tell his mother if they didn't begin."

"Dear me!"

"Pooh! That's nothing; is it, Bob?"

"Nothing at all."

"By the by, Bob," said Hopkins, with a scarcely perceptible glance at Mr. Pickwick's attentive face, "we had a curious accident last night. A child was brought in who had swallowed a necklace."

"Swallowed what, sir?"

"A necklace; not all at once, you know, that would be too much — you couldn't swallow that, if the child did — eh, Mr. Pickwick, ha! ha! No, the way was this. Child's parents, poor people, lived in a court. Child's eldest sister bought a necklace, — common necklace, large black wooden beads. Child, being fond of toys, cribbed necklace, hid necklace, played with necklace, cut string of necklace, and swallowed a bead. Child thought it capital fun, went back next day and swallowed another bead."

"Bless my heart, what a dreadful thing! I beg your pardon, sir. Go on."

"Next day, child swallowed two beads; day after that, treated himself to three beads; so on, till in a week's time he had got through the necklace, — five-and-twenty beads. Sister, industrious girl, seldom treated herself to bit of finery, cried eyes out at loss of necklace, looked high and low for necklace; but, I needn't say, didn't find necklace. Few days afterwards, family at dinner, — baked shoulder of mutton, and potatoes; child wasn't hungry, playing about the room, when family suddenly heard devil of a noise, like small hail-storm. 'Don't do that, my boy,' said father. "I ain't a doin' nothing,' said child. 'Well, don't do it again,' said father. Short silence, and then noise worse than ever. 'If you don't mind what I say, my boy,' said father, 'you'll find yourself in bed, in something less than a pig's whisper.' Gave child a shake to make him obedient, and such a rattling ensued as nobody ever heard before. 'Why, damme, it's *in* the child!' said father; 'he's got the croup in the wrong place!' 'No, I haven't, father,' said child, beginning to cry; 'it's the necklace; I swallowed it, father.' Father caught child up, and ran with him to hospital; beads in boy's stomach rattling all the way with the jostling; and people looking up in the air, and down in the cellars, to see where unusual sound came from. He's in the hospital now, and makes such a devil of noise when he walks about, that they're obliged to muffle him in a watchman's coat, for fear he should wake the patients!"

Here another knock at the door announced the rest of the company, five in number, among whom there was, as presently appeared, a sentimental young gentleman with a very nice sense of honor. The little table was wheeled out: the bottles were brought in, and the succeeding three hours were devoted to a round game at sixpence a dozen.

When the last deal had been declared, and the profit-and-loss account of fish and sixpences adjusted to the satisfaction of all parties, Mr. Bob Sawyer rang for supper, and the visitors squeezed themselves into corners while it was getting ready.

It was not so easily got ready as some people may imagine. First of all, it was necessary to awaken the girl, who had fallen asleep with her face on the kitchen table; this took time, and even when she did answer the bell, another quarter of an hour was consumed in fruitless endeavors to impart to her a distant glimmering of reason. The man to whom the order for the oysters had been sent had not been told to open them; it is a very difficult thing to open an oyster with a limp knife or a two-pronged fork, and very little was done in this way. Very little of the beef was done either; and the ham (which was also from the German-sausage shop round the corner) was in a similar predicament. However, there was plenty of porter in a tin can; and the cheese went a great way, for it was very strong.

After supper more bottles were put upon the table, together with a paper of cigars. Then there was an awful pause; and this awful pause was occasioned by an embarrassing occurrence.

The fact is, the girl was washing the glasses. The establishment boasted four; which is not mentioned to its disparagement, for there never was a lodging-house yet that was not short of glasses. The establishment's glasses were little thin, feeble tumblers; and those which had been borrowed from the public-house were great, dropsical, bloated articles, each supported on a huge gouty leg. This would have been in itself sufficient to have possessed the company with the real state of affairs; even if the young person of all work had not prevented the possibility of any misconception arising in the mind of any gentleman upon the subject, by forcibly dragging every man's glass away long before he had finished his beer, and audibly stating, despite the winks of Mr. Bob Sawyer, that it was to be conveyed down stairs, and washed forthwith.

It is an ill wind that blows nobody any good. The prim man in the cloth boots, who had been unsuccessfully attempting to make a joke during the whole time the round game lasted, saw his opportunity, and seized it. The instant the glasses disappeared, he commenced a long story "about a great public character, whose name I have forgotten, making a particularly happy reply to another eminent and illustrious individual whom I have never been able to identify." He enlarged with great minuteness upon divers collateral circumstances, distantly connected with the anecdote in hand, but said, "For the life of me I cannot recollect at this precise moment what the anecdote is, although I have been in the habit of telling the story with great applause for the last ten years. Dear me, it is a very extraordinary circumstance."

"I am sorry you have forgotten it," said Mr. Bob Sawyer, glancing eagerly at the door, as he thought he heard the noise of glasses jingling; "very sorry."

"So am I, because I know it would have afforded so much amusement. Never mind; I dare say I shall manage to recollect it, in the course of half an hour or so."

The prim man arrived at this point just as the glasses came back, when Mr. Bob Sawyer, who had been absorbed in attention, said he should very much like to hear the end of it, for, so far as it went, it was, without exception, the very best story he had ever heard.

The sight of the tumblers restored Bob to a degree of equanimity he had not possessed since his interview with his landlady. His face brightened up, and he began to feel quite convivial.

"Now, Betsey," dispersing the tumultuous little mob of glasses the girl had collected in the centre of the table, — "now, Betsey, the warm water. Be brisk, there's a good girl."

"You can't have no warm water."

"No warm water!"

"No; Missis Raddle said you warn't to have none."

"Bring up the warm water instantly, — instantly!"

"No, I can't. Missis Raddle raked out the kitchen fire afore she went to bed, and locked up the kittle."

"Never mind, — never mind. Pray don't disturb yourself about such a trifle," said Mr. Pickwick, observing the conflict of Bob Sawyer's passions as depicted in his countenance; "cold water will do very well."

"My landlady is subject to some slight attacks of mental derangement. I fear I must give her warning."

"No, don't."

"I fear I must. Yes, I'll pay her what I owe her, and give her warning to-morrow morning." Poor fellow! how devoutly he wished he could!

Mr. Bob Sawyer's attempts to rally under this last blow communicated a dispiriting influence to the company, the greater part of whom, with the view of raising their spirits, attached themselves with extra cordiality to the cold brandy and water. The first effects of these libations were displayed in an outbreak of hostilities between the youth with the nice sense of honor and Mr. Hopkins. At last the youth with the nice sense of honor felt it necessary to come to an understanding on the matter; when the following clear understanding took place.

"Sawyer."

"Well, Noddy."

"I should be very sorry, Sawyer, to create any unpleasantness at any friend's table, and much less at yours, Sawyer, — very; but I must take this opportunity of informing Mr. Hopkins that he is no gentleman."

"And *I* should be very sorry, Sawyer, to create any disturbance in the street in which you reside; but I'm afraid I shall be under the necessity of alarming the neighbors by pitching the person who has just spoken out o' window."

"I should like to see you do it, sir."

"You shall *feel* me do it in half a minute, sir."

"I request that you'll favor me with your card, sir."

"I'll do nothing of the kind, sir."

"Why not, sir?"

"Because you'll stick it up over your chimney-piece, and delude your visitors into the false belief that a gentleman has been to see you, sir."

"Sir, a friend of mine shall wait on you in the morning."

"Sir, I'm very much obliged to you for the caution, and I'll leave particular directions with the servant to lock up the spoons."

At this point the remainder of the guests interposed, and remonstrated with both parties on the impropriety of their conduct. A vast quantity of talking ensued, in the course of which Mr. Noddy gradually allowed his feelings to overpower him, and professed that he had ever entertained a devoted personal attachment towards Mr. Hopkins. To this Mr. Hopkins replied that, on the whole, he preferred Mr. Noddy to his own mother; on hearing this admission, Mr. Noddy magnanimously rose from his seat, and proffered his hand to Mr. Hopkins. Mr. Hopkins grasped it; and everybody said the whole dispute had been conducted in a manner which was highly honorable to both parties concerned.

"And now, just to set us going again, Bob, I don't mind singing a song." Hopkins, incited by applause, plunged at once into "The King, God bless him," which he sang as loud as he could to a novel air, compounded of the "Bay of Biscay" and "A Frog he would a wooing go." The chorus was the essence of the song; and, as every gentleman sang it to the tune he knew best, the effect was very striking.

It was at the end of the chorus to the first verse that Mr. Pickwick held up his hand in a listening attitude, and said, as soon as silence was restored: "Hush! I beg your pardon. I thought I heard somebody calling from up stairs."

A profound silence ensued; and Mr. Bob Sawyer was observed to turn pale.

"I think I hear it now. Have the goodness to open the door."

The door was no sooner opened than all doubt on the subject was removed by a voice screaming from the two-pair landing, "Mr. Sawyer! Mr. Sawyer!"

"It's my landlady. I thought you were making too much noise. — Yes, Mrs. Raddle."

"What do you mean by this, Mr. Sawyer? Ain't it enough to be swindled out of one's rent, and money lent out of pocket besides, and insulted by your friends that dares to call themselves men, without having the house turned out of window, and noise enough made to bring the fire-engines here, at two o'clock in the morning? — Turn them wretches away."

"You ought to be ashamed of yourselves," said the voice of Mr. Raddle, which appeared to proceed from beneath some distant bed-clothes.

"Ashamed of themselves! Why don't you go down and knock 'em every one down stairs? You would if you was a man."

"I should if I was a dozen men, my dear, but they've the advantage of me in numbers, my dear."

"Ugh, you coward! Do you mean to turn them wretches out, Mr. Sawyer?"

"They're going, Mrs. Raddle, they're going. — I am afraid you'd better go. I *thought* you were making too much noise. — They're only looking for their hats, Mrs. Raddle; they are going directly."

Mrs. Raddle, thrusting her nightcap over the banisters just as Mr.

Pickwick emerged from the sitting-room. "Going! what did they ever come for?"

"My dear ma'am," remonstrated Mr. Pickwick, looking up.

"Get along with you, you old wretch!" said Mrs. Raddle, hastily withdrawing the nightcap. "Old enough to be his grandfather, you villin! You're worse than any of 'em."

Mr. Pickwick found it in vain to protest his innocence, so hurried down stairs into the street, closely followed by the rest.

The visitors having all departed, in compliance with this rather pressing request of Mrs. Raddle, the luckless Mr. Bob Sawyer was left alone, to meditate on the probable events of the morrow, and the pleasures of the evening.